3.40

Physiological Basis
of
Human Performance

Physiological Basis

of

Human Performance

By **BENJAMIN RICCI**
Director, Laboratory of Applied Physiology
Boyden Gymnasium
University of Massachusetts
Amherst, Massachusetts

Lea & Febiger

Philadelphia 1967

To my sons

Robert Simpson   *James Benjamin*   *Thomas David*

PREFACE

Physiological Basis of Human Performance is designed to acquaint the reader with current concepts relating to the physiology of movement. Concerning some matters, agreement among exercise physiologists is less than complete. These controversies, these differing interpretations, provide a basis for continued careful research on the multicomplex human organism.

The word *exercise* is a Latin derivative (*execere:* to cause to work) and implies mental and physical effort. By definition, work is exerted effort. Apart from philosophical and psychological evaluations, work, exercise, and physical performance have synonymous meanings. To the exercise physiologist, whose attention is focused on the myriad of biochemical and physical alterations and adjustments imposed by changing metabolic requirements, there is no problem of semantics. Throughout this text, *performance, exercise,* and *work* are used interchangeably.

This book was written primarily, although not exclusively, for students whose major educational emphases include premedicine, industrial engineering, physical education, nursing, dietetics, physical therapy and physiology.

The varied scientific background of this audience is recognized. In some cases it is less than extensive. Yet to discuss exercise physiology compels one to draw upon the disciplines of physics, chemistry, engineering, and mathematics. In an attempt to provide the reader with source material for a comprehensive view, an interdisciplinary approach is employed. For detailed explanations, the reader is urged to refer to the cited literature.

Unique and important is the chapter on Calculation Methods. Through an understanding of calculation methods, the reader is certain to derive greater appreciation for and lasting meaning of the numerical expressions of physiological parameters. Conversion tables, definitions, laws, formulas, nomograms, and examples are provided.

The language of the metric system is utilized. Research and study in exercise physiology is conducted in many laboratories throughout the world. English predominates as the international, spoken language of the scientist, but the reporting of data involves use of the metric system.

I wish to acknowledge the contributions of several eminent exercise physiologists who are partially responsible for the addition of this book to the list of texts in exercise physiology. To Peter V. Karpovich, M.D., Research Professor of Physiology, Springfield College, I am indebted for basic preparation in exercise physiology, for the initial opportunity to engage in research, for the lesson of careful, diligent search, and for constant encouragement. Grateful acknowledgment is also given to Rodolfo Margaria, M.D., Director, Institute of Physiology, School of Medicine, University of Milan, Italy, for the opportunity to engage in postdoctoral study and research in the company of dedicated physiologists. To Nobel Laureate Archibald V. Hill, University College, London, England, whose name is synonymous with scholarly writing and experimentations and with learned discourses, is expressed appreciation for his suggesting that the challenge of writing this book be accepted. My visit with him, though brief, was memorable.

I wish also to express my deepest appreciation to the following scientists who willingly served as critical readers of the chapters indicated. Chapters 2 and 6, "Muscle Considerations" and "Respiration": Rodolfo Margaria, M.D., Chairman, Department of Physiology, University of Milan, Italy. Chapter 3, "Neural Control of Muscle Activity": Elizabeth B. Gardner, Ph.D., Professor of Biology and Physiology, Boston University. Chapter 4, "Kineoenergetics": John V. Basmajian, M.D., Head, Department of Anatomy, Queen's University, Kingston, Ontario, Canada. Chapter 5, "Cardiovascular Dynamics": Albert Salisbury Hyman, M.D., F.A.C.P., F.A.C.S.M., New York Medical College, New York City; Consulting Cardiologist, Veterans Administration Hospital No. 98. Chapter 7, "Regulation of Body Temperature": Elsworth R. Buskirk, Ph.D., F.A.C.S.M., Director, Laboratory for Human Performance Research Institute for Science and Engineering, College of Health and Physical Education, The Pennsylvania State University. Chapter 8, "Metabolism": J. V. G. A. Durnin, M.A., M.B., Ch.B., D.Sc., M.R.C.P., Institute of Physiology, The University, Glasgow, Scotland. Chapter 9, "Homeostasis of Body Fluids": Robert W. Bullard, Ph.D., Professor and Chairman of the Department of Anatomy and Physiology, Indiana University, Bloomington. "Formulas, Laws, and Definitions": Robert Gluckstern, Ph.D., Chairman, Department of Physics and Astronomy, University of Massachusetts, Amherst.

My acknowledgment to the critical readers bears the implication of their approval; however, I alone accept the responsibility for the views expressed.

A special expression of thanks is offered to Mr. Martin C. Hubbard, Head, Interlibrary Loan Department, University of Massachusetts Library, and to Miss Emily M. Miller, Librarian, Morrill Science Library, University of Massachusetts, Amherst, for their generous assistance which was dispensed in so cheerful a manner.

An expression of gratitude is also extended to Mr. Donald Curtis for his skillful preparation of the illustrations.

I am grateful to Dr. Ruth Abernathy, for her contribution as editor, and to Mr. John Febiger Spahr, of Lea & Febiger, for his display of patience and cooperation and for the many services he provided.

My sincerest hope is that my work reflect well on all who taught and influenced me and on those who criticized my manuscript. May the reading be challenging and rewarding.

Benjamin Ricci

Amherst, Massachusetts

CONTENTS

1. Introduction 1

2. Muscle Considerations 4

3. Neural Control of Muscle Activity 30

4. Kineoenergetics 54

5. Cardiovascular Dynamics 76

6. Respiration 110

7. Heat Regulation 141

8. Metabolism 159

9. Homeostasis of Body Fluids 201

10. Selected Topics 215

11. Calculation Methods 243

    Appendix 279

    Index 295

Chapter

1

INTRODUCTION

M<small>AN</small> has always been the subject of discussion by man. Students of all disciplines have dissected him, defined him, categorized him. Some have found him to be pretentious, pugnacious, phlegmatic, psychotic. Others have found him to be paternalistic, philosophic, provident, perspicacious. All have found him to be provocative. None has found him to be wholly predictable.

He is a composite of chemicals-in-tissues* within a framework of bones, a series of joints, a system of muscles, and a network of blood vessels and nerves. He is designed for motion.

Man finds himself a prisoner of earth—with parole status. He has succeeded in making minor penetrations into the depths of the sea and to the outer fringes of space. He has paid brief visits to the Marianas Trench and has "walked" in the vacuum of space. To be able to probe these hostile environments, man has learned to aid his dynamic internal equilibrium: he takes along an oxygen supply, compatible microclimate, and nourishment.

Irrespective of his location, man displays an amazing versatility of performance. He can accomplish delicate tasks, yet within an instant can display herculean effort—both performances being accomplished through an integrated chemoneuromuscular mechanism. Whether threatened by extinction or thrilled by excitement, his hormonal-neural

---

* Viewed as a potential energy source, man possesses amazing financial worth. Through the eyes of some E. I. DuPont biochemists, "Man's value has soared astronomically in the Atomic Age. The chemical content of a human body once was valued at 98 cents. But today, based on the fact that the atoms in a body contain a potential energy of more than 11 million kilowatt hours per pound, an average size man's body is worth $85.5 billion."[3]

responses are nondiscriminatory. Man is equipped basically for attack-or-retreat performance and his course of action is guided by his evaluation of present and past experiences.

Despite imbalances of fluid or energy or of physical effort, man's internal environment maintains a remarkable constancy in acid-base level. Man lives within rather narrow fluctuations (his blood and tissue fluid pH vary but little); pronounced fluctuations are incompatible with life. Sir F. Gowland Hopkins* noted that life is a dynamic equilibrium in an ever changing system.

Man and machine have much in common. Both consume oxygen, expel carbon, require fuel, possess joints, and perform work. A vocabulary common to both exists: work, efficiency, energy expenditure, force, electrical potential, torque. While similarities are present, dissimilarities are pronounced. In eloquent fashion, Clendening underscored the dissimilarities:[1]

> If it is a machine, it is a very complicated one—it is like no other machine we know—it is at once a heat engine and a chemical engine and an electrical engine, and besides manufactures such things as antitoxins and thought and gametes. Besides it reproduces its own parts when they break down, which is like no other machine. It is a Humpty-Dumpty machine because no one can reassemble it: when that spark which is indefinable leaves it, all the parts may be there, but it won't run. And no one knows what it is for or can predict what it will do—all of which is unmachine-like.

Unmachine-like is man's ability to perform great physical feats which require muscle action despite insufficient oxygen availability. Man is equipped to engage in deficit spending—to incur an oxygen debt—and to offer lactic acid as collateral for the debt. When incapable of maintaining his internal equilibrium, man gives in to overriding, automatic actions which are programmed to protect the protoplasm and maintain life. An example is provided by his need for oxygen. When insufficient amounts of oxygen are present, or when the oxygen transport system is inadequate, the cardiovascular, cardiopulmonary, and nervous systems undergo an immediate adjustment process in order to conserve a reduced blood-oxygen supply and to protect the organs, especially the brain. In syncope, the example becomes clear. Perhaps because of a reduced rate of blood flow (as in cardiac failure) or because of blood volume reduction (as in hemorrhage) consciousness is lost. His requirement for oxygen decreases owing to decreased metabolic activity. Oxygen use is reduced and protection is thus afforded the vital tissues such as brain and cardiac tissue which do not "go into debt" for oxygen as does muscle tissue.

---

* Sir Frederick Gowland Hopkins (1861–1947), eminent English biochemist.

Perhaps physiology should be discussed only within the framework of the "indefinable spark." Yet, to do so would be to inherit the difficult task of defining what life is. It is far more productive to accept in part the conclusion of Galilei* and merely analyze the physiological manifestations of physical performance in life.

Every phase of human expression is the result of integrated effort: nervous, muscular, circulatory, biochemical. There are no organs which are islands unto themselves. The blood which bathes the brain also bathes the small toe. Yet, within this text, discussion of function is separated into chapters. This is unfortunate but unavoidable. Except in passing, no attempt was made to discuss psychic influence on human performance.

Although the body of knowledge is broad, many questions persist. To a degree, the knowledge is of a tentative nature. New concepts are ever replacing or modifying presently held views. The search for greater understanding continues.

Enlightenment is assured, as the scientist is guided by the principle of Galilei,[2] "Measure what can be measured, make measurable what cannot be measured."

---

* Galileo Galilei (1564–1642): "It is not possible to define what life is but only to analyze its manifestations."

REFERENCES

1. Clendening, L.: *The Human Body.* 4th Ed., New York, Alfred A. Knopf, 1959.

2. Nordenskiöld, E.: *The History of Biology.* 2nd Ed., New York, Tudor Publishing Co., 1936.

3. *Protecting the Public Health.* E. I. DuPont de Nemours Co., Wilmington, Delaware, 1954.

2

MUSCLE CONSIDERATIONS

THE skeleton protects the brain, heart, lungs, and, to a lesser degree, the viscera. In addition, the skeleton provides an extensive series of levers which are acted upon by muscle tissue to produce a variety of physical expressions. It is this latter function that is pertinent to our text.

Patterns of physical expression are dependent upon arthrological construction and articular freedom (joint excursion), neuromuscular control, gradation of muscular contraction, inertia to be overcome, degree of physiological adaptation, and level of motivation. Basic to any discussion of human movement, however, is a discussion of muscle physiology.

Muscle Tissue

Within muscle tissue *potential energy*, which is chemically stored, is converted into *kinetic energy* through a vastly complex series of chemical reactions.

Muscle tissue possesses the peculiar characteristics of *irritability* and *contractility*. *Irritability* is an inherent quality of protoplasm which is manifested as a reaction to stimuli; whereas, *contractility* is evidenced by the ability of a tissue to develop increasing tension.

Within the muscular component of man, structural and functional differences in muscle tissue permit three classifications: skeletal, smooth, and cardiac.

Skeletal Muscle

As implied in the classification, skeletal muscle is usually attached by tendons to the bony framework. In certain body areas skeletal muscles may attach to other muscles or to fascia—a sheet-like arrangement of fibrous connective tissue.

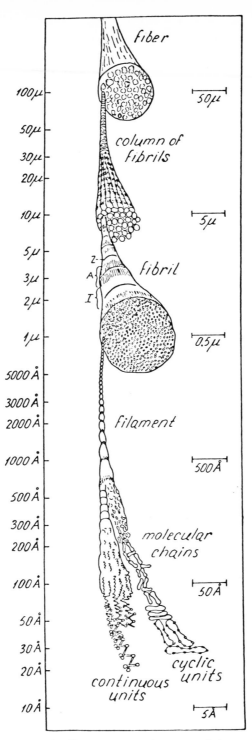

Fig. 2–1.   Skeletal muscle fiber structure. 1 micron (μ) = 1/1000 mm; 1 Ångström (Å) = 1/10,000 micron (0.0000001 mm). Number 1 is approximately 200 μ in thickness. According to Szent-Györgyi, 50% of the muscle volume is occupied by fibrils.[36] (From Buchtal and Kaiser.[5] Courtesy of Danske videnskabernes Selskab, Copenhagen.)

When viewed microscopically, skeletal muscle exhibits an alternation of light and dark areas which gives rise to such other descriptive words as *striated* or *striped* muscle. Skeletal muscle fibers are multinucleated and are distinctly separated by a delicate connective tissue sheath.

Muscle fibrils, or *myofibrils*, are embedded within *sarcoplasm*, which is muscle fiber protoplasm of protein composition. These myofibrils are composed of both actin and myosin protein filaments and represent the contractile portion. It is estimated that between 500 and 2500 myofilaments, in parallel arrangement, may be found within the myofibril, and that from several hundred to several thousand myofibrils may be found within a muscle fiber. Or, to present it in more dramatic fashion, a single muscle fiber, ranging from 1 to 45 mm in length* and from 10 to 100 microns (μ) in diameter, may contain as many as ten million muscle filaments. The interrelationship of these constituents is depicted in Figure 2–1. Each anatomically complete muscle may contain many thousands of fibers.

The striated appearance of skeletal muscle, which exists throughout the longitudinal surface of the muscle, suggests an alignment of the myofibrils with the sarcolemma.

Light and dark bands are indicative of the refractive index of the tissue segment. I bands contain *actin* filaments, are isotropic, are singly refractive to light because of the presence of thin filaments, and are therefore light in appearance. A bands contain *myosin*, are anisotropic (or birefringent), are doubly refractive because of the presence of many thin and thick filaments, and are therefore dark by comparison. Within the center of each of the A bands there is a less refractile area which is called the H band or Henson's line. Similarly, a less refractile line is located within the center of the I band and is variously called the Z line, Dobie's line, or Kraus's membrane. Lastly, the sarcomere, or unit of muscle, is recognized as the area between the Z lines.

Muscle Fiber Arrangement

Whole muscles display a substantial connective tissue framework (*stroma*) in addition to a specific arrangement of muscle fibers (*parenchyma*).

Fasciculi may be in parallel arrangement with the longitudinal axis of the muscle and may terminate at both ends in tendons which insert into bone. There are, however, two other variations in fascicular arrangement: pennate and radiated. Discussion will be limited to the pennate

---

* The *stapedius* muscle, located in the tympanum (middle ear region) possesses fibers 1 mm in length; the *sartorius* muscle of the front thigh region possesses fibers 45 mm in length.

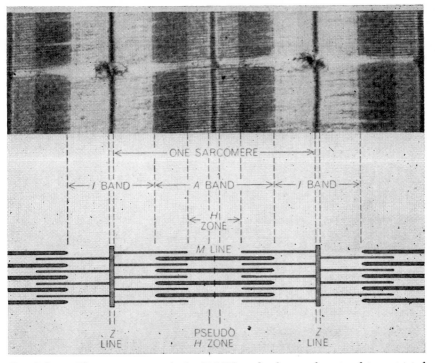

Fig. 2–2. Electron micrograph ($\times 23{,}000$) and schema of parts of two striated muscle fibers. The darkened, irregular bodies between the Z lines of the adjacent myofibrils are the mitochondria. Mitochondria contain enzymes which are essential to energy release which provides energy for contraction. (From Huxley.[22] Courtesy of Scientific American, Inc.)

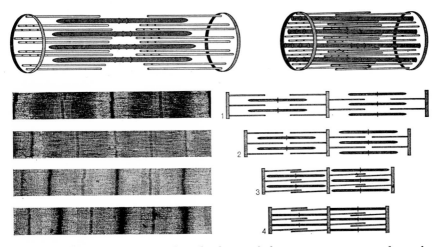

Fig. 2–3. Electron micrograph and schema of shortening contraction of muscle fiber. Note, particularly in the micrograph, that the A bands do not shorten; the filaments overlap in contraction. Schematics *1* and *4* represent uncontracted fiber (*1*) and contracted fiber (*4*). (From Huxley.[22] Courtesy of Scientific American, Inc.)

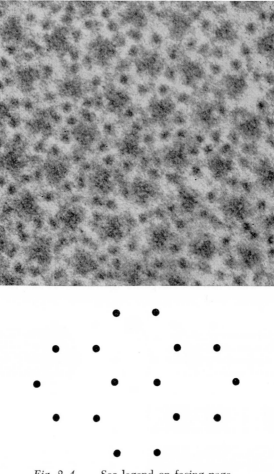

Fig. 2–4.   See legend on facing page.

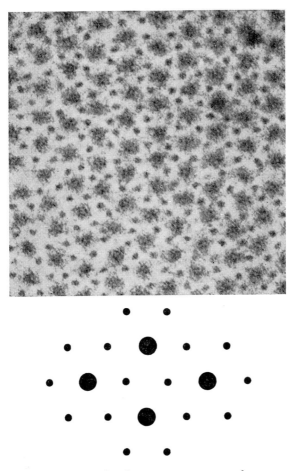

Fig. 2–4.   Electron micrograph of transverse section of uncontracted muscle
(×200,000) (p. 8) and contracted muscle (×250,000) (*above*). Schema portrays
filament arrangement. (Adapted from Huxley.[22] Courtesy of Scientific American, Inc.)

arrangement. Fasciculi may converge to a tendon located on one side of a muscle (penniform) as in the *semimembranosus* muscle. The myofibrils may converge on both sides of a tendon (bipenniform) as in the *rectus femoris* muscle. Or, the fasciculi may converge on several tendons (multipenniform) as in the *deltoideus* muscle.

The arrangement of fasciculi has been shown by Gray to be related to force and range of motion.[16] Fenn, citing Haines, notes that the length of fibers is related to the amount of shortening expected within the muscle. According to Zchakaia, also cited by Fenn, the degree of shortening contraction of a muscle in situ is equal to the absolute shortening of its fibers.

Muscles with relatively few fasciculi, as in parallel fiber arrangement, have a small cross-sectional area and reduced force capability (since force is related to cross-sectional area) but have great range of motion. In contradistinction, the penniform arrangement of fasciculi, characterized by a greater cross-sectional area, is capable of exerting greater force with reduced range of motion. These relationships are depicted in Figure 2–5.

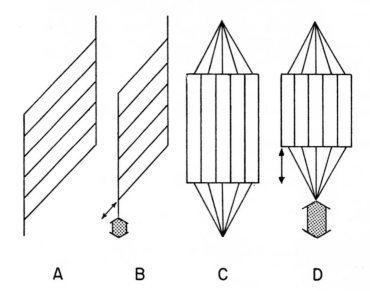

A   B   C   D

Fig. 2–5.   Pennate and parallel muscle fiber arrangement at rest (*A, C*) and at shortened contraction (*B, D*). In unipennate fiber arrangement (*A, B*) tendons are depicted as lines extending from sides of parallelogram, whereas in parallel fiber muscle (*C, D*) tendons are portrayed as lines radiating from rectangle. Although fibers are of equal length during uncontracted state (*A, C*), the pennate muscle (*B*) shortens to a lesser degree than does the parallel myofibril muscle (*D*). Thin double arrows indicate direction and magnitude of muscle fiber shortening; broad double arrows indicate range of movement. (From Zierler,[39] in Bard's *Medical Physiology.* Courtesy of C. V. Mosby Co.)

Muscle Contraction—Historical Perspective

Skeletal muscle contraction is an enormously complex chain of chemimal processes, the understanding of which is constantly expanding.

Muscle contraction is older than man; it enabled insects to crawl, to fly, to adjust to changing environments, and to exist. It is philosophically and scientifically fitting to mention here the name of René Descartes (1596–1650) who contributed a mechanical explanation of the nervous system in terms of animal spirits conveyed through nerves to muscles.[32]

Gian Alfonso Borelli (1608–1679) was among the first to explain scientifically the causes of muscle action, a process which he ascribed to fermentation.[32] He did not explain the physicochemical reactions, but he did assume the involvement of complicated chemical reactions.

The discovery by Luigi Galvani (1737–1798), that an electric current could elicit muscle contraction, added important knowledge to the physiology of contraction.[15]

Hermann Ludwig von Helmholtz (1821–1894) introduced a graphic method of studying muscle contractions. He also measured the speed of motor nerve impulses in frogs.[7]

In a classic experiment, Carlo Matteucci (1811–1868) offered convincing proof of the relationship of electrical activity (*action potential*) to muscle contraction.[7]

Although the protein *myosin* had been extracted from muscle tissue in the 1860's, it was Szent-Györgyi who demonstrated that myosin in skeletal muscle is actually two proteins *actin* and *myosin*, both of which are involved in muscle contraction.[36]

Chemical Composition

Fresh muscle tissue is composed of 75% water, 20% protein, and 5% minerals and organic compounds. The principal minerals are potassium (K), magnesium (Mg), sodium (Na), phosphorus (P), and calcium (Ca). Glycogen, glucose, and hormones of the adrenal cortex constitute the organic compounds. Creatine, phosphocreatine, adenosinetriphosphate, and urea constitute the nonprotein nitrogenous substances.

Chemistry of Contraction

To begin, it is well to underscore several points. (1) The energy for contraction of muscle tissue is derived from the combustion of carbohydrates in glycogen form. (2) Like all living tissue, muscle tissue requires oxygen for the combustion of glycogen. The anaerobic phase of contraction serves to point out the complexity of the chemical reactions which occur within the isotropic regions of skeletal muscle. The adenosinetriphosphate (ATP) source is by no means limitless and requires the presence of oxygen in the reconstitution process. (3) As the glycogen stores diminish, lactic acid concentration increases. Here again the ultimate importance of oxygen at muscle tissue level is recognized. As long as the physicochemical activity of muscle is maintained at a low level, as during rest, oxygen availability is adequate and the formation rate of lactic acid is low. This is evidenced by the low concentrations of blood lactic acid, on the order of 8 to 20 mg% during basal and resting states. Increased muscle activity requires increased oxygen availability and utilization. At this juncture in discussion, more complexities are recognized. The oxygen molecule is carried predominantly in chemical combination in the blood and is in great abundance; however, its delivery rate is dependent upon the rate of blood circulation. Further complexities are cited: increased levels of metabolic activity are reflected in an increased demand for oxygen by *all* body cells and tissues.

Muscle tissue that is rested contains an abundance of adenosinetriphosphate (ATP),* phosphocreatine, and glycogen. According to Szent-Györgyi, muscles contain approximately 20% actomyosin, 10% dissolved protein *myogen,*† and 70% water.[36]

Muscle fiber contraction is the result of a "violent"‡ separation of phosphoric acid from adenosinetriphosphate caused by the influence of acetylcholine on actomyosin in the presence of potassium. "The adsorption (inactivation) of this adenosinetriphosphate depends on potassium adsorption which property is very labile (unstable)."

Acetylcholine, shown by Dale to be produced by nerve action,[9,10] causes changes in membrane permeability thereby permitting an influx of sodium ions. The resulting ionic imbalance triggers the activity of adenosinetriphosphate. Szent-Györgyi cites the findings of Erdös and Rózsa who reported the level of activity of adenosinetriphosphate to be dependent upon the salt concentration within the muscle fiber. Szent-Györgyi also indicated that "at the concentration of potassium plus sodium in muscle . . . myosin can inactivate adenosine diphosphate."[36]

The separation of ATP is not dependent upon the presence of oxygen; however, ATP is quickly synthesized through interaction of the compound phosphocreatine with adenosine diphosphate ADP (which is formed from the separation of ATP). In summary, the energy for muscle fiber contraction is brought about by the explosive separation of phos-

---

* In rested muscle, the supply of ATP is certainly adequate and is believed to be 5000 times greater than necessary to elicit contraction.[36]

† Through enzymatic reaction (fermentation) myogen is converted into myosin.

‡ In this discussion, words or sentences within quotation marks are from Szent-Györgi.[36]

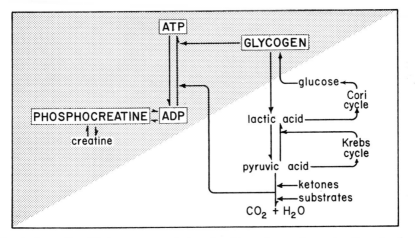

Fig. 2–6. Simplified summary of the chemistry of muscle contraction. In the breakdown of each of the essential compounds (within blocks) energy is liberated. Energy serves as a source for muscle contraction, as in ATP breakdown, or serves to resynthesize the compounds. The breakdown of ATP, phosphocreatine, and glucose is accomplished in the nonoxidative or anaerobic phase (shaded area). Reconversion of lactic and pyruvic acid requires the presence of oxygen (clear area). Anaerobic phase is a relative term; true anaerobiosis is incompatible with animal metabolism.

phoric acid from ATP. Simultaneously ADP and adenylic acid (adenosine monophosphate, AMP) are formed. Oxygen is not required in this reaction; enzyme activity provides the energy source.

Often attempts are made to discuss in step fashion the vastly complex series of enzymatic reactions and oxidations involved in muscle contraction. While there is undoubtedly some merit to this approach, there is also an inherent tendency to fail to underscore the *simultaneous* nature of chemical reactions.

Following muscle fiber contraction, phosphoric acid, which is separated from ATP through enzyme involvement, combines with glycogen to synthesize ATP. This is also a nonoxidative phase.

The conversion of muscle glycogen to lactic acid, through a series of intermediate enzymatic reactions, liberates energy that is necessary for the synthesis of phosphocreatine. This also is a nonoxidative phase. Note also that this reaction represents another source of energy for the synthesis of ATP, i.e., in addition to the phosphocreatine reaction.

To this point in discussion, oxygen has played a *seemingly* unimportant role.

In actuality, the nonoxidative phases represent an extremely important chemical reserve which enables man to express himself in a variety of strenuous physical ways. At rest, physiological homeostasis is maintained at relatively low caloric cost; however, during strenuous muscular effort the rate of ATP utilization greatly exceeds the rate of muscle oxygen consumption and is reflected in increased end-products of muscle metabolism. Following energy release, nonoxidative synthesis restores an abundant supply of ATP, thereby assuring continued muscle contraction, *provided* lactic acid and pyruvic acid can be reconstituted. These acids, end-products of muscle metabolism, are converted through oxidative means. Their rates of formation bear an inverse relationship to oxygen availability at tissue level.

Lactic acid diffuses from muscle tissue into the blood stream. Its presence may be viewed as beneficial as well as detrimental to continued muscular activity. Persons possessing great tolerances to discomfort may attain a blood lactic acid concentration of 200 mg%. Excess lactic acid can also effectively halt the synthesis of ATP and muscle contraction by failing to liberate energy that is necessary for the synthesis of glycogen. Glycogen provides the energy source for phosphocreatine synthesis; phosphocreatine liberates the energy necessary for the reconstitution of ATP.

Margaria et al. present evidence indicating that 10% of the total lactic acid which is oxidized serves as the energy source for the reconversion of the remaining 90% (lactic acid) into glycogen.*

The lactic acid which diffuses into the blood stream is converted through oxidation in the liver into glycogen. This conversion process, greatly simplified and schematically represented in Figure 2–7, is known as the Cori cycle.

Lactic acid is released by the liver into the blood stream as glucose. (Another normal liver function includes the conversion of glucose to glycogen.) The blood sugar is then utilized by the tissues or is converted into glycogen—a form utilized within the muscle—or is converted to fat.

TABLE 2–1.   Body Carbohydrate Distribution of 70 kg Male (Adapted from Short[35])

Mass		Carbohydrate	gm %	gm
Muscle	28.0 kg	glycogen	0.4–0.6	112–168
Liver	1.8 kg	glycogen	1.0–6.3	18–113
Extracellular fluid	15.0 L	glucose	0.06–0.16	9–24
			TOTAL	139–305

---

*Margaria[28] more recently calculated a coefficient of combustion of lactic acid of 1:13, which he considers to be more precise than the oft quoted figure of 1:4 by Meyerhof, cited by Margaria,[28] and of 1:5 also by Meyerhof and cited by Williams.[38]

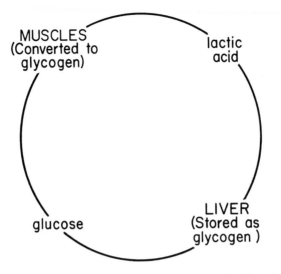

Fig. 2–7. The Cori cycle. Muscles and liver are capable of performing glyco-genic functions. During vigorous muscular effort, lactic acid is formed at a rate which exceeds its oxidation; hence, it escapes into the blood stream (repre-sented by the circular line above). In the liver the lactic acid is converted into glycogen (glycogenesis) and is stored or is converted to glucose (glycogenolysis), released into the blood stream, and carried to the muscles where it is converted into glycogen.

Pyruvic acid, shown by Margaria[28] to form at approximately one-tenth the rate of lactic acid, is convertible. During steady state, it is eventually reduced through a series of complex reactions (Krebs cycle) into carbon dioxide and water; during maximal exercise, however, it is converted to lactic acid. Lactic acid and pyruvic acid are interconvertible. During work, some lactic acid may be converted to pyruvic acid and eventually synthesized via the Krebs cycle.

Steady State

As previously stated, during basal and resting levels of metabolic activity, oxygen availability and utilization are adequate to sustain muscle cellular activity. An analysis of blood drawn during such periods would reveal the presence of a high concentration of oxygen and a low concentration of lactic acid. Even at moderately increased levels of metabolic activity, the blood oxygen-lactic acid relationships would remain essentially unchanged. Slightly elevated levels of muscular activ-ity can be maintained for extended periods of time because the increased rate of oxygen consumption is maintained by an adequate rate of oxygen transport and delivery. Stated another way, homeostasis, or *steady state* is maintained because the rate of oxygen delivery to the muscle tissue is sufficient for the level of consumption. The system is in balance. Supply equals demands.*

At markedly elevated levels of metabolic activity, there exists an imbalance between oxygen demand and supply; the rate of oxygen consumption is in excess of the rate of delivery. The arterial oxygen saturation level remains high. As a result of the imbalance between oxygen demand and supply, the blood lactic acid concentration rises. Since oxygen is necessary for the resynthesis of lactic acid, any discrepancy between oxygen demand and supply will be indicated by an increase in blood lactic acid levels. This level of activity is described as being above steady state.

Oxygen Debt

Oxygen debt is also discussed in a later chapter; however, a discussion of it is appropriate here. This term was introduced by A. V. Hill[17] as the quantity of oxygen required by the contracting muscles over and above the quantity actually supplied to them during their activity. Recall the inverse relationship which exists between oxygen availability and lactic acid formation. Thus, when the oxygen requirement of the muscle tissues is in excess of the oxygen available to the tissues, the rate of lactic acid formation is increased and the muscle tissues go into temporary debt for oxygen. The repayment of the debt—the oxidation of the increased concentration of lactic acid—is accomplished after the work has been performed and is reflected in the elevated rate (i.e., above resting rate) of oxygen consumption in the recovery process.

Red Muscle and White Muscle

When analyzed chemically, striated muscle fibers are found to differ in relation to the quantity of myoglobin within the fiber. Myoglobin is a protein substance that is chemically related to hemoglobin (Hb) and like hemoglobin possesses an affinity for the oxygen molecule.

Myofibers that possess a preponderance of myoglobin are called *red* fibers (myoglobin contains red pigment). Those that possess lesser quantities of myoglobin are called *white* fibers. Both types of fibers are found within single muscles; however, the predominance of one fiber type gives rise to one of two terms: *red muscle* or *white* muscle.

Because of high oxygen affinity, red muscles are capable of much greater endurance than are the white muscles. Red muscles are exemplified by such muscles as the anti-gravity skeletal muscles generally—the trunk and leg extensors, cardiac muscle, and the diaphragm.

---

* The term *steady state* was introduced by A. V. Hill and was related to muscular activity[17]; however, it might also be used to describe the maintenance of any physiological or chemical equilibrium.

There are relative degrees of redness within the red muscles. For example, within two muscles of the calf group, both anti-gravity muscles, the soleus muscle possesses greater amounts of myoglobin per unit area than does the gastrocnemius.

Generally, flexor muscles possess a preponderance of white fibers. Muscles of this type are characterized by speed of contraction rather than by magnitude of exerted tension.

Even a brief discussion of red and white muscle fibers is incomplete unless reference is made to the publication of Huxley.[21] Huxley cites the research of Krüger who found the cross section of muscle fibers which gave long lasting responses to differ from those fibers which gave only quick responses. Krüger also noted differences in motor nerve terminations within muscle fibers producing quick responses as compared with fibers which gave long lasting responses. This research was conducted during the early 1930's.

Chemical differentiation of skeletal muscle fibers into red and white categories has been established and accepted; however, the effect of tendon transplantation and the role of innervation have barely been investigated.

The transfer of muscle characteristics shown by Bach is of great interest. Surgical attachment of a red muscle to a white muscle tendon resulted in a reduction of myoglobin content and decrement in endurance. It appears in this example that the function of a muscle determines its chemical structure.

Buller et al. have shown that the soleus muscle of the cat, normally capable of slow sustained contraction (a red muscle characteristic) may become transformed into a fast acting muscle (a white muscle characteristic) by being denervated from its normal neural source and reinnervated through the neural pathway of a fast acting muscle. They concluded that differentiation of slow muscle activity is influenced by neural pathways in the spinal cord.

At the present time one can only speculate whether the differences in nerve conduction properties are influenced primarily chemically or primarily by frequency conductance properties. At any rate, many questions have been raised. The neat categorization and simplicity of description of red muscle properties of sustained slow contraction versus white muscle properties of quick responses and low endurance cannot be stated with absolute authority.

Gradation of Muscle Contraction

Individual muscle fibers are contained within a tough elastic membrane called the *sarcolemma*. Bundles of approximately one hundred fibers are enveloped within connective tissue to form a *fasciculus* (Latin,

fascis: a bundle of fibers, usually with reference to muscles or nerves).
Any skeletal muscle belly, e.g., that of the biceps femoris, is in reality a
collection of fasciculi. A preponderance of connective tissue at the
muscle ends constitutes the muscle *tendons* which attach the muscle
to bone. The biceps femoris is capable of exerting great force on its
tendinous attachments, especially at its point of insertion on the head of
the fibula. Yet, the biceps femoris is also capable of exerting extremely
little force through its attachments. Stated another way, the biceps
femoris is capable of exerting a force which extends along a continuum
from delicate to powerful. Its *gradation of contraction* is extensive.
Gradation implies varying degrees of force which can be exerted by
a muscle and is the resultant of the degree of motor unit involvement
or degree of *recruitment.*

Functionally then, the *motor unit,* or motoneuron, is of extreme
importance because its involvement determines the extent of contraction—the gradation, the magnitude of the response, the degree of recruitment. A motor unit is composed of a single axon and the muscle fibers
innervated by the axon.

The obvious differences in tension and speed between such muscles
as the rectus superior, which controls eye movement, and the biceps
femoris are further explained by the innervation ratio. The innervation
ratio of a muscle is the ratio of the number of muscle fibers to the
number of motor axons within the nerve which serve it. Lower innervation ratios permit more precise gradation of contraction.

Clark calculated innervation ratios ranging between 1:120 and 1:165
in the leg muscles of a cat.[8] Based upon size differences, motor units
within the biceps femoris in man are assumed to be greater. By contrast
the rectus superior muscle possesses innervation ratios between 1:3
and 1:6.

Smooth or Involuntary Muscle

In comparison with skeletal muscle, smooth muscle does not exhibit
the light and dark striations. It is innervated by the autonomic nervous
system and performs a myriad of functions such as controlling the
lumen of blood vessels, the ducts of glands, the peristaltic actions of
the intestinal tract and stomach, and ocular movements. Each muscle
fiber unit possesses a single nucleus. It is characterized by slowness
of contraction and relaxation—the slowness of recovery being attributed
by Bozler[4] to its viscosity. He also reported smooth muscle fibers to be
short, i.e., up to 200 μ in length.

Bozler also distinguished two types of smooth muscle: those within
the viscera which display autorhythmicity (a physiological property
similar to that exhibited by cardiac muscle tissue) and those within the

vascular walls which are innervated via the efferent pathway (a striated muscle characteristic). He presented the comparison which follows:

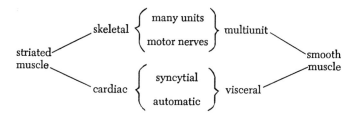

Tonicity is maintained in smooth muscle for extended periods of time and, as suggested by Johnson et al., may be related to its characteristic labile (unstable) molecular arrangement.

Cardiac Muscle Tissue

Again by comparison with smooth and striated muscle, cardiac muscle tissue exhibits a less clearly defined myofibril-nucleus arrangement. This multinucleated protoplasmic mass is referred to as a syncytium. It is dually innervated via the involuntary nerve system by the vagus nerve (cardio-inhibitory) and the cardiac nerves (cardio-accelerator).

As stated in Bowditch's law, any stimulus applied to cardiac muscle tissue will result in maximal response. Because of the syncytial arrangement, cardiac muscle tissue responds as a whole to a stimulus. Unlike skeletal tissue, cardiac muscle tissue does not exhibit graded responses from graded stimuli (Fig. 2–12).

To a small degree, skeletal and smooth muscle tissues are capable of being regenerated whereas cardiac muscle tissue is not. Scarring—connective tissue replacement—is a matter of concern in tissue hypoxia following coronary occlusion.

End-Plate Potentials

The axon terminates within a specialized part of the muscle membrane, an area referred to as the end-plate region or myoneural junction.

Fatt described one type of end-plate chemical receptor which is depolarized by acetylcholine, thus initiating the contraction of the actomyosin fibers.[12] Within milliseconds the enzyme acetylcholinesterase inactivates acetylcholine causing repolarization of the muscle end-plate and thereby creating a situation favorable to the initiation of another contraction. The importance of acetylcholine was described by Dale and Feldberg,[9,10] by Nachmansohn and Wilson, and by Fatt and Katz. Acetylcholine is common to excitable tissue and is essential to nerve impulse propagation by virtue of its action on the end-plate to increase membrane permeability.

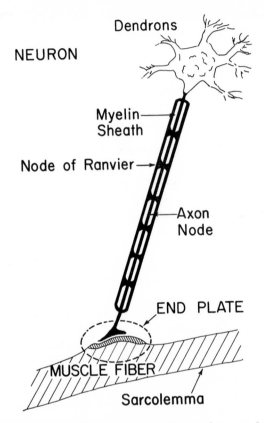

Dendrons

NEURON

Myelin—
Sheath

Node of Ranvier→

Axon
Node

END PLATE

MUSCLE FIBER

Sarcolemma

Fig. 2–8.   Neuron and end-plate region. Arising in the ventral horn of the spinal cord, motor nerve fibers through a single axon ramify the muscle quite extensively. Each muscle fiber is innervated by at least one motor nerve fiber. (Adapted from Acheson.[1] Courtesy of American Physiological Society.)

Nerve and Muscle Fiber Action Potential

Action potential, an electric current elicited in active nerve and muscle tissue, was first described by du Bois Reymond.[7]

As described by Hodgkin[18] and by Rushton, the normal means for conducted action potential (excitation) is by a circulating electric current, above threshold intensity, resulting from muscle and nerve activity.

In particular, the propagation of the impulse involves muscle and nerve membrane permeability to sodium (Na^+), potassium (K^+), and chloride (Cl^-). Fundamentally, nearly all cells accumulate K^+ and expel Na^+, and normally, cell membranes are moderately permeable to K^+ and Cl^- and almost impermeable to Na^+. The *resting potential* of muscle and nerve fibers signifies that the membrane is *almost* imperme-

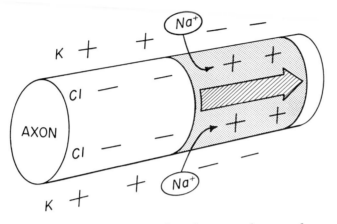

Fig. 2-9. Propagation of an impulse along the axon indicates a change of membrane permeability which permits an influx of Na^+ ions across the membrane. During the *resting potential* state, the K^+ concentration on both sides of the membrane is constant. During the *action potential* state the influx of Na^+ ions through the membrane results in depolarization of the membrane (shaded area).

able to Na^+, but at the zenith of *action potential* the membrane *is* permeable to Na^+. Repolarization* was shown by Desmedt to be a function of membrane permeability to K^+ and rate of repolarization to be directly related to the internal K^+ concentration.[14]

Hodgkin and Keynes described the functioning of a sodium-potassium pump.[19] During the period of recovery from muscular activity the sodium-potassium pump serves to maintain constancy of chemical composition in the cells, but is only indirectly involved in the mechanism of the action potential.

Stimulus and Response

The magnitude of striated muscle response is dependent upon a number of factors. One factor relates to the stimulus. Although initially induced through a variety of ways—chemical, electrical, mechanical, and thermal—all muscle responses are the result of a chemo-electrical phenomenon. The chemical reaction at the end-plate region effects polarity. Additional factors which affect magnitude and duration of striated muscle contraction include: number, frequency, and strength of stimuli; length of refractory period; temperature; and fatigue products resulting in pH changes.

---

* Polarity signifies opposite electrical charges; following depolarization, the outer muscle and nerve membrane surface is positive with respect to a negative membrane inner surface.

3

Bowditch's all-or-none law was formulated for cardiac muscle tissue; however, the law has also been applied to striated muscle tissue. As it relates to striated muscle fiber, the all-or-none law provides that a stimulus that is of sufficient intensity to evoke a response results in maximal response of the muscle *fiber*, i.e., the fiber responds maximally in relation to its capability. Further, contraction capability is dependent upon muscle temperature and pH. *Gradation of contraction* and *recruitment* present evidence of varying degrees of stimulus intensities as well as number of motor units innervated in whole muscles.

As it relates to a single fiber, a stimulus that is of insufficient intensity to evoke a response is termed *subminimal, subliminal,* or *subthreshold.* By comparison, a stimulus that elicits a muscle fiber response is called *minimal, liminal,* or *threshold.* As the stimulus relates to a striated muscle *fiber*, the *fiber* either responds maximally or it does not respond at all. Within the whole muscle, where recruitment and gradation of contraction are much in evidence, muscle fibers continue to obey the all-or-none law; however, *muscle fibers differ in threshold levels.* Thus, varying the intensity of the stimuli will result in progressively greater responses. Additional myofibrils with varying threshold levels are *recruited.* Obviously, a plateau is attained at a time when all myofibers within the muscle are stimulated and the muscle is responding maximally. Increases in intensity of stimuli will evoke no further response: the stimulus intensity is described as *supramaximal.*

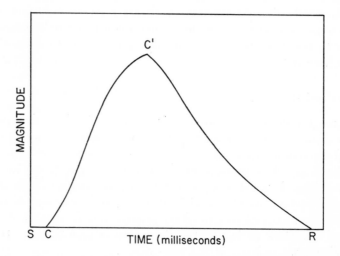

Fig. 2–10.   Pattern of simple muscle contraction. Stimulus applied at S, muscle begins to contract at C. Time interval between S and C is designated the latent period. C to C′ represents shortening contraction phase. C′ to R represents relaxation (or recovery) phase. Heat is liberated throughout the period from S to R.

The response of a striated muscle fiber to a single stimulus is illustrated in Figure 2–10.

With the aid of delicate, precise apparatus and under controlled laboratory conditions, the latent period may be reduced. Despite the refinements, a latent period will be present. The latent period is the interval of elapsed time between application of stimulus and manifestation of contraction. During this period, which is characterized by the development of tension, molecular rearrangement and depolarization within the muscle fiber occur.

The movement of a whole limb or even part of a limb in response to a stimulus may be characterized by a more pronounced latent period. This pronounced latent period may be due to one or a combination of such factors as joint structure, inertia to be overcome, level of physiological development of muscle, degree of muscle fatigue, and number of muscle groups involved.

Normal Patterns of Striated Muscle Response

Depicted in Figure 2–10 is a twitch, a spasmodic momentary contraction of a single muscle fiber.

A whole muscle, composed of many myofibrils with varying threshold intensities, exhibits several different patterns of contraction. A number of factors affect the pattern of contraction. One of these is the refractory state of the muscle, the receptivity of the muscle to more than single stimuli. Furthermore, refractory states are either absolute or relative. For example, if a second stimulus of like intensity, closely following the first and applied during the contraction phase, fails to elicit a greater contraction amplitude than one elicited by a single stimulus, the muscle is said to be *refractory,* or unresponsive, or in *absolute refractory state.* Yet, if a second *stronger* stimulus closely following the first is applied during the contraction phase, the muscle is once again responsive and provides an example of a *relative refractory state.* By varying the interval between threshold intensity stimuli, a second contraction may be elicited; the responsiveness of the muscle has assumed more normal characteristics. Thus, it is possible to alter the magnitude and the pattern of skeletal muscle contraction by varying the frequency and the strength of the stimuli. Ramsey[33] points out that an increase in muscle temperature is related to a shortening of the relative refractory period.

Again, complete or incomplete tetanus is a relative concept which includes a consideration of the frequency and the strength of stimuli.

Under constant, regulated stimuli, an isolated muscle clamped to laboratory apparatus exhibits an eventual decrease in amplitude which reflects a decrease in tension, hence exerted force. In addition, the latent

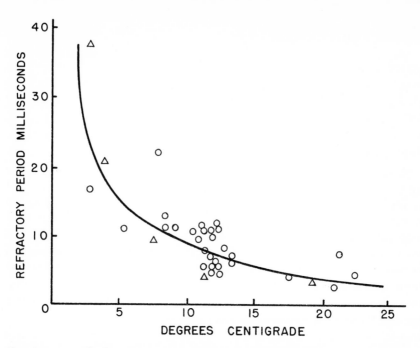

Fig. 2–11.   Absolute refractory periods of single muscle fibers as a function of temperature. The triangles represent refractory periods of a single muscle fiber at different temperatures; the circles represent absolute refractory periods at indicated temperatures. (From Ramsey,[33] in Rodahl and Horvath: *Muscle As a Tissue.* Courtesy of McGraw-Hill Book Co.)

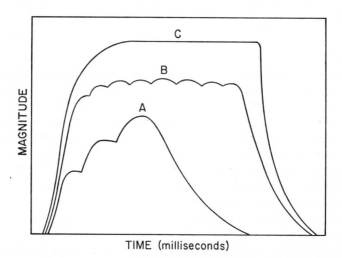

Fig. 2–12.   Response of skeletal muscle to varying frequency of stimuli. *A,* Summation pattern, is produced by low rate, ca 15/sec; *B,* incomplete tetanus, is produced by a moderate rate, ca 50/sec; *C,* complete tetanus is produced by a high rate, ca 100/sec. The usual type of contraction in situ is that of complete tetanus.

24

period is increased, the contraction and refractory periods are longer, and the muscle fails to return to its initial length. These are patterns of depleted chemical stores and of accumulated end-products of muscle metabolism. In short, these are patterns of fatigue.

Tonicity (Tonus)

Man's muscle system is extensive and its functioning is dependent upon stimuli and upon a series of complex chemical reactions. The end result is a variety of physical feats performed under a variety of conditions.

Even during complete rest, skeletal muscles respond to stimuli through the efferent neural pathway. During this period, a very small percentage of the myofibrils is being stimulated. The evidence is present in the form of tonicity, that is, the feeling of muscle firmness, of tension within the muscle. A minimal degree of force is exerted. There is an active yet involuntary resistance to stretch. With gravitational force and body weight as the combined inertia to be overcome, a variety of inactive body positions is maintained through skeletal muscle tonicity. Thus, skeletal muscle tonicity is greatest in standing, less in sitting, and least in lying positions. The transformation from a passive to an active body position represents a change in tension which demands an increase in frequency and intensity of stimuli, a greater degree of recruitment, and a greater gradation of contraction.

Muscle Contraction

Skeletal muscle actions are variable and are mechanically antagonistic but functionally *associated antagonistic;* physical expression is the resultant of associated antagonistic muscle action.

As exemplified in the freely moveable joint *diarthroses enarthrosis,* muscle action may produce flexion *or* extension, abduction *or* adduction, and medial *or* lateral rotation. The flexor muscle group exerts a force which is diametrical to that of the extensor group, but through *reciprocal innervation** either flexion or extension may be accomplished. The role of the stabilizer muscles must also be recognized.

Some of the terms which are in current use to describe muscle contraction are precise; some meaningless. The functional classification of muscle contraction is based upon the terminology of Adolph Fick[14] who in 1882 used the words *isotonic* to denote constant load and *isometric* to denote constant length.

---

* An increase in tension in the principal effectors of movement is accompanied by a decrease in tension in the antagonists thus allowing movement.

A scheme of classification of the three types of skeletal (as well as smooth and cardiac) muscle contraction was proposed by Fenn and is presented in Table 2–2.

TABLE 2–2.   Types and Characteristics of Muscle Contraction

Type of Contraction	Work	Application	Effect on Tension of Increasing Velocity	Rate of Energy Supply
Shortening	Positive	Acceleration	Decreases	Increases
Isometric	Nil	Maintenance		
Lengthening	Negative	Deceleration	Increases	Decreases

The "nil" external work accomplished in isometric contraction is explained in the scientific sense: work is the product of force acting against mass through a distance.

$$W = Fs$$

where: W (work) = F (force) s(distance mass is moved)

In the physical sense, merely holding a 20 kg weight in the hands is not work because the weight is not moved; however, energy is expended and the exercise is fatiguing because of the effort required to exert an upward force to counteract the downward force of the 20 kg load.

Less precise words or terms which are used to describe isotonic muscle contraction include concentric contraction (shortening contraction), eccentric contraction (lengthening contraction), and dynamic contraction. Isometric contraction is often referred to as static contraction.

Other descriptive words which are used to describe muscle contraction are *pliometric* and *miometric*. Of Greek derivation, miometric, from *meiosis*, describes a *lessening* (in tension); pliometric, from *pleio*, means more or *increasing* (in tension).

Warming-Up

Warming-up, in athletic parlance, is descriptive of a routine which induces body temperature gains. These gains may be accomplished through a myriad of forms but fall basically into two categories. In the first example, heat may be obtained from an external source; the continuum extends from the application of analgesic preparations to the use of microwave therapy. Or, heat may be generated from an internal source as exemplified by the elevation of body shell and core temperatures that result from vigorous physical movement. Attendant increases in cardiac frequency, respiration rate, and blood pressure level are also noted.

Often, warm-up is a feeling, a psychological state.

Karpovich has maintained a perennial interest in the effect of warm-up on physical performance.[25] In a study conducted by Karpovich and Pestrecov subjects who engaged in warming-up (ergocycle riding without load prior to endurance riding against load) performed more poorly than subjects who were denied the warm up trial. In 1934 Karpovich introduced the terms *formal warming-up* and *general warming-up* to denote physical exercises which are either related to the task or activity (formal) or informal or unrelated exercises (general).[24] Asmussen and Bøje reported, in 1945, the beneficial effects of exercise, short-wave diathermy, and hot showers to sprint running events and to bicycle ergometer performance. Massage as a warm-up technique produced no beneficial effect. In 1956, Karpovich and Hale presented evidence of the nonbeneficial effect of massage and warming-up on running or ergocycle sprint riding.

The study by Massey et al. sheds light on one of a multiplicity of considerations affecting physical performance. Under the influence of suggestion (no conscious awareness of having warmed-up) prior to the induction of deep hypnosis, warmed-up subjects performed less well on an ergocycle than did the group who had no prior warm-up.

The accomplishment of great athletic feats is usually accompanied by elevated body temperatures as well as by increased cardiovascular-pulmonary responses. Just as cardiovascular-pulmonary efficiency is negated in sprinting events, so might warm-up be negated in distance running events. The data are conflicting; much additional, carefully conducted research is needed before conclusive results can be gleaned.

Because man is receptive to many influences, he is also quite unpredictable. Warming-up may be a fetish. Depending upon man's physical and physiological responses as well as his pattern of behavior, warming-up may or may not be necessary. Man, after all, is a psychophysiological being.

REFERENCES

1. Acheson, G. H.: Physiology of neuro-muscular junctions: chemical aspects. *Fed. Proc.*, 7:447–457, 1948.

2. Asmussen, E., and Bøje, O.: Body temperature and capacity for work. *Acta Physiol. Scand.*, 10:1–22, 1945.

3. Bach, L. M. N.: Conversion of red muscle to pale muscle. *Proc. Soc. Exper. Biol. and Med.*, 67:268–269, 1948.

4. Bozler, E.: Smooth Muscle. *In* Rodahl, K., and Horvath, S. M. (Eds.): *Muscle As A Tissue*. New York, McGraw-Hill Book Co., 1962.

5. Buchthal, F., and Kaiser, E.: The rheology of the cross striated muscle fiber with particular reference to isotonic conditions. *Dan. Biol. Medd., 21*:(7) 1–318, 1951.

6. Buller, A. J., Eccles, J. C., and Eccles, R. M.: Differentiation of fast and slow muscles in the cat hind limb. *J. Physiol, 150*:399–416, 1960.

7. Castiglioni, A.: *A History of Medicine*. 2nd ed., Edited by E. B. Krumbhaar, New York, Alfred A. Knopf Co., 1958.

8. Clark, D. A.: Muscle counts of motor units: a study in innervation ratios. *Am. J. Physiol., 96*:296–304, 1931.

9. Dale, H. H., and Feldberg, W.: The chemical transmitter of vagus effects to the stomach. *J. Physiol., 81*:320–334, 1934.

10. Dale, H. H., and Feldberg, W.: Chemical transmission at motor nerve endings in voluntary muscle? *J. Physiol., 81*:39P–40P, 1934.

11. Desmedt, J. E.: Electrical activity and intracellular sodium concentration in frog muscle. *J. Physiol., 121*:191–205, 1953.

12. Fatt, P.: Biophysics of functional transmission. *Physiol. Rev., 34*:674–710, 1954.

13. Fatt, P., and Katz, B.: An analysis of the end-plate potential recorded with an intra-cellular electrode. *J. Physiol., 115*:320–370, 1951.

14. Fenn, W. O.: Muscles. *In* Höber, H. (Ed.): *Physical Chemistry of Cells and Tissues*. Philadelphia, The Blakiston Company, 1948.

15. Fulton, J. F.: *Selected Readings in the History of Physiology*. Springfield, Charles C Thomas, 1930.

16. Gray, H.: *Anatomy of the Human Body*. 28th Ed. Edited by C. M. Goss, Philadelphia, Lea & Febiger, 1966.

17. Hill, A. V.: *Muscular Movement in Man*. New York, McGraw-Hill Book Co., 1927.

18. Hodgkin, A. L.: Evidence for electrical transmission in nerve. *J. Physiol.,* Part I, *90*:183–210, 1937; Part II, *90*:211–232, 1937.

19. Hodgkin, A. L., and Keynes, R. D.: Experiments on the injection of substances into squid giant axons by means of a microsyringe. *J. Physiol., 131*:592–616, 1956.

20. Huxley, A. F.: Muscle structure and theories of contraction. *In Progress in Biophysics and Biophysical Chemistry*. Vol. 7, London, Pergamon Press, 1957.

21. Huxley, A. F.: Skeletal Muscle. *In* Rodahl, K., and Horvath, S. M. (Eds.): *Muscle As A Tissue*. New York, McGraw-Hill Book Co., 1962.

22. Huxley, H. E.: The mechanism of muscular contraction. *Scientific Am., 213*: 18–27, 1965.

23. Johnson, W. H., Kahn, J. S., and Szent-Györgyi, A. G.: Paramyosin and contraction of "catch muscles." *Science, 130*: 160–161, 1959.

24. Karpovich, P. V.: The physiology of athletics. *Scholastic Coach, 4*:22–23, 1934.

25. Karpovich, P. V.: *Physiology of Muscular Activity.* 6th Ed., Philadelphia, W. B. Saunders Co., 1965.

26. Karpovich, P. V., and Hale, C.: Effect of warming-up upon physical performance, *J.A.M.A., 162*:1117–1119, 1956.

27. Karpovich, P. V., and Pestrecov, K.: Effect of gelatin upon muscular work in man. *Am. J. Physiol., 134*:300–309, 1941.

28. Margaria, R.: Physiology of exercise. *In* Jokl, E., and Simon, E. (Eds.): *International Research in Sport and Physical Education.* Springfield, Charles C Thomas, 1964.

29. Margaria, R., Edwards, H. T., and Dill, D. B.: The possible mechanisms of contracting and paying the oxygen debt and the role of lactic acid in muscular contraction. *Am. J. Physiol., 106*:689–715, 1933.

30. Massey, B. H., Johnson, W. R., and Kramer, G. F.: Effect of warm-up exercise upon muscular performance using hypnosis to control the psychological variable. *Res. Quart., 32*:63–71, 1961.

31. Nachmansohn, D., and Wilson, I. B.: Molecular basis for generation of bioelectric potentials. *In* Shedlovsky, T. (Ed.): *Electrochemistry in Biology and Medicine.* New York, John Wiley & Sons, 1955.

32. Nordenskiöld, E.: *The History of Biology.* New York, Tudor Publishing Company, 1936.

33. Ramsey, R. F.: Cardiac Muscle. *In* Rodahl, K., and Horvath, S. M.: *Muscle As A Tissue.* New York, McGraw-Hill Book Co., 1962.

34. Rushton, W. A. H.: The initiation of the nervous impulse. *J. Physiol., 90*: 5P–6P, 1937.

35. Short, R.: *A Synopsis of Physiology.* 5th Ed. Edited by C. C. N. Vass, Baltimore, The Williams & Wilkins Co., 1961.

36. Szent-Györgyi, A.: *Chemistry of Muscular Contraction.* New York, Academic Press Inc., 1947.

37. Szent-Györgyi, A. G.: Aspects of the chemistry of muscle contraction. *In* Rodahl, K., and Horvath, S. M. (Eds.): *Muscle As A Tissue.* New York, McGraw-Hill Book Co., 1962.

38. Williams, G. R.: Metabolism in muscular activity. *In* Best, C. H., and Taylor, N. B. (Eds.): *The Physiological Basis of Medical Practice.* 7th Ed. Baltimore, The Williams & Wilkins Co., 1961.

39. Zierler, K. L.: Mechanism of muscle contraction and its energetics. *In* Bard, P. (Ed.): *Medical Physiology.* 11th Ed. St. Louis, C. V. Mosby Co., 1961.

Chapter

3

NEURAL CONTROL OF
MUSCLE ACTIVITY

Through an extensive maze of afferent and efferent neural pathways, an efficient functioning and integration of the entire organism called man is effected. All movement involves the coordinated functioning of these neural pathways which may be classified into either structural or functional categories. The structural classification incorporates two integral subdivisions: central and peripheral. The brain, consisting of all nervous matter within the cranium, and the spinal cord constitute the central nervous system. A connecting nerve system, the peripheral nervous system, also ramifies extensively throughout the body.

A functional, rather than structural, classification produces greater meaning. Within the functional classification, somatic and autonomic systems are recognized and each of these systems possesses central as well as peripheral portions. The somatic system becomes essential to nervimuscular discussion. The autonomic system, consisting of parasympathetic and sympathetic divisions, is composed of nerve tissue which forms an integral part of the hypothalamus, medulla, midbrain, and spinal cord where its peripheral fibers travel with those of the somatic nervous system in the cranial and spinal nerves.

The somatic nervous system is frequently called the voluntary system, a term which describes a degree of control of voluntary muscle contraction. By contrast, parasympathetic and sympathetic divisions of the autonomic system exert an involuntary influence over cardiac muscle as well as smooth muscle within the viscera and blood vessels as well as glands. Because of the diametrical effects produced on these structures through dual innervation, from sympathetic and parasympathetic divisions, the autonomic system also functions as an antagonistic system and is variously called the visceral or involuntary or vegetative nervous system.

Of interest is the evolution of the word sympathetic. In 1723 a segment of the nervous system, thought by the Dane, Jakob Winslow, to deal with the "sympathies" of the body, thus became known as the sympathetic nervous system. Almost two hundred years later, in 1916, Gaskell, who showed this system to emerge from the spinal cord in the cranial, thoracolumbar, and sacral regions, was instrumental in changing the name to involuntary nervous system. It was later renamed the autonomic nervous system by Langley (1852–1925) who also coined the term parasympathetic nervous system.[8]

Both divisions of the autonomic system possess centers within the hypothalamus, midbrain, and medulla oblongata; however, as seen in Table 3–1, each division is specific.

TABLE 3–1. Functional Classification of the Autonomic Nervous System

Parasympathetic or Craniosacral Division	*Sympathetic or Thoracolumbar Division*
Cranial segment: cranial nerves 3, 7, 9, 10	Thoracic segment: thoracic nerves 1 through 12
Sacral segment: sacral nerves 2, 3, 4	Lumbar segment: lumbar nerves 1, 2, 3

Movement is dependent upon reflex as well as voluntary control; however, movement implies more than the use of muscles and nerves. It involves sense organs and stimuli. For example, movement often involves the perception of the nature or source of stimulation. Perception, a recognition through memorization and association of the quality and nature of an object, involves sense organs. These sense organs are described by Granit as ". . . our 'private' measuring instruments and like instruments, they have properties such as sensitivity, range, speed, and power of resolution."[12] In a real sense, one lifts an object with his eyes as well as with his muscles; the integrative action of the nervous system assures success in lifting. While not focusing primarily on the neural mechanism, A. V. Hill noted that intact muscles [sensed] the inertia to be overcome and regulated their energy release accordingly.[18-20] A simple experiment can be employed to demonstrate this. Three fruit juice cans of identical size (approximately 1 liter) and label are required. After the contents of two cans have been removed through bottom openings, one of the two cans is filled with sand before both

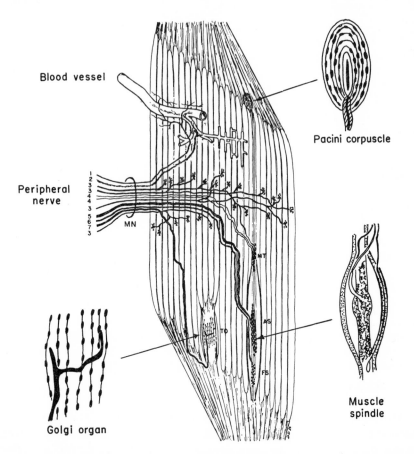

Fig. 3–1.   Schematic drawing of anatomic relationship between muscle, nerve, and proprioceptors. Arising from the anterior horn of the spinal cord, efferent and afferent fibers of the peripheral nerve, *MN*, ramify into the muscle. Innervation of motor end-plates is accomplished through the larger efferent fibers (3,3,3,3) while the end-plates of muscle spindles, *MT*, are innervated by smaller efferent fibers (4,4). Afferent fibers such as (5) innervate the annulospiral ending, *AS*, of the muscle spindles; (7) serves the Golgi end organ, *TO*. Medium sized afferent fibers (6) innervate the muscle spindle, *FS*, through the flower-spray organ of Ruffini. Smaller afferent fibers (1) innervate the connective tissue coating of blood vessels; (2) represents a sympathetic nerve fiber which controls diameter of small arteries and arterioles. Ruffini ending is not to be associated with the muscle spindle alone. These endings are located in fasciae, tendons, and joints as well. Likewise, Pacini corpuscles are widely distributed in similar locations. (Adapted from Adams and Denny-Brown.[1] Courtesy of Paul B. Hoeber, Inc. Insert, muscle spindle, from Barker.[5] Courtesy of Royal Microscopical Society of London.)

are resealed. The three cans are placed in an upright, adjacent position on a table. For most dramatic effects, the cans should be placed in the following order: sand-filled, A; empty, B; juice-filled, C. An unsuspecting subject who is instructed to lift each can in ABC order will be momentarily unable to lift A and may literally fling can B over his shoulder before he can accomplish a neuromuscular adjustment. The response to C will be highly variable among subjects.

The fruit juice can represents a recognizable degree of inertia which the subject, through memorization and association, will normally and easily overcome by the recruitment of sufficient muscle fiber bundles. The ensuing gradation of contraction is usually equal to the task of overcoming inertia.

Past experience and association have led the subject to anticipate the degree of inertia which is offered by a fruit juice can. His mental image has been reinforced by virtue of his having previously lifted fruit juice cans of similar size. Mainly through somatic nervous system involvement, both central and peripheral, a "sufficient" number of muscle fibers are activated. Can A, however, offers more resistance than the number of activated muscle fibers are capable of overcoming and momentarily the can is unmoved. Simultaneously the autonomic nervous system becomes involved as manifested by an increased cardiac frequency, increased blood pressure, and an increased respiration rate. The predetermined effort, guided by visual afferents and thought to be "sufficient," was soon found to be embarrassingly inadequate to the task; however, within an interval of milliseconds, the nervimuscular mechanism is successfully adjusted.

The subject, now faced with can B (empty), is perplexed. The experience with can A is translated into an excessive force which is converted to speed and distance before conscious and unconscious feedback modify the impulse to the muscle groups involved in the act.

In such a simple act as lifting three cans with familiar labels, many nervimuscular adjustments were required. Reflex activity was in evidence as characterized by an involuntary motor response to the stimulus. More specifically, muscle spindles were deeply involved as were such receptors as Golgi tendon organs and corpuscles of Pacini (Fig. 3–1). The can-lifting act also provides a classic example of the functioning of the gamma loop.

Proprioception

Accomplishment of a coordinated motor act is dependent upon constant sensory stimuli set up by the act itself which "feed back" the results of the act and produce correction in the nervous system. In a word, the "feedback" of sensory information—specifically information from those sense organs which are stimulated by body position and movement—which evokes responses in skeletal muscles is called proprioception. Proprioceptors,* widely distributed throughout the body, may be classified as kinesthetic and vestibular. Both perform essential roles in the accomplishment of skillful performance. All receptors respond to stimuli in a similar manner. Provided the stimulus is of sufficient intensity, the sense receptors respond by producing generator potentials which, in turn, initiate impulses in neurons. Excitation of the effector, by neural transmission, produces the response.

Receptor organs, variously called afferent end-organs or sensory receptors, are widely distributed over the body and are specific to stimuli. Receptors may also be classified as interoceptive (those located within the viscera, gastrointestinal tract, respiratory tract, and cardiovascular system) or exteroceptive (receptors located within the integument, ears, eyes, and mucous membranes).[11] They also may be classified according to the type of stimulus to which each is sensitive, viz. chemoreceptors, cryoreceptors, mechanoreceptors, nociceptors, osmoreceptors, phonoreceptors, photoreceptors, tactoreceptors, and thermoreceptors.

Each receptor is particularly sensitive to a particular type of stimulus (law of adequate stimulus). Thermoreceptors possess much greater sensitivity than do the nociceptive receptors.

Kinesthetic sense receptors include the muscle spindles, Golgi tendon organs, and corpuscles of Pacini. All contribute to the kinesthesia, or muscle sense, which enables man to perceive. Even if blindfolded or placed in a darkened room, each of us would possess a mental image of the position of our limbs and body parts. The sense of vision is unnecessary. Sensory endings within the skeletal muscles, tendons, and joints enable us to "feel" the location of our body parts. This muscle sense was described by Sherrington as an ". . . impression that my mind, aware of the limb (without looking at it) and its posture, then in its effort at attention to that experience, conjures up a visual memory of what the limb looks like in that posture."[37]

Granit placed great importance on the muscle spindle in kinesthesia and stressed its role as an "autogenetic governor" of activity.[18] He referred to the self-regulating role of the "autogenetic governor" as the "muscle machine . . . first aiding it to contract, then dampening the discharge from its motoneurons."

Alpha and Gamma Efferent Fibers

The designations alpha (α) and gamma (γ) serve as a descriptive basis for the differentiation of the diameters of the efferent axons which

---

* The word proprioceptor was coined by Sherrington.[38]

terminate on extrafusal fibers of the muscle and on the intrafusal fibers of the neuromuscular spindle respectively. The relationship between axon diameter and propagation velocity is an essentially positive one. Hursh noted that propagation velocity is generally greater in neurons that are medullated and larger in diameter (Fig. 3–2).

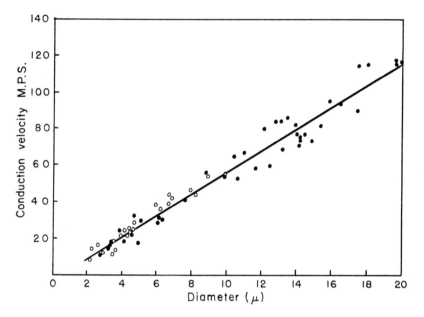

Fig. 3–2. Conduction velocity plotted as a function of nerve diameter. The best curve relating velocity and diameter is a straight line. Solid dots denote conduction velocity in adult cats; open circles, kittens. (Adapted from Hursh.[24] Courtesy of American Physiological Society.)

Rossi was among the first to visualize the role of muscle spindle innervation. Hunt noted the richness of spindle efferent innervation: approximately 30% of the efferent fibers are directed to the muscle spindle and are designated gamma efferent fibers. By comparison, the remaining efferent fibers which innervate the extrafusal (skeletal) fibers possess larger diameters and are designated alpha efferent fibers. Afferent (sensory) fibers which innervate the muscle spindle are alpha in size, but to avoid confusion are designated Ia (annulospirals) and II (flower sprays). Golgi tendon organ afferents, also of alpha size, are designated Ib. The locus of innervation is specific: afferent fibers innervate the muscle spindle along its equatorial region, whereas efferent fibers innervate the spindle ends.

Feedback Loop

A description of the stretch reflex, presented on page 40, serves to point out the interrelationships among extrafusal and intrafusal muscle fibers and the "proprioceptive triad." Coordinated physical expression involves far more extensive and complex neural involvement and control. Irrespective of the extent of involvement and of skill level exhibited, the muscle spindle is in the midst of all physical expression.

Discharge of the alpha efferent neurons is excitatory to muscle fibers. An inhibiting capability accomplished by a decrease in the discharge frequency of motor neurons, is also in evidence. The combined effect of alpha efferent discharge and of inhibition provides an important control mechanism which constitutes the feedback loop. Control mechanisms, called "servomechanisms" by Granit,[13] involve collateral axons as well as inhibitory interneuronal cells within the spinal cord. These inhibitory interneurons, some of which are called Renshaw cells, control motoneural activity by either inhibiting additional motoneural activity (negative feedback) or by inhibiting an already existing inhibition (disinhibition).

Muscle Spindles

Muscle spindles are macroscopic, fusiform, sensory end-organs which are located between skeletal muscle fibers. Each spindle may consist of as many as ten intrafusal muscle fibers enclosed within a sheath of connective tissue. Differences between the muscle spindles and muscle fibers (extrafusal) are pronounced. Within their central portion, the intrafusal fibers lack the characteristic cross striations of skeletal muscle tissue.

Located within the central (equatorial) portion of these intrafusal fibers* are the annulospiral (or primary) nerve endings. Situated at the juxta-equatorial region of the spindle, toward the polar ends, are the secondary or flower-spray endings of Ruffini.

When a muscle begins to contract, as in lifting can A (pp. 31, 33), the number of contracting motor units, being insufficient for the weight of the can, contributes to muscle stretching and spindle discharging. Any distortion of either annulospiral or flower spray endings elicits a response along specific neural pathways. Annulospiral distortion produces an afferent discharge in its large, fast conducting, Ia afferent fibers and results in a motor response by direct (monosynaptic) excitation of motor neurons to extrafusals. The muscle which had become momentarily stretched (by can A) now contracts. An example of the functioning of

---

* Eldred has recently presented evidence for two types of intrafusal fibers.

the gamma loop, of gamma bias, and of muscle spindle involvement may be observed in the can lifting experiment. Previous experience with can lifting (which was memorized) had the effect of voluntarily "setting" a gamma bias. Because cans A and B offered resistance outside the "setting" of the gamma bias, the effects of the actual load prompted feedback correction. All cans elicited reflex modification of the contraction. Muscle spindle stretch was increased or decreased in comparison to the initial, existing gamma bias.

The precise nature of the simultaneous, flower-spray ending discharge has not been fully described. Small, gamma-2 neurons have been identified; however, their function is not fully understood. Mountcastle describes the gamma-2 as slower acting; their propagation velocity is approximately one-half the velocity of the gamma-1 efferents.

Receptors may become less responsive or even cease to respond to stimuli of constant intensity. This phenomenon, of *adaptation*, offers an explanation for varying sensory experiences. Adrian demonstrated this phenomenon (Fig 3–3). An initial direct relationship between strength of stimulus and strength of discharge is exhibited; however, the discharge of the receptor organ diminishes in response to stimuli which

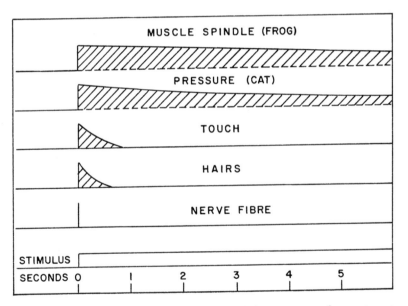

Fig. 3–3. Response of nerve fiber and of different types of receptors to a continued stimulus. Receptor organs differ in their response to stimuli of constant intensity. The muscle spindle (top) is said to fire at a high rate which decreases slightly as stimulus is maintained. By comparison, hair follicle receptors (next to bottom) fire at low rate. Adaptation is most rapid in the nerve fiber and slowest in the muscle spindle. (From Adrian.[2] Courtesy of W. W. Norton Company.)

are maintained at constant levels. On the basis of Adrian's data it is understandable how people (especially those with a shock of hair) fail after awhile to "feel" the lightweight hat or even the heavy helmet they wear. Likewise, a leg immersed in a hot or cold whirlpool bath "feels" more comfortable a few minutes after the initial and sometimes "agonizing" exposure.

In the above example, the sense receptors, in the expression of Guyton, adapted to "extinction" within a short period.[15] By contrast, muscle spindles and Golgi tendon organs adapt very little. By this means, an individual is constantly aware of the positions of his body segments or of the status of the tension within his muscle groups. Man becomes unaware of the glasses perched atop his nose and over his ears and soon becomes unaware of the fact that he is holding a textbook, but he is constantly aware of the fact that his forearms are flexed.

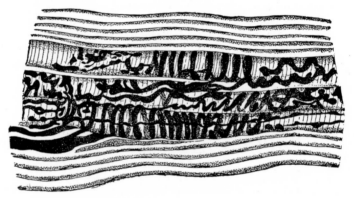

Fig. 3–4.   Muscle spindle embedded within skeletal muscle fibers. (After Ruffini.) (From Gray.[14] Lea & Febiger.)

The muscle spindles were classified by Ruffini as being among the most developed of the sense receptors in the body, "Apart from the organs of special sense (eye, ear, etc.) the body possesses no terminal organ that can compare with these [spindles] in richness of nerve fibers and of nerve endings."

Hunt reported the extensiveness of spindle innervation. Roughly 30% of the efferent fibers distributed into skeletal muscle innervates the intrafusal fibers of the muscle spindles.

Vestibular Proprioception

Perceiving sounds is the particular function of the ears; however, the ears must be considered in another important light, that of equilibration. More precisely termed vestibulocochlear organs, the ears play an important role in equilibrium as well as hearing. Adrian referred to the ear as "the most elaborate of the mechanically operated sense organs."[4]

Of the three portions, the innermost recess of the ear is most complex and comprises a series of fluid-filled spaces which is collectively termed the labyrinth. The bony labyrinth houses the membranous labyrinth.

The cochlea, perhaps the most familiar vestibular apparatus, functions essentially as the hearing organ. The utricle and semicircular ducts, which also comprise the vestibular apparatus, play a more significant role in equilibration; however, visual stimuli and proprioceptive impulses play major roles in the maintenance of posture in particular.

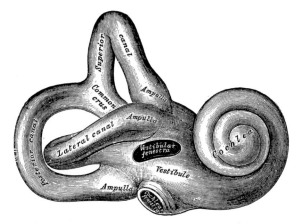

Fig. 3–5. The osseous labyrinth of the inner ear. Within this labyrinth is located the membranous labyrinth which contains fluid (endolymph). Pressure exerted upon the fluid within the ampullae plays an important role in equilibration. (From Gray.[14] Lea & Febiger.)

A simplified discussion of the complex inner ear compels one to focus attention on the series of cavities—the cochlea, vestibule, and semicircular canals—which comprise the labyrinth (Fig. 3–5).

Because of their importance to equilibration, particular attention is focused upon the vestibule and semicircular canals only.

The utricle and saccule portions of the membranous labyrinth are joined by a common duct. The role of the saccule in equilibration is not fully understood. (It plays a major role in the perception of vibration.) The utricle, however, is intricately involved in spatial orientation. An otolithic* membrane within the utricle is sensitive and responsive to pressures generated by body tilting or by linear acceleration.

---

* *Otolites,* also called *otoliths,* are calcium carbonate crystals or ear stones (literally translated from the Greek *ous,* ear; *lithos,* stone) located within the utriculosaccular ducts.

Three semicircular ducts, which communicate with the utricle and saccule, are arranged at right angles to each other. This arrangement assures effective monitoring in anteroposterior, lateral, and transverse planes (Fig. 3–5). Any pressures upon the ampullae, e.g., those pressures caused by movement, stimulates the nerve endings and results in the correction of temporary disturbances. Motion sickness, the nemesis of some airplane and ship passengers, appears to be associated with the stimulation within the semicircular canals.

In addition to the muscle spindles and vestibular proprioceptors, other proprioceptors such as Golgi organs and Pacini corpuscles mediate reception and response. Both are stimulated by tension. Golgi organs, located at the musculotendinous junction, play an important role in the reflex mechanism. By comparison, Pacini corpuscles are more widely distributed and are located within joints, periosteum, skin, and mesentery as well as tendons.

Interrelationships among this "proprioceptive triad"* may be observed in the stretch reflex.

Stretch or Myotatic Reflex

Reflex may be defined as an involuntary movement or reaction to a stimulus. Further, the impulses induced by reflexogenic stimulation may travel only to the spinal cord or to higher brain centers. The term *reflex arc* is descriptive of the anatomical neural pathways involved in mediating a reflex. Reduced to essential components, a reflex arc is composed of receptor organs, an afferent (sensory) neural pathway, an association area or center located within the gray matter of the spinal cord, an efferent (motor) neural pathway, and an effector organ (muscle) (Fig. 3–6).

The stretch reflex is characterized by the contraction of muscle which is elicited by stimulation of the muscle spindles. Basically, stretching of intrafusal muscle fibers distorts the annulospiral and Ruffini flower-spray endings within the muscle spindle. This distortion evokes an afferent discharge in the fast conducting Ia afferent fibers and motor response is effected. Within the region of the musculotendinous junction, the Golgi organ, distorted by tension within the muscle (which was initially accomplished by the spindle discharge), also discharges. Simultaneously the corpuscles of Pacini, excited by the induced pressure of vigorous muscle response, also discharge and by so doing contribute to an even greater motor response.

---

* Terminology of Gardner.[11] Proprioceptive triad consists of muscle spindles, musculotendinous organs (Golgi organs), and pacinian corpuscles (Pacini corpuscles).

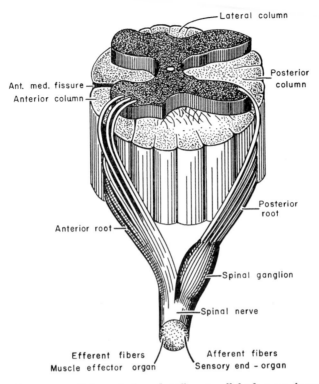

Fig. 3–6. A segment of the spinal cord. Efferent cell bodies are located within the anterior horn of the gray matter of the cord. Afferent bodies are located within the posterior ganglia. Efferent fibers of peripheral nerve are depicted entering the anterior root; afferent fibers are shown entering the posterior (or dorsal) root of the nerve. An association area, located entirely within the spinal cord, lies between afferent and efferent fibers. Reflex arc is composed of receptor organs, afferent and efferent neural pathways, and the association area. (Adapted from Gray.[14] Lea & Febiger.)

Functional differences between muscle spindles and Golgi tendon organs have been noted. The spindle, being in parallel neural circuitry with the extrafusal muscle fibers, discharges only when stretched. Golgi organs, being in series with the extrafusal fibers, discharge when the muscle tendon is under strong tension from stretch or when the muscle shortens under contraction. By discharging only when stretched, the muscle spindle facilitates contraction. By comparison, Golgi organs serve an important inhibitory and sometimes protective role. In the words of Granit, the tendon organs "apply the brakes" to muscular contraction and thereby prevent the development of excessive tension which could conceivably result in injury to the muscle or tendon.[12,13]

Some of the more common myotatic reflexes are listed in Table 3–2.

TABLE 3–2. Commonly Observed Myotatic Reflexes

Reflex	Action
Achilles tendon	Contraction of calf muscle group; foot extension
Acromial (or biceps)	Contraction of biceps brachium
Biceps femoris	Contraction of biceps femoris
Front tap (area of shin)	Contraction of gastrocnemius
Olecranon	Extension of forearm
Phillipson's	Contraction of knee extensors when extensors of opposite knee are inhibited
Quadriceps tendon (or patellar)	Contraction of quadriceps muscles group; extension of lower leg

Sherrington was the first to describe the functional significance of protection afforded by the flexion reflex, which is manifested in the withdrawal of an extremity from a painful stimulus.[36] He coined the term *nociceptive reflex.*

The role of the stretch reflex in the maintenance of the erect posture was also recognized by Sherrington,[35] and later by Liddell and Sherrington.[26,27] Further elucidation of the postural reflexes was contributed by Adrian,[4] and by Cannon and Haimovici[7] relative to the functioning of the muscle spindle and the Golgi organ.

Although the effective functioning of these reflex actions demands a state of consciousness,* the actions are consensual, i.e., the responses to stimuli do not involve conscious effort. Thus, the presence of the myotatic reflex, at spinal level, contributes to the maintenance of voluntary muscle control. There is, however, high brain center control of postural tonicity. In particular, the impulses from the reception within the labyrinths,† as well as those from the joint receptors of the neck, play a significant role in the maintenance of muscle tonus.

Semantics in physiology is equally as interesting as is the semantics of other disciplines. Reflex, according to Merton, originally implied ". . . that nervous messages traveling up sensory nerves were 'reflected' in the central nervous system and passed out again into motor nerves."

---

* Any act which renders an individual insensible results in a loss of tension of the antigravity muscles and subsequent collapse. Generally speaking, the extensor muscles are considered the antigravity muscles. This includes the extensors of the head, trunk, lower legs, and feet. In addition, the flexors of the mandible and of the upper limbs are also antigravity muscles.

† The influence of labyrinthine receptors is profoundly indicated during periods of inner ear infection as exemplified by the difficulty in maintaining equilibrium. There is a practical lesson to be drawn from this fact. Individuals suffering from upper respiratory tract infections should refrain from participation in physical activity in order to minimize the chances of inner ear infection and an attendant, extended recovery period.

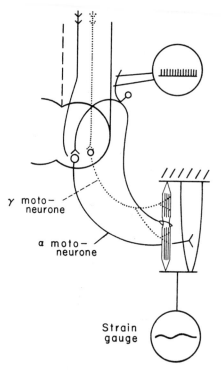

Fig. 3–7.   Diagram illustrating arrangement of experiment for reflex work with simultaneous spindle control. Muscle with parallel intrafusal fiber containing spindle connected to strain gauge. Afferent fiber discharge from spindle isolated in dorsal root and projected on oscilloscope. Destination of alpha α and gamma γ fiber from ventral root of spinal cord shown. (From Granit.[12] Courtesy of Yale University Press.)

Facilitation, denoting a reinforcement of nervous activity, was derived from the Latin word *facilitas* meaning *easy.* Low frequencies of impulses propagated along the afferent pathway of the reflex arc may fail to elicit responses in the efferent neuron; however, when additional inadequate impulses from other origins are summated with the afferent impulses, liminal synaptic intensity is attained and response is elicited in the effector neuron. Thus, an individual who has apparently reached the tension limit of his quadriceps muscle group can elicit greater tension through facilitation induced by attempting to "break" a self-induced hand clasp. Well known is the ergogenic effect of excitement or of encouragement ranging from soft whispers to loud cheering, which is accomplished in large measure through facilitation.

Another type of control which is exerted by the central nervous system is that of inhibition as exemplified in reciprocal innervation. For example, whether a movement is involuntary or voluntary has no bearing on the act of flexion of a leg in response to a nocioceptive stimulus. Yet, before the leg can be flexed, inhibition of the extensor myotatic reflex must be accomplished. Because of the antagonistic action of skeletal muscle groups, reciprocal innervation through stimulation—inhibition of the opposing muscle groups assures coordinated movement.

While both muscle spindle and Golgi organ are sensitive to stretch, Granit observed that muscle spindles possess a lower threshold level.[13] He also observed that during muscle stretch, facilitation tended to dominate over inhibition.

Although receptors may convey sensations to cortical level, movement will be effected without conscious effort; however, perception of the movement usually occurs. The myriad of sense organs, distributed throughout the body, enables man to protect himself without thinking. It enables man to perform first and evaluate the experience later.

Voluntary Movement and Brain Control

To paraphrase the prominent English neurophysiologist, Hughlings Jackson (1835–1911), from the simplest to the most complex reflex act the nervous system ". . . 'thinks' in terms of movement not muscle." In the words of Nobel Laureate E. D. Adrian, "The chief function of the central nervous system is to send messages to the muscle which will make the body move effectively as a whole."[3]

Luria views the cerebral cortex as "a higher-level center for analysis and integration of signals received by the organism from its internal and external environments. . . . The principle of feedback is universal in the operation of the central nervous system."

Much is known about the effects of cerebral dysfunction. The classic example of temporary cerebral dysfunction caused by a jarring blow is known to all. If the force on the jaw or on any part of the skull is transmitted to the cerebrum in sufficient intensity, the individual loses equilibrium by losing muscular control. If, however, the transmitted force only partially interrupts cerebral function, the participant is staggered and dazed and attempts to remain standing. In this latter instance, the individual, though unable to think about the act, remains standing through reflex control. The football player or boxer who is dazed is carried through precarious situations through reflex actions which have been conditioned through practice. Obviously, these periods of haziness represent periods of grave physical danger to the person who cannot cope with the complex situations. The football player who runs for a touchdown—in the wrong direction—provides an excellent example of the controlling role of the conditioned reflex (catch and carry the ball, then run) despite cerebral disorientation (fails to exhibit discrimination by running generally in the direction of goal posts and not specifically in the direction of the opponents' end zone).

Although he possesses the most highly developed cerebral cortex, man has barely unlocked its secrets. Through electrical stimulation of the cerebral cortex, notably by Wilder Penfield, cytoarchitectonic features have been mapped (Fig. 3–8).

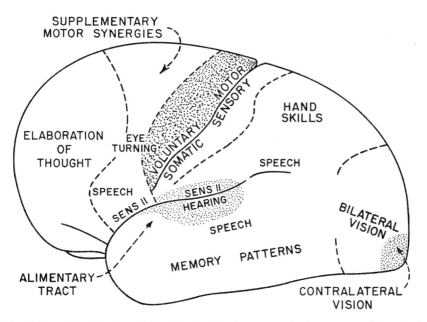

Fig. 3–8. Localization of function in the human cerebral cortex as determined by electrical stimulation. Cortex representation is contralateral: the right hemisphere controls the left side of the body, and vice versa. (From Penfield and Rasmussen.[32] Courtesy of Macmillan Co.)

Descending motor pathways, or pyramidal tracts, mediate the motor cortex area with the ventral horn of the spinal cord. The pyramidal system exhibits the characteristic decussation: neurons in the right cortical hemisphere communicate with the left body hemisphere.

Within the third of six layers present in the voluntary motor area of the cerebral cortex is located distinctively large, pyramid-shaped cells called Betz cells. The propagation velocity of the axons which serve these cells is high. Earlier neurophysiologists ascribed to the Betz cells the complete motoneural source of the pyramidal system. However, recent estimations by such authorities as Guyton place the number of motoneurons within the pyramidal system at approximately 2 million and the number of Betz cells at less than 70,000 or approximately 3%.

Of particular interest is the topic of cortical representation. Greater cortical representation is equated with greater functional control. As pointed out by Penfield and Rasmussen, large areas of the cortex are given over to the control of the hands as well as the mouth. In other words, the innervation ratio for hand and mouth muscles is higher than for postural muscles. A high ratio of motoneurons to muscle fibers permits a high degree of precision in coordinated movement.

An extrapyramidal or supplementary motor system is represented within the brain stem and serves both cortical and cerebellar regions. Although the extrapyramidal system covers a more extensive area than does the pyramidal system, it is functionally associated with gross, coordinated movement patterns. Neural communication between the cortical portion of the system and the lower motorneurons of the spinal cord is accomplished by an extremely complex network of tracts and nuclei* within the subcortical midbrain region. Synchronization of muscle function is accomplished within this region. It serves as an integral part of a feedback loop which coordinates muscle action.

The cerebellum is essential to coordinated physical expression. Proprioceptive data from muscle spindles, Golgi organs, Pacini corpuscles, and Ruffini endings, in addition to data provided by the vestibulocochlear organs and the photoreceptors, are representative of the myriad of sensory data which are received in the cerebellum. Irrespective of the

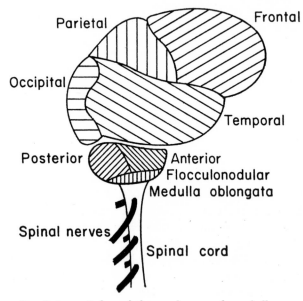

Fig. 3–9. Lobes of the cerebrum and cerebellum.

---

* More important nuclei are those of the substantia nigra, red nuclei, and corpus striatum (striate body).

degree of simplicity or complexity of the physical expression, the integrative function of the cerebellum is assured. Although the coordination function rests generally within this section of the brain, there are areas of more specific involvement, namely, the anterior lobe which regulates control of posture, the flocculonodular lobe which is involved in the maintenance of equilibrium, and the posterior lobe which is associated with movement (Fig. 3–9).

Changing Postures

The adjective *static* (Greek *statikos:* causing to stand) is often used to describe a stationary body position. Hence, reference is made to a static posture. Static posture, however, is a relative term and the degree of stability is dependent upon its center of gravity. The most stable equilibrium is exhibited in the lying position and the least stable equilibrium is found in the unassisted standing position.

As was demonstrated by Hellebrandt et al.,[17] and by Hellebrandt and Braun,[16] the term static standing posture is a term wrongly applied for it implies an unchanging center of gravity. These researchers found the center of gravity of the body to shift "incessantly" during the maintenance of "natural, comfortable standing."

Movement may be defined as a series of dynamic physical positions or postures conducted in a spatial setting and extending along a continuum from mild to vigorous. Movement or motion is better defined as a series of changing equilibria whereas a fixed posture is descriptive of a body in equilibrium, i.e., there is no change in its motion. Within these definitions, shifts in centers of gravity are recognized as inherent. In the unassisted standing position, maintenance of equilibrium is assured through stretch reflex involvement, whereas during movement, stretch reflex involvement is supplemented by conscious effort and other sensory feedback.

A comparison of three body postures reflects, through an increased oxygen consumption, the degree of reflex involvement of motor units, which is necessary to overcome the effect of gravity in the maintenance of equilibrium.

TABLE 3–3. Oxygen Cost of Maintaining Three Body Postures
(♂ 81.7 kg, 43 years)

Position	$\dot{V}O_2$ ml/min
Lying	230
Sitting	253
Standing	278

The statement of anthropologist Hooton, that "man is a made-over animal," underscores the difficulties of adaptation to bipedism and gravitational forces. Man the biped has not completely erased some of the functional and structural quadriped characteristics. Kahn outlines a number of these. Yet man has acquired some characteristics which are not possessed by any other animal including primitive man. In particular, the development of the lower jaw is of great significance to Kahn who also cites the upright posture and the freeing of the forelimbs as contributing factors:

> . . . primitive man, of whose capacity for speech we are ignorant, had no chin. The development of the lower jaw to its modern human form is therefore not simply a decrease in the size, but rather a transformation of this organ from an animal eating-and-biting apparatus operated by brute force to a supporting structure for the human mouth. Man no longer bites and eats like an animal, but partakes of and enjoys his prepared food in a "decorous manner". And instead of gnashing his teeth, he utters words. The history of the lower jaw is the history of humanity.*

Man's erect posture represents a victory for the numerous and rapid muscular reactions to an ever present series of temporary mechanical imbalances. Sherrington described standing as "a complex neuromuscular act dependent upon the integrity of the myotatic reflex."[39] The automaticity of response of leg and foot muscles to a variety of trunk and upper appendage movement patterns was shown by Houtz and Fischer (Fig. 3–10). These researchers also observed compensatory upper limb realignment, which served to assist the foot as a supporting base.

Walking and running represent more spectacular accomplishments, for in both instances the movement is a resultant of a series of controlled imbalances. These mechanically unstable postures, ever affected by gravitational forces, are maintained and controlled primarily through reflex muscular reactions which are transmitted to the higher brain centers. While at times the process of coordination of impulses along afferent and efferent pathways involves conscious levels, many bodily activities are regulated at subconscious levels and are termed reflex actions.

---

* In evolutionary matters man has reached a point of no return. Were man suddenly transformed into a quadriped, he would find himself extremely uncomfortable. While he might rid himself of low back problems, he would probably acquire a variety of knee problems (were he to maneuver on hands and knees), and should he emulate the ambulation pattern of the lower primates, his hamstring and quadriceps muscle groups would cry out in discomfort.

While recognizing the importance of such stimuli as sound, pressure, and temperature to varied body functions, one must underscore the importance of the visual afferents in the maintenance of balance. As the lifting of objects is partly dependent upon the visual afferents, so is the maintenance of equilibrium in standing and walking postures. Body sway and an unsteady gait are the risks of the blindfold or the darkened room.

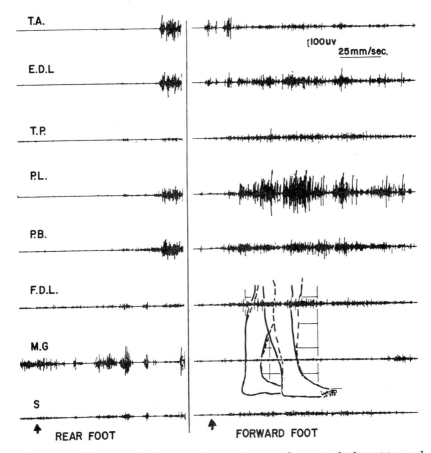

Fig. 3–10. Evidence of reflex muscular reactions to changes in limb position and center of gravity as evidenced by electromyographic tracings. Arrows indicate initiation of activity. Broken outline of limb indicates starting position and solid line indicates terminal position. Right limb is forward, left is rear limb. *TA*, tibialis anterior; *EDL*, extensor digitorum longus; *TP*, tibialis posterior; *PL*, peroneus longus; *PB*, peroneus brevis; *FDL*, flexor digitorum longus; *MG*, medial gastrocnemius; *S*, soleus. (From Houtz and Fischer.[22] Courtesy of American Physiological Society.)

Reaction Time

Reaction time is represented by the minimal time interval which elapses between stimulus application and the beginning of a voluntary response. The agile athlete is one who possesses the ability to make quick reactions, to respond to stimuli. Thus, the runner and swimmer react to the sound of the starter's gun. Members of the offensive football unit respond to the quarterback's signals and members of the defensive team react to movement. In these situations (and with varied degrees of success) the participants may anticipate the stimulus. In baseball, however, the fielder must respond to the sound of bat on ball as well as to the direction of the ball.

Reaction time varies within the same individual and is dependent upon such factors as the nature of the stimulus, the pattern of response, limb dominance, age, fatigue level, shell and core temperature, and ambient temperature and humidity. Reaction time obviously varies between individuals as well.

To the physiologist, reaction time includes a fast component, the *reflex time,* and a slower component, the *conditioned reflex* time. Depending upon the level of neuromuscular development and the degree of sophistication and reliability of timing apparatus, the conscious response interval can be reduced. Also included in reaction time is an interval of time required for reciprocal innervation to be effected. This interval is not specifically measured. Because of practicality, the categorization of each of the phases mentioned is overlooked and the intervals are summated into a convenient designation called *reaction time.*

To the psychologist, reaction time is classified as being either simple or complex.[10] *Simple reaction time* includes the interval between a prearranged signal and a predetermined response. *Complex reaction time* may take several forms:

> *discrimination* (response to one of several stimuli), or
> *cognitive* (response after recognition of stimulus), or
> *choice* (specific responses to particular stimuli).

Rather than reaction time, *intentional response time* has been suggested as a more accurate term, "Since the stimulus to be expected is in some way stipulated and the response to be made is agreed upon in advance."[10]

Stato-Tonic and Stato-Kinetic Reflexes

Magnus described three types of attitudinal reflexes which are currently designated as postural or stato-tonic reflexes. The first, or local static reaction was discussed earlier as the *myotatic reflex.* General static reactions were also presented by Magnus in the discussion of *tonic neck* as well as *tonic labyrinthine reflexes.*

In addition to these stato-tonic reflexes, another category of righting reflexes is exhibited. Irrespective of its position at time of release, a cat lands feet first. This maneuver would be accomplished even if the cat were blindfolded (thus denied visual stimuli) and released from an inverted position. In describing this maneuver, Magnus identified five principal sequential reflexes: labyrinthine righting reflexes, body-on-head righting reflexes, neck righting reflexes, body righting reflexes acting on body, and optical righting reflexes.

Of initial consequence are the *labyrinthine righting reflexes* which originate within the labyrinths and are therefore structurally dependent upon the labyrinths but also structurally and functionally dependent upon the otolites. Gravitational forces initiate the labyrinthine righting reflexes which, in turn, serve as a stimulus for neck muscle involvement in providing orientation of the head in space.

Body-on-head righting reflexes are initiated by asymmetrical presso-receptor stimulation on the body surface. This results in reflexly elicited neck muscle involvement and proper positioning of the head in space.

As a consequence of head rotation, resulting from labyrinthine righting reflexes, and body-on-head righting reflexes, proprioceptive stimulation of the neck muscles elicits still further reflex movements in the trunk and limbs. This *neck righting reflex* results in attempted symmetrical trunk and limb positioning with respect to the head.

Body righting reflexes acting on body are evidenced in the labyrinthectomized cat by an attempted positioning of the hind limbs in the horizontal position independent of the position of the forelimbs, which may be held in vertical position.

Lastly, Magnus identified the *optical righting reflexes* which enables a cat to maintain righting reactions through neck, trunk, and limb involvement even when both labyrinths have been destroyed.

Even more astonishing than the cat-act itself is the fact that it is performed in a fraction of a second despite the high degree of neuromuscular involvement.

Man does not allow himself to be manipulated (as does the cat) for he is prudent in such matters. Man does, however, possess the anatomic structures and physiologic mechanisms for reflex and volitional neuromuscular acts. These he displays in such examples of complex physical expressions as pole vaulting, trampolining, tumbling, and springboard diving. Each of these physical expressions, as even the simple physical expression of flexing the index finger, is also performed within seconds and is accomplished through an integrated neuromuscular system involving cerebellar coordination and cortical control.

REFERENCES

1. Adams, R. D., and Denny-Brown, D.: *Disease of Muscle, A Study in Pathology.* 2nd Ed., New York, Hoeber Medical Books, 1962.

2. Adrian, E. D.: *The Basis of Sensation.* New York, W. W. Norton Co., 1928.

3. Adrian, E. D.: *The Mechanism of Nervous Action; Electrical Studies of the Neurone.* Philadelphia, University of Pennsylvania Press, 1932.

4. Adrian, E. D.: *The Physical Background of Perception* (The Waynflete Lectures, 1946). Oxford, Clarendon Press, 1947.

5. Barker, D.: The innervation of the muscle spindles. *Quart. J. Micr. Sci., 89*: 143–186, 1948.

6. Campbell, H. J.: *Correlative Physiology of the Nervous System.* London, Academic Press, 1965.

7. Cannon, W. B., and Haimovici, H.: The sensitization of motoneurones by partial "denervation." *Am. J. Physiol., 126*:731–740, 1939.

8. Castiglioni, A.: *A History of Medicine.* 2nd Ed. Edited by E. B. Krumbhaar, New York, Alfred A. Knopf Co., 1958.

9. Eldred, E.: The dual sensory role of muscle spindles. *J. Am. Phys. Therapy Assn., 45*:290–313, 1965.

10. English, H. B., and English, A. C.: *A Comprehensive Dictionary of Psychological and Psychoanalytical Terms.* New York, Longmans, Green and Co., 1958.

11. Gardner, E.: *Fundamentals of Neurology.* 4th Ed., Philadelphia, W. B. Saunders Co., 1963.

12. Granit, R.: *Receptors and Sensory Perception.* New Haven, Yale University Press, 1955.

13. Granit, R.: Reflex self-regulation of the muscle contraction and autogenic inhibition. *J. Neurophysiol., 13*:351–372, 1950a.

14. Gray, H.: *Anatomy of the Human Body.* 28th Ed. Edited by C. M. Goss, Philadelphia, Lea & Febiger, 1966.

15. Guyton, A. C.: *Textbook of Medical Physiology.* 2nd Ed., Philadelphia, W. B. Saunders Co., 1961.

16. Hellebrandt, F. A., and Braun, G. L.: The influence of sex and age on the postural sway of man. *Am. J. Phys. Anthropol., 24*:347–360, 1939.

17. Hellebrandt, F. A., Crigler, E. F., and Kelso, L. E. A.: Variations in intramuscular pressure during postural and phasic contraction of human muscle. *Am. J. Physiol., 126*:247–253, 1939.

18. Hill, A. V.: The heat of shortening and the dynamic constants of muscle. *Proc. Roy. Soc.* (London) B, *126*:136–195, 1938.

19. Hill, A. V.: Work and heat in a muscle twitch. *Proc. Roy. Soc.* (London) B, *136*:220–227, 1949.

20. Hill, A. V.: A discussion on muscular contraction and relaxation: their physical and chemical basis. Introduction. *Proc. Roy. Soc.* (London) B, *137*:40–50, 1950.

21. Hooton, E. A.: An anthropologist looks at medicine. *Science, 83*:271–276, 1936.

22. Houtz, S. J., and Fischer, F. J.: Function of leg muscles acting on foot as modified by body movements. *J. Appl. Physiol., 16*:597–605, 1961.

23. Hunt, C. C.: The effect of stretch receptors from muscle on the discharge of motoneurons. *J. Physiol., 117*:359–379, 1952.

24. Hursh, J. B.: Conduction velocity and diameter of nerve fibers. *Am. J. Physiol., 127*:131–139, 1939.

25. Kahn, F.: *Man in Structure and Function.* Vol. I. Translated and edited by G. Rosen, New York, Alfred A. Knopf Co., 1956.

26. Liddell, E. G. T., and Sherrington, C.: Reflexes in response to stretch (myotatic reflexes). *Proc. Roy. Soc.* B, *96*:212–242, 1924.

27. Liddell, E. G. T., and Sherrington, C.: Further observations in myotatic reflexes. *Proc. Roy. Soc.* B, *97*:267–283, 1925.

28. Luria, A. R.: *Higher Cortical Functions in Man.* New York, Basic Books, Inc., 1966.

29. Magnus, R.: Some results of studies in the physiology of posture. *Lancet, 211*:531–585, 1926.

30. Merton, P. A.: The central nervous system. *In* Winton, F. R., and Bayliss, L. E. (Eds.): *Human Physiology.* 5th Ed., Boston, Little, Brown and Co., 1962.

31. Mountcastle, V. B.: Reflex activity of the spinal cord. *In* Bard, P. (Ed.): *Medical Physiology.* 11th Ed. St. Louis, C. V. Mosby Co., 1961.

32. Penfield, W., and Rasmussen, A. T.: *The Cerebral Cortex in Man: Clinical Study of Localization of Function.* New York, Macmillan Co., 1950.

33. Rossi, G.: Asimmetrie toniche posturale, ed asimmetrie motorie. *Arch. Fisiol., 25*:146–157, 1927.

34. Ruffini, A.: Observations on sensory nerve-endings in voluntary muscles. *Brain, 20*:368–374, 1897.

35. Sherrington, C. S.: Decerebrate rigidity, and reflex coordination of movements. *J. Physiol., 22*:319–332, 1898.

36. Sherrington, C. S.: Flexion-reflex of the limb, crossed extension-reflex, and reflex stepping and standing. *J. Physiol., 40*:28–121, 1910.

37. Sherrington, C. S.: *Man on His Nature.* Gifford Lectures, Edinburgh 1937–8, Cambridge, University Press, 1951.

38. Sherrington, C. S.: Problems of muscular receptivity. *Nature, 113*:732, 892–894, 929–932, 1924.

39. Sherrington, C. S.: Some function problems attaching to convergence. *Nature, 123*:998–999, 1929.

C h a p t e r

4

KINEOENERGETICS

M_{AN} is designed for motion.

By means of levers which are formed by the skeletal system and powered by the muscle system, man exhibits machine-like characteristics. Thus, the definition applied by the physicist or engineer to the machine* may also be applied to man. Energy undergoes a transformation from potential to kinetic, a process by which heat is liberated, motion is produced, and work is performed. Both man and machine require oxygen for the combustion processes which result in such end-products as carbon dioxide and water. Both require electrical systems, fuel lines, and pumps. In referring to either man or machine, a common vocabulary is employed. *Motion, speed, velocity, torque, acceleration, work, efficiency,* and Sir Isaac Newton's *laws of motion* serve as examples of this vocabulary.

The admonition of Clendening is too audible (p. 2); the analogy is continued no further.

Arthrological Considerations

Man's articulations dictate the form of motion permitted. Classification of articulations may be divided into two categories: those which permit movement and those which do not. For example, articulations between the bones of the skull are fixed, thus eliminating the possibility of movement. Such joints are classified as *synarthroses* (Greek: *syn* = joined; *arthrosis* = articulation). The majority of articulations, how-

---

* An accepted definition of machine: that which presupposes power source, and mechanical devices (levers) which change the application of energy.

54

TABLE 4–1. Classification of Articulations

Classification	Example of Articulation	Movement Permitted
Synarthroses	Bones and sutures of skull (e.g., temporo-occipital)	None
Diarthroses Arthrodial	Between carpals*	Gliding, sliding
Ginglymus	Humero-ulnar	Flexion, extension
Trochoid	Radio-ulnar (proximal articulation)	Rotation
Condyloid	Radius-scaphoid-lunate	Flexion, extension, abduction, adduction circumduction (no rotation)
Saddle joint	Carpometacarpal of thumb	Flexion, extension, abduction, adduction, circumduction (no rotation)
Enarthrosis	Glenohumeral	All movement evidenced: flexion extension, abduction, adduction, circumduction, rotation

* Except capitate, scaphoid and lunate.
Note: All diarthrodial articulations permit gliding movements.

ever, permit movement and are classified as *diarthroses* (Greek: *dis =* two, *arthrosis =* articulation). Some authors recognize the existence of a third classification: *amphiarthroses* or slightly moveable articulations.[22]

Within the diarthrodial classification, movement may range from limited to pronounced and extensive. Classifications and examples of articulations are presented in Table 4–1.

For an excellent review of joint physiology, the reader is referred to Gardner.

Power Source and Levers

Additional considerations relative to motion incorporate myological-mechanical factors.[40] From the mechanical point of view, a primary consideration involves a sufficient degree of force which can be exerted by a muscle group to overcome inertia. Further, the amount of force required to overcome inertia may vary directly or inversely with the inertia and is dependent upon such additional considerations as class of lever and interrelationship between force arm and resistance arm.

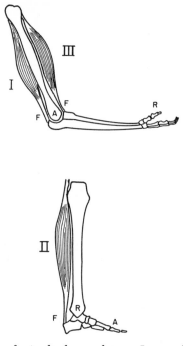

Fig. 4–1.   Examples of simple lever classes. Lever class is determined by relative positions of force application (*F*), axis (*A*), and resistance (*R*). In class I, A is between *F* and *R*; in class II, *R* is between *F* and *A*; in class III, *F* is between *A* and *R*. Force in first class lever is provided by principal forearm extensor, the triceps brachii. In the third class lever the principal forearm flexors, the biceps brachii and brachialis anterior muscles, provide the force. In both of the above examples, the axis is located at the humero-ulnar articulation. Principal foot extensors, the gastrocnemius and soleus muscles, provide the force for the second class lever. The axis, in this example, is located at the metatarsophalangeal joints. See discussion in text relative to changing nature of lever at ankle during standing-on-toes movement. Note that the femur is *not* represented. (See Figs. 4–2 and 4–8.)

In man, third class levers predominate over first class levers. Second class levers are few in number. Examples of each are depicted in Figure 4–1.

A lever is a mechanical device, in reality a simple machine, which produces rotary motion about an axis or fulcrum. Furthermore, the effort force tends to rotate the lever in a direction which is opposite to that exerted by the resistance force. The degree of force (a reflection of tension, recruitment, gradation of contraction) necessary to produce motion is basically dependent upon the mechanical advantage afforded by the lever system (Fig. 4–4). The mechanical advantage of levers is expressed as a ratio of the length of the force arm to that of the resistance arm.* Man is an anatomical configuration of short force arms and moments of force; however, the reduced torque† afforded by such lever systems is offset by rapid speed of motion.

The act of rising-on-toes provides a basis for interesting and controversial discussion relative to lever action. Proponents of each lever class may be identified. Gerstein describes such an act as an example of first class lever involvement, whereas De Coursey describes the accomplishment in terms of second class lever involvement. Steindler labels the act as an example of the functioning of a third class lever. Interestingly enough, the ankle-foot region does provide an incontrovertible example of second class lever action. This is best demonstrated by the act of sitting, with the lower leg perpendicular to the foot, and merely elevating the heel; however, the forces at the thigh must be in equilibrium (Fig. 4–2).

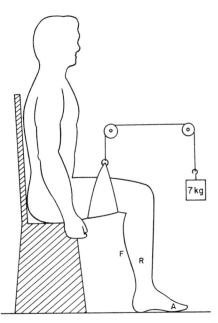

Fig. 4–2. A second class lever. The thigh is cradled in a sling. A force of approximately 7 kg is required to produce equilibrium. (Weight of thigh, 6.81 kg; of leg, 2.95 kg; of foot, 1.13 kg.) Without condition of equilibrium, weight of thigh would cause resistance (*R*) to shift to a position *behind* point of force application (*F*) and lever would become third class. (See Fig. 4–8.)

---

* Force arms are variously called effort arms or power arms; resistance arms may also be labeled weight arms.

† Torque and moment of force are synonymous and equal the product of the force and the length of the moment arm on which it acts.

By calculating the forward displacement of the center of gravity* during several phases of the toe rise, one must conclude that the lever action is second class *during* the body raising stage, but becomes first class in the maintenance of the toe-stand position, with the metatarsophalangeal articulations serving as axes.

In the ankle-foot region, however, movement about a number of axes is essential to the toe-rising act. One must not focus attention on the tibia-fibula-talus axis to the exclusion of the metatarsophalangeal axis of rotation, for one cannot negate the forces exerted by the toes (against the floor) in the execution of such an act.

When viewed as an organ of support and movement, the lower leg-ankle-foot region exhibits lever actions which can only be classified as compound. The seemingly simple act of rising-on-toes is accomplished by forces exerted not only by the powerful foot extensors, but also by the extensors of the toes as well.

As indicated by Fenn, the lever class designation is immaterial and should be subordinated to a discussion of torques.[15] Nevertheless the lever class, though arbitrary, remains controversial and thus is in need of clarification through research.

Motion

Displacement of the body along terrain or through water is accomplished at the expense of forces opposing progression and is reflected in the level of metabolic activity.

An explanation of these forces is rooted in the three laws of motion which were advanced at the turn of the seventeenth century by Sir Isaac Newton.

The first law, the law of inertia, may be so stated: *a body continues in its state of rest or uniform motion unless compelled by unbalanced forces to change its state.* In relation to the human body, one might observe that a body which is either at rest or in uniform motion is in *equilibrium* in that there is no change in its rate of motion, i.e., its velocity† is constant. Since the stability of the body is related to its center of gravity and base of support, one must also recognize that a

---

* Calculation of center of gravity can be accomplished through employment of the technique of Reynolds and Lovett or that of Cureton and Wickens, which was adapted from the Reynolds-Lovett technique. The equilibrium principle is employed: the sum of moments about a selected point equal zero, $\Sigma M = 0$.

†Velocity is expressed as a continuum from zero to the present limits of human locomotion: 6.96 meters/second. This figure is based on the accomplishments of Kansas track star, Ryun, who established a world's record for the mile (1609.344 meters) at 3 minutes 51.3 seconds. Even higher velocities can be attained in the final spurt of the dashes.

lowered center of gravity coupled with an increased base of support results in greater stability. Hence, greater stability requires a greater unbalanced force to produce a change in its state.

In such an athletic expression as wrestling, man is required to assume a quadriped position during the course of a full encounter (Fig. 4–3). In order to disrupt the stability which is afforded by such a position, the opponent must muster sufficient force—must unbalance the forces— to produce acceleration and hence overcome the inertia of his opponent. Since opposing wrestlers are equally desirous of victory, each offers resistance to the very forces which tend to unbalance him. Such an athletic expression, though brief, is accomplished at high energy cost.

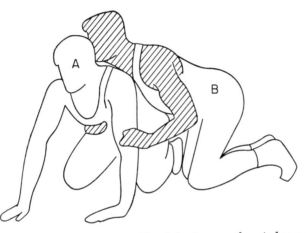

Fig. 4–3. Referee's position on mat. The defensive wrestler, A, has a wide base of support. Wrestler, B, on offense; must unbalance the force.

Newton's second law of motion, the law of acceleration, is expressed in the following way: *a body is accelerated in the direction of and in direct proportion to the force exerted on it but in inverse proportion to its mass.* According to this law, and verified by ergonomic research, greater force is required to accelerate a mass which is stationary than one which is already in motion. Related to this discussion is the concept of momentum which is defined as the product of the mass of an object and its velocity.

Opposing linemen in American football, separated by approximately one meter, exchange momentums which enhance fatigue but which are of lower magnitude than the momentum generated by the ball carrier who is tackled by the defending linebacker. The ball carrier, with velocity and mass operating in his favor, presents a vexing problem to the linebacker who must meet him head-on.

Finally, the third Newtonian law, the law of interaction, may be stated: *for every action there is an equal and opposite reaction.* In locomotion, the ground exerts a force which is equal and opposite to the force exerted by the foot. The composition of the terrain has much effect on the energy cost of locomotion. Walking in loose sand at the seashore requires a greater caloric expenditure than walking on the boardwalk. Forces exerted by the feet against the differing surfaces are unequal and are less uniform in loose sand and more uniform on wood.

The action of arms and legs which exert a force against the water (which exerts an opposite force) enables the swimmer to propel himself.

Dynamogenesis

Kinetics presupposes myological involvement in the application of force which is necessary to overcome inertia and result in movement. Some myological factors were discussed in Chapter 2 under such topics as innervation ratio, tension, recruitment, and gradation of contraction. In the ensuing discussion, additional factors which affect man in motion will be presented.

Assessment of work, expressed mathematically as efficiency—the ratio of output to input—reveals that man compares favorably with the machine. A. V. Hill reported man's mechanical efficiency to be 25% and Steindler reported 26%.

Man in motion displays intra-individual as well as interactivity variation as is expressed in the percent efficiency of the following performances. For sprint running, Fenn reported 22.7%,[14] whereas Furusawa, Hill, and Parkinson reported a mean of 37.7% for the 60 yard run (range 27.8 to 44.5%).[18] For swimming, Karpovich and Pestrecov[30] reported 0.5 to 2.2% for the crawl stroke and 0.88 to 1.35% in the execution of the back stroke. For bicycle ergometry, Dickinson reported efficiencies from 11.4 to 21.5%. Grade walking on the treadmill was reported by Erickson et al. to range from 24.8 to 40.3%; Knehr et al. reported a range from 15.3 to 16.9%.

Mechanical work, the product of force times distance, $W = F\ s$, is affected by many factors including inertia to be overcome, speed of contraction or rate of work, duration of effort, environmental conditions, somatotype, as well as numerous physiological and psychophysiological factors.

Ontogenetic and phylogenetic limits to efficiency have been imposed on man. The delivery of the oxygen molecule to active tissue and the removal of end-products of metabolism is dependent upon rate of blood flow which has mechanical limits. Gas molecules enter into chemical combination at a rate which assures a high degree of saturation of arterial blood with oxygen and rapid removal of carbon dioxide from the active tissues.

Anatomical limits also exist. For example, the mechanical efficiency of work performance expressed through forearm flexion has an anatomically imposed ceiling. In Figure 4-4, the attachment of the distal portion of the biceps brachii (through tenontomyoplastic surgery) from its position of normal attachment A to position B would result in an appreciable reduction of force required for the performance of equal amounts of work.

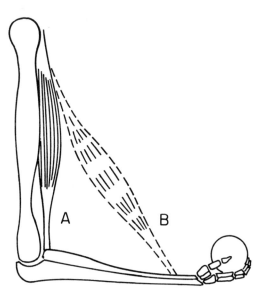

Fig. 4-4.   Man revised. Through tenontomyoplastic surgery, mechanical efficiency of levers can be increased, but only at the expense of beauty and at decreased speed and range of motion. At 90 degrees, position A forearm flexors must exert a 30 kg force to maintain a 5 kg load (including weight of arm). At position B a force of only 6 kg would be required. See Chapter 11 for calculation procedure. For an excellent, concise discussion of biomechanics, see Williams and Lissner.[44]

Anatomical economies are also pronounced. A number of muscles within the body span more than one joint; thus, each muscle is capable of producing simultaneous motion at two or more locations within the trunk or appendage. The economy of motion afforded by such biarticular muscles was shown by Elftman to be substantial (Fig. 4-5). Biarticular muscles capitalize on the kinetic energy imparted by limb momentum.* For running, Elftman calculated an actual expenditure

---

* Fenn discussed the storage of mechanical energy in muscles and tendons and the subsequent transfer of momentum and energy between body areas.[14]

of 2.61 horsepower. If the biarticular muscles of the limbs were to be replaced by uniarticular muscles, an increase of 1.36 horsepower would be required to initiate and maintain the same motion.

A number of other factors relate to dynamogenesis. While these factors are discussed elsewhere in this text, a mention of them is in order here.

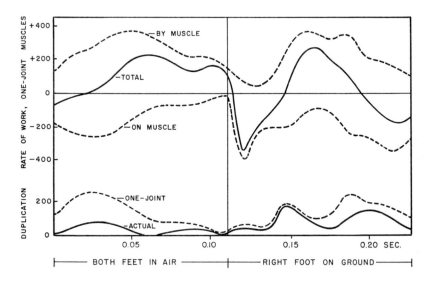

Fig. 4–5. The work of running. Above, summation for each phase, of rate at which work is done *by* uniarticular muscle (positive work) and *on* uniarticular muscle (negative work) and the algebraic total. Below, rate at which duplicate work is performed by uniarticular muscle (broken line) and by biarticular muscle (solid line). Note the economy of effort of the biarticular muscle. Work rate in kilogram meters/second. (Adapted from Elftman. Courtesy of American Physiological Society.)

Speed of work and performance expressed as a function of energy expenditure exhibits a relationship which is depicted in Figure 4–6.

The same parabolic curve is exhibited in the plotting of load expressed as a function of either caloric expenditure or efficiency.

A curvilinear relationship is exhibited in energy expenditure expressed as a function of grade walking (Fig. 4–7).

What is readily apparent is the presence of an optimal rate of performance for each task.

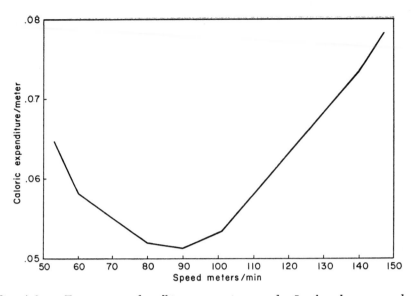

Fig. 4–6. Energy cost of walking at varying speeds. In the above example, walking at 90 meters/min. represents the optimum speed. (Plotted from data of Benedict and Murschhauser.)

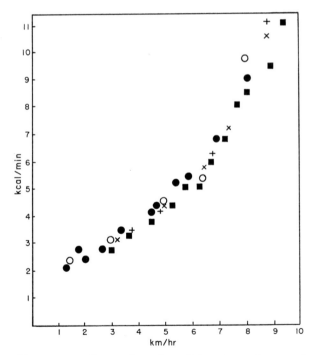

Fig. 4–7. Energy expenditure of grade walking at varying speeds. The relationship is curvilinear, except between 3 and 6.5 km/h where the relationship is linear. Symbols represent data gathered at five laboratories in four countries: England, Germany, Italy, and the United States. (Adapted from Passmore and Durnin. Courtesy of American Physiological Society.)

Analysis of Physical Accomplishment

Accomplishments which are measured in mechanical units* are expressed through such words as *work* or *power*. Common to both definitions is the concept of force: the production of motion. A consideration of work focuses on force† acting on matter and the distance through which the matter is displaced. Power represents the *rate* at which the work is performed and the force expended. Although the words occasionally are used interchangeably, each has a specific meaning.

Constantly changing internal and external forces would seem to present problems of such magnitude as to preclude the mathematical calculation of muscle forces. By separating each force into component forces acting in specific directions, a resolution of muscle forces can be calculated through the use of trigonometry. Basic to an understanding of the resolution of forces is a comprehension of the force, that is, its composition and its resolution.

In the analysis of body mechanics, force represents a basic concept. The scientific definition of it is broad: *that which tends to or in actuality produces or prevents motion.* Essential to a thorough understanding of muscular force are such considerations as magnitude and direction (quantities) as well as point of force application.

Within the human body, attachment of muscle to bone serves to direct the application of the force generated within the muscle to a specific area. Force magnitude and direction are represented by vector quantities, or more simply, force vectors. Displacement, as an expression of movement or motion, is in reality a net displacement which is usually labeled the resultant or resultant vector. Other vectors are called component vectors or simply components.

Resultants also reflect the nature of the displacement. Two component vectors acting in the same direction or in opposite directions produce a resultant with a magnitude equal to the algebraic sums of the component magnitudes and acting in the direction of the component possessing the greater magnitude. These may be described as either parallel forces or as linear forces in that they act in the same or in opposite directions. Forces that are linear, i.e., along a line, require simple algebraic addition (Fig. 4–8).

---

* Accomplishment also may be measured in biochemical units as indicated by oxygen consumption.

† The unit of force is the meter-kilogram (or the inch-pound or derived units, such as the newton and the dyne) and is expressed as meter-kilogram, centimeter-kilogram, or centimeter-dyne.

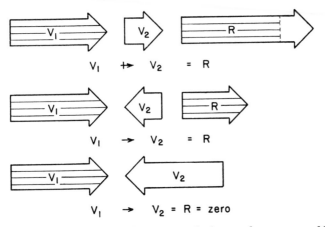

Fig. 4–8.   Linear vectors. Displacements which are linear are added alge-
braically. The resultant, in the upper diagram, depicts *added* force vectors since
the component force vectors, V_1 and V_2, act in the *same* direction. In the middle
diagram, the force vectors are *subtracted* and the resultant, R, reflects the magnitude and direction of the greater force, V_1. In the bottom diagram, the resultant
is zero since V_1 and V_2 are equal and opposite. (Note: The symbol $+\!\!\rightarrow$ signifies
vector addition; → vector subtraction.)

Perhaps often overlooked is the algebraic addition of the forces
exerted by the body segments into a total force called body weight;
the scale reading is an indication of the force exerted by the head, the
upper and lower appendages, and the trunk.

Most often, force vectors in man are neither linear nor parallel and
hence must be described in terms of resultant forces, a single force
which possesses the same effect as two or more forces acting together.
Further, the resultant force is in the direction of the greater force
(assuming only two forces). Through application of either the triangle
law or the parallelogram law, resultant vectors may be graphically presented (Fig. 4–9). Through algebraic and trigonometric application,
the force vectors are easily calculated. (For a description of the mathematical basis of calculation as well as for examples, turn to Chapter 11.)

Resistance to Motion

Displacement of the body along terrain or through water is accomplished at the expense of forces opposing progression. These forces,
ever present, can be minimized in order that accomplishment may be
attained at low metabolic cost.

Energy cost is a reflection of the degree of resistance (the opposition)
to motion.

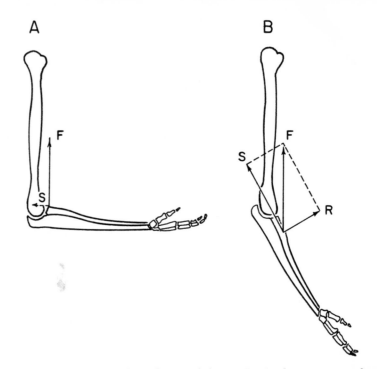

Fig. 4–9. Composition and resolution of forces. In A, the upper arm-forearm relationship is at 90 degrees. The force of the forearm flexor, *F*, is optimal because it is applied in the direction of motion; the stabilizing component, *S*, is minimal. In position *B* the arm is flexed at 150 degrees. The force vector *F* is decreased in magnitude since a great portion of the force is expended in joint compression, *S* (the stabilizing component), but not usefully in producing rotation about the humero-ulnar joint (vector *R*). $F = S +\!\!\to R$. Although not in linear fashion, force vectors increase in magnitude, whereas vector components decrease as the forearm is flexed from 90 degrees. Because of the acute angle which is formed by the insertion of the majority of skeletal muscles to bone, the magnitude of the stabilizing component is much more pronounced than is the rotational component. This contributes to postural stability. For calculation procedure, turn to Chapter 11.

In walking or running, one is literally at the mercy of the headwind. The end result of such an experience is manifested in reduced rates of progression coupled with an increased energy cost of performance. Somatotype cannot be quickly altered; however, changes in configuration of body mass are easily accomplished by such representative acts as flexion, abduction, or rotation. Bicycle riding offers an example of the effectiveness of assuming a more streamlined, advantageous posture. A marked reduction of body surface area exposed to the wind is accomplished through trunk flexion. This posture represents the only advantageous physical adjustment the bicyclist can readily make. An added condition, discouraging and unalterable, concerns the fact that the resistance offered by the wind varies with the square of the velocity —increases in displacement are met by increases in resistance.

Displacement in water offers additional problems and considerations. The retarding effect of body density (not immediately alterable) may be partially offset by technique. Speed of swimming, however, is directly related to resistance offered by the water since resistance to movement increases as a function of speed. Resistance, according to Karpovich and Millman,[29] accounts largely for the reduced efficiency of any swimming technique.

Electromyography

Analysis of muscular involvement in the production of motion may be accomplished through the employment of electromyography (EMG). This method of muscle analysis incorporates the amplification and recording of electrical potentials which are generated within active muscle tissue. Detection of electrical activity is accomplished with the aid of either surface electrodes (variously called skin or percutaneous electrodes) or needle electrodes, with the results of such detection made visible through either an oscilloscope or recorder. A high gain amplifier and audio system also may be used to render audible the potential within muscle. (The frequency of the electromyographic signal, ranging between ten and several thousand cycles per second, is readily audible after it is amplified.) However, this technique serves merely for purposes of demonstration.

With the observation by Galvani of the effects of electricity on muscle tissue and with the analysis of current by Volta, a new perspective in physiology was gained; however, it remained for G. B. Duchenne, in the mid-1800's, to use electricity for the purpose of diagnosis and treatment of nervous diseases. For his deeds, Duchenne has earned the title of "father of electrophysiology."[77] Matteucci, in 1844, detected bioelectricity during muscle contraction.[36] Yet much of the credit for the introduction of the technique of electromyography must go to such English neurophysiologists as Nobel Laureate E. D. Adrian,[1] D. W. Bronk, and D. E. Denny-Brown. In 1929, Adrian and Bronk introduced the concentric needle electrode.[36]

Essential for diagnostic purposes, precise location and exploration are afforded by the use of needle electrodes. These electrode types may vary from unipolar (for detecting potential within a radius of several centimeters—considered a large volume of muscle) to multiple coaxial (for detecting potential of a small volume of muscle), i.e., it is highly sensitive to potential changes at the immediate tip of the needle.

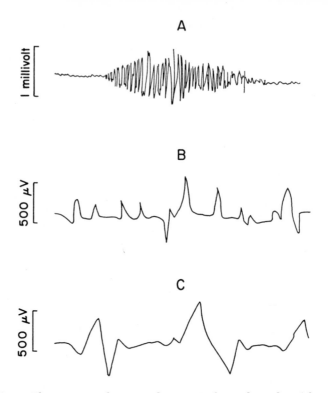

Fig. 4–10. Electromyographic records. *A,* Surface electrodes (slow recorder speed); *B* and *C,* needle electrodes (fast speed). Calibration wave appears at left of recording. Base-line disturbances are more pronounced with surface electrodes.

By contrast, percutaneous or skin electrodes are placed in surface contact with motor units. (Good skin-to-electrode contact and lowered electrical resistance of the skin [to approximately 3000 ohms] is practically assured through use of a saline electrode paste.) Also by comparison with the needle electrode, the percutaneous electrode detects potentials from many motor units and, as such, produces a less precise record. Representative tracings may be seen in Figure 4–10.

The statement of Basmajian,[4] "Electromyography is unique in revealing what a muscle actually *does* at any moment during various movements and postures [and] reveals objectively the fine interplay of coordination of muscles," has been demonstrated by many researchers, but in particular by the eminent authority himself.

Selected examples of preclinical research which attest to the unique feature of electromyography are presented.

Impressive is the scientific substantiation by Basmajian[3] of the mathematical treatise of skeletal muscle action by MacConaill.[34,35] MacConaill used the words "spurt" and "shunt" to distinguish those muscles which "produce acceleration along curve of motion" (spurt) from muscles acting "chiefly during rapid movement which is directed along the long axis of the moving segment" (shunt).

Through electromyographic research, Houtz and Fischer[24] have revealed a muscular mechanism which is constantly adjusting to postural deviations caused by externally applied forces or to changes in center of gravity.

The research of O'Connell substantiated the earlier results obtained by Basmajian and Bentzon relative to the precise action of the tibialis anterior. Contrary to actions described in authoritative anatomy texts, the tibialis anterior fails to function as an inverter of the foot unless extension of the foot occurs simultaneously.

A multivariate approach to the physiology of movement has been demonstrated by the simultaneous monitoring of additional parameters with electromyograms. Portnoy and Morin recorded cardiac response simultaneously with electromyograms (Fig. 4–11).

Electromyograms and electrogoniograms are obtained simultaneously. This serves not only as an important teaching aid, but also serves the purpose of research in the determination of specific muscle involvement in joint range of motion.

Telemetering of electromyographic data has been successfully accomplished.

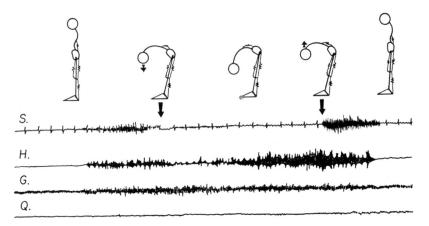

Fig. 4–11.   Electrocardiogram and electromyographs of trunk flexion and extension. On uppermost channel was recorded the myographs of the sacrospinalis muscles, *S*, as well as the electrocardiogram. Other channels (in descending order) recorded the activity of the hamstring muscles, *H*, the gastrocnemius, *G*, and the quadriceps muscles, *Q*. Interval between "critical points" designated by arrows indicates cessation of sacrospinalis involvement. The term "critical points" was introduced by Floyd and Silver to signify an abrupt change in muscle electrical activity. (From Portnoy and Morin. Courtesy of American Physiological Society.)

6

Electrogoniometry

Precise analysis of locomotion and of physical movement may now be accomplished through electrogoniometry, an inventive contribution of Karpovich.[28]

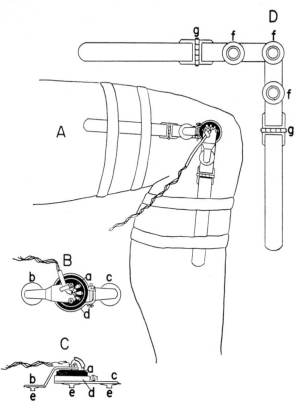

Fig. 4–12.   A, Electrogoniometer (elgon) attached to a chassis, which is strapped to the leg. B, Top view of the elgon; a, potentiometer; b and c, snap buttons; d, a clamp for attaching the arms to potentiometer. C, Side view of the elgon; a, potentiometer; b and c, arms; d, clamp; e, studs of snap buttons. D, Chassis; f, sockets for the elgon studs; g, hinges. (From Karpovich.[28] Courtesy of W. B. Saunders Co.)

Fig. 4–13.   A, Elgon control panel with calibration protractor. (Laboratory of Applied Physiology, Boyden Gymnasium, University of Massachusetts, Amherst.) B, Elgon calibration curve recorded on visicorder. The magnitude of the deflection on the recording instrument may be varied. To assure uniformity of recording and reading. Karpovich has suggested that flexion, abduction, and pronation movements be recorded as deflections to the *right*. These will be read as *downward* strokes on the light-sensitive paper. Extension, adduction, and supination are recorded as deflections to the *left* and read as *upward* strokes.

A

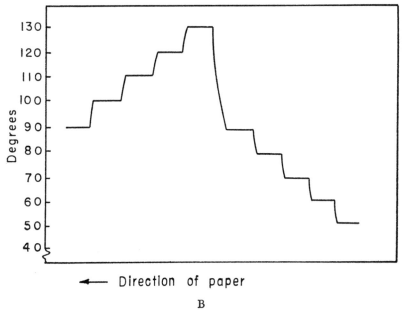

← Direction of paper

B

Fig. 4–13.   Legend on opposite page.

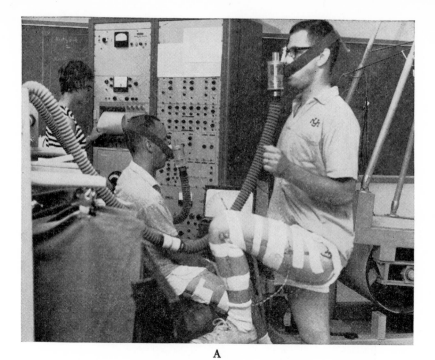

A

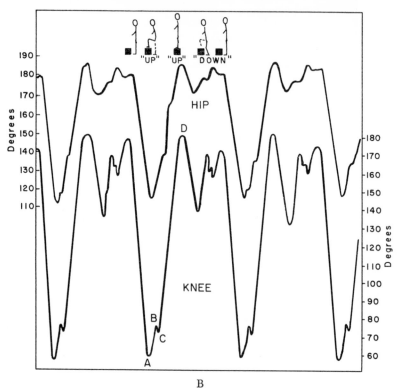

B

Fig. 4–14.   Legend on opposite page.

Through the use of a potentiometer which is supplied a constant voltage, and which obeys Ohm's law, a record of the degree of angular motion is easily obtained. The potentiometer and chassis to which it is attached is called an elgon (contraction of the words electric goniometer), and is pictured in Figure 4–12.

Decreases and increases in resistance within the wire-wound potentiometer, resulting from changing positions of the body part, are inversely related to current flow: $I = E/R$. The current is then delivered to an oscilloscope or recorder.

After initial calibration with a protractor has been accomplished (Fig. 4–13A, B), the elgon is used as a substitute for it and the range of joint movement is expressed as a deflection on the recorder which is translated into degrees of movement.[2]

The versatility of the direct wire elgon has been demonstrated.[11,16,21,25,27,31,32,43] Elgons also have been used in the analysis of the gaits of dogs and horses.

Telemetry units, currently undergoing extensive laboratory testing, will soon free the subject from wires and will enable researchers to analyze such complex gyrations as are performed by the diver and gymnast, as well as the long distance locomotion of walking or running and the physical movement of astronauts.

Fig. 4–14. A, Electrogoniometry in research involving energy cost of daily participation in, Harvard step-testing. (Laboratory of Applied Physiology, Boyden Gymnasium, University of Massachusetts, Amherst.) B, Electrogoniograms of left hip and knee of dominant and lead leg. Dotted appendage in stick figure depicts nondominant right leg. Encircled portion of knee goniogram focuses on high step action of foot which is reflected in acute knee angle, A. Knee angle B indicates that foot is in contact with bench surface. Interval between B and C depicts weight shifting phase. Torque phase is represented between C and D.

REFERENCES

1. Adrian, E. D.: Interpretation of the electromyogram. *Lancet:* 5311:1229–1233 and 5312:1283–1286, 1925.

2. Adrian, M., Tipton, C. M., and Karpovich, P. V.: *Electrogoniometry Manual.* Physiological Research Laboratory, Springfield College, Springfield, Massachusetts.

3. Basmajian, J. V.: "Spurt" and "shunt" muscles: an electromyographic confirmation. *J. Anat.*, 93:551–553, 1959.

4. Basmajian, J. V.: *Muscles Alive: Their Functions Revealed by Electromyography.* Baltimore, The Williams & Wilkins Co., 1962.

5. Basmajian, J. V., and Bentzon, J. W.: An electromyographic study of certain muscles of the leg and foot in the standing position. *Surg. Gynec. & Obst.,* 98:662–666, 1954.

6. Benedict, F. G., and Murschhauser, H.: Energy transformations during horizontal walking. Carnegie Institute of Washington, Publication 231, 1915.

7. Castiglioni, A.: *A History of Medicine.* 2nd Ed. Edited by E. B. Krumbhaar, New York, Alfred A. Knopf Co., 1958.

8. Cureton, T. K., and Wickens, J. S.: The center of gravity of the human body in the antero-posterior plane and its relation to posture, physical fitness, and athletic ability. *Res. Quart. Supplement,* 6:93–105, 1935.

9. Dickinson, S.: The efficiency of bicycle-pedalling, as affected by speed and load. *J. Physiol.,* 67:242–255, 1929.

10. DeCoursey, R. M.: *The Human Organism.* New York, McGraw-Hill Book Co., 1955.

11. Doss, W., and Karpovich, P. V.: A comparison of concentric, eccentric, and isometric strength of elbow flexors. *J. Appl. Physiol.,* 20:351–353, 1965.

12. Erickson, L., Simonson, E., Taylor, H. L., Alexander, H., and Keys, A.: Energy cost of horizontal and grade walking on the motor driven treadmill. *Am. J. Physiol.,* 145:391–401, 1946.

13. Elftman, H.: Work done by the muscles in running. *Am. J. Physiol.,* 129:672–684, 1950.

14. Fenn, W. O.: Frictional and kinetic factors in the work of sprint running. *Am. J. Physiol.,* 92:583–611, 1930.

15. Fenn, W. O.: The mechanics of standing on the toes. *Am. J. Phys. Med.,* 36:153–156, 1957.

16. Finley, F. R., and Karpovich, P. V.: Electrogoniometric analysis of normal and pathological gaits. *Res. Quart.,* 35:379–384, 1964.

17. Floyd, W. F., and Silver, P. H. S.: Electromyographic study of standing in man. *J. Physiol.,* 111:5P, 1950.

18. Furusawa, K., Hill, A. V., and Parkinson, J. L.: The energy used in "sprint" running. *Proc. Roy. Soc. B,* 102:43–50, 1927.

19. Gardner, E.: Physiology of movable joints. *Physiol. Rev.,* 30:127–176, 1950.

20. Gerstein, J. W.: Mechanics of body elevation by gastrocnemius-soleus contraction. *Am. J. Phys. Med.,* 35:12–16, 1956.

21. Gollnick, P. D., and Karpovich, P. V.: Electrogoniometric study of locomotion and of some athletic movements. *Res. Quart.,* 35:357–369, 1964.

22. Gray, H.: *Anatomy of the Human Body.* 28th Ed. Edited by C. M. Goss, Philadelphia, Lea & Febiger, 1966.

23. Hill, A. V.: The maximum work and mechanical efficiency of human muscles and their most economical speed. *J. Physiol.,* 56:19–41, 1922.

24. Houtz, S. J., and Fischer, F. J.: Function of leg muscles acting on the foot as modified by body movements. *J. Appl. Physiol.,* 16:597–605, 1961.

25. Karpovich, P. V.: Electrogoniometer for measuring degree of forearm rotation. Report to U. S. Army Medical Research and Development Command, Office of the Surgeon General, Washington, D. C., 1960.

26. Karpovich, P. V.: *Physiology of Muscular Activity.* 6th Ed. Philadelphia, W. B. Saunders Co., 1965.

27. Karpovich, P. V., and Ikai, M.: Relation between reflex and reaction time. *Fed. Proc., 19*:300, 1960.

28. Karpovich, P. V., and Karpovich, G. P.: Electrogoniometer. A new device for study of joints in action. *Fed. Proc., 18*:79, 1959.

29. Karpovich, P. V., and Millman, N.: Energy expenditure in swimming. *Am. J. Physiol., 142*:140–144, 1944.

30. Karpovich, P. V., and Pestrecov, K.: Mechanical work done and efficiency in swimming crawl and back stroke. *Arbeitsphysiol., 10*:504–514, 1939.

31. Karpovich, P. V., and Wilklow, L. B.: Goniometric study of the human foot in standing and walking. *U. S. Armed Forces M. J., 10*:885–903, 1959.

32. Karpovich, P. V., Herden, E. L., and Asa M. M.: Electrogoniometric study of joints. *U. S. Armed Forces M. J., 11*:424–450, 1960.

33. Knehr, C. A., Dill, D. B., and Neufield, W.: Training and its effect on man at rest and at work. *Am. J. Physiol., 136*:148–156, 1942.

34. MacConaill, M. A.: Some anatomical factors affecting the stabilizing functions of muscles. *Irish J. M. Sc., 6*:160–164, 1946.

35. MacConaill, M. A.: The movements of bones and joints. 2. Function of the musculature. *J. Bone & Joint Surg., 31* B:100–104, 1949.

36. Norris, F. H.: *The EMG, A Guide and Atlas for Practical Electromyography.* New York, Grune & Stratton, 1963.

37. O'Connell, A. L.: Electromyographic study of certain leg muscles during movement of the free foot and during standing. *Am. J. Phys. Med., 37*:289–301, 1958.

38. Passmore, R., and Durnin, J. V. G. A.: Human energy expenditure. *Physiol. Rev., 35*:801–840, 1955.

39. Portnoy, H., and Morin, F.: Electromyographic study of postural muscles in various positions and movements. *Am. J. Physiol., 186*:122–126, 1956.

40. Rasch, P. J., and Burke, R. K.: *Kinesiology and Applied Anatomy.* 3rd Ed. Philadelphia, Lea & Febiger, 1967.

41. Reynolds, E., and Lovett, R. W.: Method of determining the position of the center of gravity in its relation to certain body landmarks in the erect position. *Am. J. Physiol., 24*:286–293, 1909.

42. Steindler, A.: *Kinesiology of the Human Body Under Normal and Pathological Conditions.* Springfield, Charles C Thomas, 1962.

43. Tipton, C. M., and Karpovich, P. V.: Clinical electrogoniometry. *J. Phys. Ment. Rehab., 18*:90–95, 1964.

44. Williams, M., and Lissner, H. R.: *Biomechanics of Human Motion.* Philadelphia, W. B. Saunders Co., 1962.

5

CARDIOVASCULAR DYNAMICS

ANALYSIS of blood gas from any part of the arterial system reveals uniform levels of oxygen and carbon dioxide saturation because oxygen and carbon dioxide transfers do not take place in these vascular channels. The one notable exception is provided by the blood within the pulmonary artery. This vascular pathway, from the right ventricle of the heart to the lungs, contains blood which possesses a reduced oxygen content and an increased carbon dioxide content. The pulmonary veins channel the oxygenated blood from the lungs to the left atrium of the heart. Analysis of venous blood mirrors cell metabolic activity; carbon dioxide levels are elevated and oxygen levels are found to be reduced. Blood gas analyses from arterial, venous, and tissue sources scientifically establish the fact that the transfer of oxygen from arterial blood to tissue and of carbon dioxide from tissue to venous blood takes place in the capillary bed. It is interesting to note that more than a century ago Gustav Magnus[11] had inferred this occurrence.

The vital process of gaseous exchanges between blood and tissues represents an important role of the circulatory system. However, effective gas exchange can take place only when the composition, the pH, and the temperature of the blood is maintained within rather narrow limits. An added consideration is blood quantity. Although the discrepancy between capacity of the vascular system and blood volume favors capacity, adequacy of blood quantity is maintained through vasomotor (neural) control—through vasodilation and vasoconstriction and through shunting. An underlying assumption of the preceding discussion is that the rate of circulation is maintained at an adequate level. Normally, this is assured through the constancy of varying degrees of blood pressure at diverse body locations, which is maintained in part through alteration in lumen size and in part by the property of extensibility of vascular tissue.

Relatively stable, low levels of metabolic activity present a sufficiently great challenge to the dynamics of adequate circulation. Within an interval of milliseconds, metabolic intensities can vary greatly, yet the logistics of support—the maintenance of adequate rates of gas exchange, of adequacy of nutrients and removal of metabolites, of sufficiently great blood pressures and flows effected principally by changes in vasomotor activity—while even more challenging, are adequately provided.

The rate of blood circulation—volumetric quantity per unit of time— is initiated by the heart and assured by pressure gradients. In short, the muscular pumping mechanism, the heart, ejects blood into an elastic vascular system, the aorta and arteries, in which potential energy is converted into kinetic energy.

The Heart

This clenched-fist-sized, four-chambered muscular organ, weighing approximately 350 grams, serves the important function of initiating the propelling force of blood and lymph to the cells.

For purposes of discussion, the heart may be separated into right and left sections. Each section contains a collecting chamber, the atrium, and a more muscular, larger chamber, the ventricle. The biologic concept "function makes structure" is much in evidence in the comparative cross-sectional areas of the myocardium. Physical demands placed upon and functions performed by the atria are decidedly less pronounced than the functions of the ventricles and are reflected in the relative thinness of the atria. So, too, does the thickness of each ventricle reflect its role. The right ventricle, which propels blood through a relatively short distance, the pulmonary circulation, is less muscular than the left ventricle, which performs the task of propelling blood under greater pressure through an extensive circulatory system.

Tracing the flow of blood through the cardiovascular system might begin in the systemic veins. Venous blood from all cells, tissues, and organs of the body is ultimately channelled through the superior or inferior *venae cavae* into the right atrium of the heart (Fig. 5–1). Blood flow from right atrium to right ventricle is through the *tricuspid valve*. The propelling force generated by contraction of the ventricle, and the closing of the tricuspid valve, directs the blood through the *pulmonary valve* into the pulmonary artery to the lungs and through the pulmonary vein into the left atrium. From here, systemic circulation (as opposed to the previously mentioned pulmonary circulation) is directed through the *mitral valve* into the more muscular left ventricle. Contraction of this chamber forces the blood through the *aortic valve* into the aorta, arteries, arterioles, and capillaries, and from capillaries into venules, veins, and venae cavae.

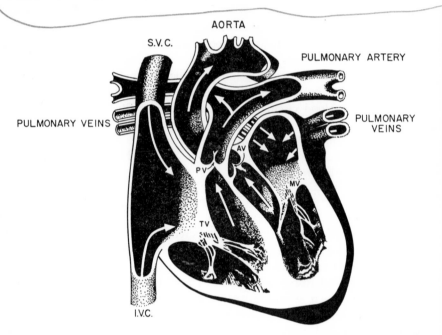

Fig. 5–1.   The muscular pump. Blood flows into right atrium through the superior and inferior venae cavae (SVC) (IVC). From here the blood passes through the tricuspid valve (TV) into the right ventricle then through pulmonary valve (PV) into pulmonary arteries to the lungs. Oxygenated blood from lungs is received into the left atrium via the pulmonary veins. From here it passes through the mitral valve (MV) into the left ventricle then through aortic valve (AV) and into systemic circulation via the aorta.

Cardiac Tissue

Cardiac muscle tissue combines the characteristics of skeletal muscle tissue as well as visceral muscle tissue.* It exhibits the structural characteristics of skeletal (voluntary) muscle in that it possesses cross striations, i.e., regions within the tissue which are alternately singly and doubly refractive to light; however, it is innervated by the sympathetic and parasympathetic tissue of the involuntary nervous system. Cardiac and smooth (involuntary) muscle tissues bear another similar property:

---

* The contraction of all three types of muscle tissue is explained by the law of Bowditch, commonly called the "all-or-none" law, which implies maximal response provided the stimulus is of sufficient intensity. *Gradation of contraction* (force) and *recruitment* of muscle fiber bundles explains differences in magnitude of response.

both tissue types are composed of a protoplasmic mass which is multi-nucleated.

In function, heart muscle tissue is capable of rapid contraction—a characteristic of skeletal muscle tissue; unlike skeletal muscle, however, it possesses a sustained, inherent systolic-diastolic rhythm.

Because of its wide frequency-of-contraction range and its variable volume of blood ejected per ventricular contraction, the output of the heart may range from 5.0 L/min during rest to 35.0 or 40.0 L/min during work states which tax the cardiovascular-pulmonary systems. These interrelations are expressed by the formula:

$$MV = SV \times HR$$

MV = minute volume (volume of blood flow per minute)[*]
SV = stroke volume (volume of blood ejected per stroke or contraction of ventricle)
HR = heart rate per minute

by
rearrangement
$$SV = \frac{MV}{HR}$$

While cardiac muscle is peculiar in that it possesses anatomical and functional characteristics of skeletal and smooth muscle tissues, it is also peculiar in its requirement of an *uninterrupted* supply of oxygen. Unlike skeletal muscle, cardiac tissue (and brain tissue as well) cannot tolerate an interrupted oxygen supply without incurring irreversible tissue damage, necrosis (tissue death). Unlike skeletal tissue, the heart will not incur an oxygen debt and it is much more sensitive to changes in blood composition and blood temperature. Alterations in composition and temperature of blood will effect changes in cardiac frequency. Variations in the metabolic rate of the pacemaker, the sinoatrial (SA) node,[†] are reflected in blood temperature.

Decreased blood temperatures effect a reduction in heart rate, whereas elevated temperatures result in an increased rate.

The contracted force of each of the chambers reflects its role. Wiggers describes the contraction force of each of the atria as being approximately equal. Rushmer aptly describes the right ventricle as a low pressure, volume pump and the left ventricle as a pressure pump.[37]

Direction of blood flow is determined by pressure gradient and valve action. In the heart, the low pressure exerted on the blood in each of the atria is sufficient to open the one-way atrioventricular valves and drive the blood into the ventricles. During contraction, ventricular

---

[*] Q or $\dot{Q}$ml/min are other symbols which might be used in place of MV to represent cardiac output.

[†] The SA node, or pacemaker, is also called the node of Keith and Flack, who described its role in establishing cardiac rhythm.

blood pressure against these atrioventricular valves is ineffective and serves merely to close these unidirectional valves more securely. This low resistance to flow results in blood flow from the right ventricle into pulmonary circulation and from left ventricle into systemic circulation. The elasticity of the pulmonary artery and of the aorta plays an extremely important role in the transfer of potential energy (e.g., during distention of the muscular wall) to kinetic energy (e.g., during recoil of the circular muscular wall).

Control of Cardiac Output

One of the peculiar characteristics of cardiac muscle tissue is its inherent rhythmicity of contraction; however, the frequency of contraction is alterable within limits (40 to 210 contractions/min) and is determined by neural impulses. Force of contraction is also dependent upon direct neural control, or reflex action.

The hypothalamus portion of the brain has been shown to effect changes in cardiac frequency. Stimulation of the posterior hypothalamic region may evoke an increased cardiac frequency (tachycardia), whereas stimulation of the middle portion may evoke a decreased frequency (bradycardia). This regional influence, however, has been questioned.

The hypothalamus also modifies the cardioinhibitor-accelerator centers of the medulla oblongata.

Dual innervation of the heart is accomplished through the autonomic nervous system. Stimulation of the vagus neurons (parasympathetic fibers) evokes a reduced cardiac response in both force and frequency of contraction, whereas stimulation of the augmentor neurons (sympathetic fibers) produces a diametrical effect. During any instance, impulses to the heart are received from parasympathetic and sympathetic fibers. Since the neural impulses are continuous, an altered cardiac frequency is the consequence of altered neural activity of either the vagus or the augmentor nerves. Acting independently, the vagus or augmentor nerve can alter the cardiac frequency, e.g., a decrease in vagus stimulation results in a decrease in cardiac frequency.

Reflex control of the heart is extensive and is influenced by baro-, chemo-, and pressoreceptors. The oxygen and carbon dioxide content of the blood influences the chemoreceptors which activate the cardio-accelerator center of the medulla oblongata, whereas the pressor receptors influence the cardioinhibitor center.

Located within the walls of the venae cavae and pulmonary veins are nerve fibers, under vagal control, which bear a striking resemblance to pressoreceptors. In 1915, Bainbridge pointed out that cardiac frequency could be altered under certain conditions and within established limits. Introduction of blood or physiologic (saline) solution into venae cavae of anesthetized animals resulted in an acceleration of cardiac frequency, *provided* the heart frequency was low; cardiac frequency that was high at the time of infusion remained unaltered. Provided heart frequency is within normal range (50 to 100 beats/min), increases in pressure in the venae cavae and right auricle cause an increase in heart rate. This is called the Bainbridge effect. Its acceptance among physiologists is not complete because of conflicting results obtained in research involving stimulation of the right heart. For example, as pointed out by Keele and Neil, stimulation of vagal receptors within the right heart results in a *decrease* in cardiac frequency. Heymans and Neil present evidence in support of the reflex. Others would agree that attempts to support the existence of the Bainbridge effect through logic must be minimized, that much more careful research is needed before the question can be settled.

In scientific jargon, laws are statements of scientific fact. Occasionally, outcomes of carefully conducted research performed under similar conditions may yield conflicting results. Such is the case with *Starling's law* also called the *law of the heart* which has gained complete acceptance by some but has also been totally rejected by others. According to Starling, "The energy of [cardiac muscle] contraction is a function of the length of the fiber." Stronger contractions resulting from greater initial lengths of muscle fibers have been interpreted to mean that the greater the initial filling of the ventricles, the greater will be the amounts of blood ejected per ventricular contraction. In short, the blood volume output of the heart is directly related to the input. Although the output-input relationship seems logical, there are eminent authorities on cardiac function who would replace logic with factual evidence. Rushmer[38] points out that the complete and universal acceptance of the law of Starling has resulted in the disregard of contradictory evidence. The evidence of Stead and Warren and of Sjöstrand also serves to contradict the "law." (Read discussion of stroke volume, pp. 103–107.)

Notable examples of alterations of heart rate are produced by such chemical substances as epinephrine (adrenaline) and thyroxin, which increase the frequency, and by norepinephrine (noradrenaline), which decreases the frequency. Epinephrine causes an increase in cardiac output, norepinephrine a slight decrease (see p. 91). The influence of epinephrine is extensive and predictable enough to warrant the formulation of a law. In accordance with *Elliott's law*, epinephrine effects action upon the structures innervated by the sympathetic system.

The function of the heart is to propel the blood at a·uniform rate to every cell throughout the body. How this is accomplished is most precisely explained in terms of the hemodynamics, the operating forces, of the greater (systemic) and lesser (pulmonary) circulatory systems.

TABLE 5–1. Approximate Blood Volume in the Adult Human Circulatory System

System or Location		Volume (ml)	%
Veins, venules		2750	50
Lungs		1100	20
Arterial		825	15
	Arteries	550 ⎤	10 ⎤
	Aorta	165 ⎬	3 ⎬
	Arterioles	110 ⎦	2 ⎦
Heart		550	10
Capillaries		275	5
Total		5500	100

Before discussing arterial and venous blood pressures, physical principles must be presented, but more basic to the discussion is an awareness of the blood volumes within different areas of the circulatory system.

In any instance, approximately one-half of the total blood volume is contained within the venous system, yet, in a discussion of circulation dynamics the important contribution of the venous system is often not cited. As a result, the important milking action of adjacent muscles, the so-called *muscle pump* is often downgraded.

Although Poiseuille's observations were directed to water flow within inelastic cylindrical tubing, the application of his findings to blood flow has contributed immeasurably to a clearer understanding of hemodynamics. By application of *Poiseuille's law* the flow rate of viscous fluids is observed as being directly proportional to the pressure gradient, fluid viscosity, and diameter of tubing. Blood is a viscous fluid which possesses considerable internal resistance. The cohesive force between the blood and the walls of the blood vessel bears an inverse relationship, i.e., the fluid layer adjacent to the blood vessel wall is prevented from flowing by the cohesive force exerted by the wall; at the center of the vessel the cohesive force is minimal and the blood flow (axial flow) is maximal. Through mathematical reasoning, Hagen calculated fluid flow and presented the formula:

$$F = P_1 - P_2 \times \frac{(\pi r^4)}{(8L)} \frac{(1)}{(v)}$$

$P_1 - P_2 =$ pressure difference at tube or vessel ends

$\pi, r^4, L =$ specifics of vessel dimensions

$1/v$ = coefficient of fluid measured in poise units

8 = Hagen's integration; calculus derivation.

Of great physiologic significance is the interpretation of the formula. Factors which *increase* the power of the numerator aid blood flow; factors which *decrease* the power of the numerator retard blood flow. However, of particular importance is r^4. At constant pressure and viscosity, doubling the radius results in a 16-fold increase in blood flow. Likewise, a decrease, by one-half, of the blood vessel radius results in a flow reduction of one-sixteenth of the initial value. Changes in blood viscosity, which increases in direct relationship to hematocrit levels but inversely to blood temperature, also affect blood flow. From the above formula it becomes obvious that blood flow and pressure are proportional, hence, doubling the blood pressure will result in a doubling of the blood flow rate. Elevated blood pressures are to be expected in heavy, prolonged work states; however, a doubling of pressures might embarrass the cardiovascular system or even terminate life.

Arterioles serve principally to distribute blood to more active regions through involuntary muscle control of arteriole diameters. Thus, diverting of blood, precipitated by hormonal influences or by neural impulses, is effectively accomplished. Changes in levels of metabolic activity are reflected in the lumen and in the degree of involvement of vascular beds.

Through rearrangement of Poiseuille's law, resistance to flow may be obtained:

$$R = \frac{P}{F} = \frac{(8L)}{(\pi r^4)} \frac{(v)}{(1)}$$

Changes in blood viscosity and vessel length (numerator above), as well as changes in radius of blood vessels, affect resistance levels. The flow-pressure curves drawn from the in vivo experimentation of Burton[9] and of Girling reveal the presence of a "critical closing pressure." At critical pressure levels, blood flow is halted due to vasoconstriction (especially of arterioles); however, at considerably elevated blood pressures (greater than critical closing pressure) flow becomes proportional to pressure of blood. In effect, resistances are maintained at fairly constant levels.

Application of *Pascal's laws* renders understandable the importance of the cardiovascular reflexes in maintaining constant blood flow to all tissues irrespective of body position or of temporary changes in gravitational forces. Pascal's first law embodies the concept that pressure applied on a confined fluid is transmitted equally in all directions; in his third law: fluid pressure increases with increasing fluid depth.

With the body in the horizontal position, the mean arterial pressures are approximately equal in the feet and head; however, with a vertical body position, the pressure in the feet exceeds that within the head. Rapid changes in body positions are usually accomplished without danger of dire consequences. On occasion, however, a feeling of "light headedness" or of "spotted vision" is experienced and is indicative of an inadequate cardiovascular reflex mechanism. This condition is termed postural hypotensive syndrome.

Maintenance of Even Flow Rates

During cardiac contraction, the left ventricle forces blood into the aorta. Because of its high degree of elasticity, the capacity of this vessel not only increases with blood volume increases, but also decreases with decreased blood volumes. Thus, during the cardiac diastolic phase, the pressure exerted on the blood volume within the aorta is maintained at a high level. These pressures, however, are of an intermittent or pulsating nature (pulsatile pressure) and are in obvious rhythm with the cardiac frequency. The elasticity of the large arteries serves to maintain a sufficiently high and constant pressure on the blood volume within its walls to drive it along to arterioles and capillaries (Figs. 5-2 and 5-3). It is interesting to note that changes in the nature of blood pressure from pulsating (in the aorta and large arteries) to steady (in the capillaries) follows the principle of circulation statics first described in

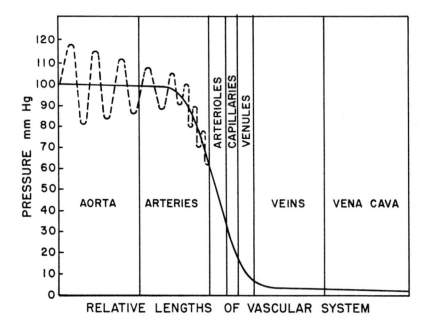

Fig. 5-2.   Pressures of blood within the vascular system. Blood pressure begins to fall in the terminal arteries but the most pronounced fall is in the arterioles. Borelli principle is depicted by pulsating (broken) line. (Adapted from Green. Courtesy of Year Book Medical Publishers, Inc.)

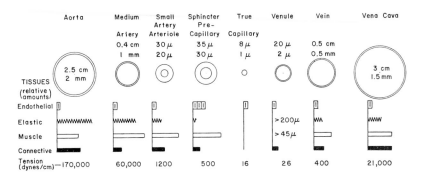

Fig. 5–3. Elastic properties and composition of blood vessels. Figures beneath each vessel indicate diameter of lumen and thickness of vessel wall. Relative amounts of tissue as well as tensions of vessel walls are also indicated. The highly elastic property of the aorta is followed by that of the arteries, vena cava, arterioles, pre-capillary sphincters, veins, venules, and capillaries. (Adapted from Burton.[10] Courtesy of American Physiological Society.)

the 1600's by Gian Alfonso Borelli, hence changes in blood flow from pulsatile to steady are described in terms of the Borelli principle. (Borelli regarded the human organism as a machine and applied the laws of statics and mechanics to it—the influence of his teacher, Galileo.)

Pressure Gradients

The elastic quality of the aorta and large arteries serves effectively to transform potential energy (occasioned by an increase in blood volume resulting from left ventricular systole) into kinetic energy—blood flow. Within the arterioles, blood flow is actively regulated through muscular control of the vessel diameters. In the venous system, the influence of the external forces provided by the overlying muscles and by one-way valves within the vessels serves effectively to propel the blood to the heart.

The tension exerted upon the blood vessel walls is explained by the law of Laplace and expressed as the product of pressure (of blood) and the radius of the vessel. $T = Pr$.

Arterial and Venous Blood Pressure—History

Although the accounts of the reaction of the English antivivisectionists to Hales' horse have been lost to history, the accomplishments of the Reverend Stephen Hales have been preserved.[13] It was the Reverend Hales who, in 1733, obtained the first direct determination of arterial blood pressure by vertically attaching a glass tube to a major equine artery: the blood rose to a height of $8\frac{1}{4}$ feet.

7

In 1896, S. Riva-Rocci[11] invented the mercury sphygmomanometer which made possible a technique of indirect assessment of blood pressure. The Riva-Rocci principle serves us to this day—the quantification of external air pressure to arrest arterial blood flow. The auscultation technique introduced by the Russian physician Korotkoff, in 1905, was a further improvement.[11]

For the researcher, electronic apparatus, capable even of telemetering blood pressure measurements of astronauts in space, has replaced the stethoscope (auscultoscope). Yet, the principle of measurement remains the same. Although a further engineering breakthrough is expected, at present the obtainable blood pressure data are from rather immobile subjects only and it is assumed that blood pressure readings taken immediately after the cessation of work are truly representative of the values during work. Thus, until the problem of artifact is solved, the important changes in arterial blood pressure *during* work remain elusive.

Unless specific reference is made to venous pressure, the term blood pressure signifies arterial (systolic and diastolic) blood pressure.

Physical Principles

Mindful of the laws of Pascal and cognizant of the convenient heart-level location of the elbow joint, the researcher most often selects the brachial artery as the site of blood pressure measurement. The amount of air pressure within the pneumatic cuff which is sufficient to stop brachial artery flow is then estimated by a mercury column or anaeroid manometer. In the Korotkoff technique, the stethoscope head is placed below the break of the elbow to a position atop the brachial artery. While four sounds of Korotkoff are documented, two are of a sufficiently challenging nature to be detected through the stethoscope by those persons of little training. Blood flow within the vascular system is inaudible; however, turbulent flow is detectable and is used as an end point in measurement.

Systolic and diastolic values vary between the sexes, but for both sexes the systolic and diastolic values climb slowly but steadily during advancing years (Fig. 5–4).

Although a stethoscope serves the useful purpose of aiding the physician to obtain clinical evidence, it plays a questionable role in carefully conducted research. As an example, in a study conducted by Ertel et al. sound conduction through stethoscopes was found to vary considerably.

More precise systolic and diastolic readings are obtained with the aid of microphone-amplifier-transducer-recorder apparatus or microphone-amplifier-speaker arrangements for audio signals (Fig. 5–5).

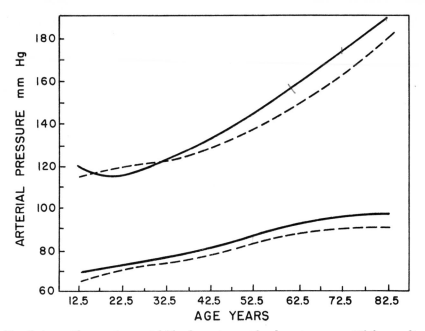

Fig. 5–4. Changes in arterial blood pressure with advancing years. While systolic and diastolic values climb steadily during advancing years, the rate of systolic climb is decidedly greater. Females represented by solid line, males by broken line. (Adapted from Hamilton et al.[22] Courtesy of Cambridge University Press.)

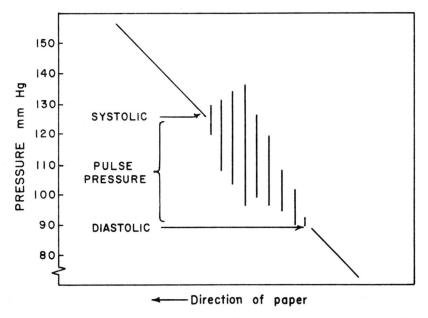

Fig. 5–5. Diagrammatic representation of blood pressure. Microphone imbedded within pneumatic cuff detects impulses (phases of sound of Korotkoff) which are fed through a pressure transducer into amplifier and recorder. Vertical lines indicate sound.

87

Blood Pressure Regulation

Maintenance of blood pressure levels is an ever impressive reflection of the control forces within the human organism. Blood is directed through a vascular system of varying lengths and diameters and of varying degrees of distensibility. Physiological or psychological adjustment to elevated metabolic states is required within seconds. To satisfy the increased needs of the tissues an increased cardiac output ensures an increased circulation rate. Although all systems within the organism are integrated, attention is presently focused upon the regulation of arterial blood pressure—the resultant of cardiac output and the peripheral resistance.

Dynamics of Cardiac Output

In the mid-seventeenth century, Blaise Pascal formulated his laws of hydrostatics: on a confined liquid, fluid pressure is transmitted in all directions and the force is exerted at right angles to the direction of flow.

Liquids and gases are fluids, i.e., both substances are incapable of withstanding any degree of shearing force. Liquids, unlike gases, are incompressible. In particular, blood does not behave in total conformity with Sir Isaac Newton's first two laws of motion and is, therefore, described as a non-Newtonian liquid; its viscosity, within small limits, is variable. Further, the mathematical treatment by Hagen of Poiseuille's law demonstrated that blood flows in layers, that the axial flow is greatest, and that the velocity of flow is reduced in direct relation to the proximity of blood to the blood vessel wall. Through rearrangement of the law of Poiseuille, resistance to blood flow is shown to be directly proportional to the viscosity of the fluid and to the length of the blood vessel.

$$R = \frac{P}{F} = \frac{(8L)}{(\pi r^4)} \frac{(v)}{(1)}$$

In the human, at any given instant, the relative viscosity of blood remains at fairly constant levels as does the length of the blood vessels; but the diameters of the vessels undergo constant alterations.

Metabolic requirements of the tissues are quickly alterable and are highly dependent upon blood flow. Because within the circulatory system blood volumes remain practically unchanged, the adequacy of the available blood volume is assured through alteration of blood vessel diameters. Through shunting, active tissues are supplied more blood through vasodilation, while less active tissues are supplied less blood through vasoconstriction. Should the metabolic intensity of work or exercise remain at high levels, a shunting of blood from the viscera would be effected.

The French physiologist Claude Bernard discovered, in 1851, nerve control of vasoconstriction.

For the most part, neural control of the lumen of arterioles, venules, and veins is located in the medulla oblongata of the brain. Within this vasomotor center are located arteriolar vasoconstrictor centers and arterial vasodilator centers. Constriction of the vascular lumen is accomplished through impulses along the sympathetic nerve pathways to the involuntary (smooth) muscles which encircle the arteries and arterioles. Dilatation of these vessels is the result of a decreased level, or rate, of innervation along the same nerve pathways, in effect, a passive dilatation. A more precise concept includes reference to pressor and depressor medullary regions, i.e., the pressor region effects vasoconstriction through excitation and effects vasodilation by inhibition. While a degree of constriction takes place in the arteries, pronounced constriction takes place in the more abundant arterioles; hence, the degree of peripheral resistance is the resultant of arteriolar influence.

Active vasodilation nerve fibers are present, though not in great numbers. Katz and Jochim point to vagal control of vasodilatation of the coronary arteries.

A rise in arterial blood pressure during the anticipatory phase of work or exercise is caused by neural impulses travelling from higher brain centers (hypothalamus or cerebral cortex) to the vasomotor center of the medulla.

Indirect Neural Control

An abundance of sensory nerve fiber endings in the atria and ventricles of the heart and within the internal carotid artery serves to maintain the blood pressure at fairly constant levels. An increased pressure of the blood within the areas served by the endings* results in an increased capacity of these vessels, and of the cardiac chambers. These sensory endings are therefore effective in maintaining a constancy of blood pressure: the vessels and cardiac chambers enlarge and decrease directly with the pressure of the blood within them.

Cardiac frequency, however, is inversely related to blood pressure. Thus, a rise in systemic pressure (caused by the pressure of the blood within the areas served by the nerve endings) reflexly elicits dilatation and distention and a reduced cardiac frequency (bradycardia). The afferent nerve pathways, the sino-aortic nerves, located within the subclavian artery, aortic arch, and internal carotid artery (coined "buffer nerves" by Wright[28]), serve to maintain blood pressure homeostasis through reflex regulation.

---

* Called proprioreceptors by Barron.

Direct Chemical Regulation

It is also well to recall the sensitivity of these carotid and aortic bodies (chemoreceptors) to blood gases and pH. The end result of their sensitivity is reflected in an increased cardiac output, through an increased blood pressure, despite an increased cardiac output, through an increased blood pressure, despite an increased peripheral resistance. Except under extreme conditions, e.g., in the studies of Astrand[3] and Dill[14] in which the blood pH level was reduced to 6.9 through severe work, this regulatory mechanism is of less importance, because of its infrequency of activation, than are the buffer nerves.

Certain of the end-products of metabolism carried in blood circulation also exert a direct effect on blood pressure through alteration of arteriole diameters. One ever present and highly important end-product is carbon dioxide which dilates the arterioles by direct action on the circular muscle walls. (By contrast, an increase in the partial oxygen pressure produces vasoconstriction.) Thus, through increased blood volume (flow) and through arteriolar dilatation, carbon dioxide provides directly for its own removal—more carbon dioxide, greater dilatation, more blood volume, more carbon dioxide removal. As exemplified in the Astrand study, the increase in carbon dioxide and lactic acid, and the decreased blood pH and partial oxygen pressure effected the removal of carbon dioxide.

	Pressure	Effect
P_{O_2}	increased decreased	vasoconstriction vasodilatation
P_{O_2}	increased decreased	vasodilatation vasoconstriction

A lowered partial carbon dioxide pressure, induced by voluntary overbreathing, results in a slight change in blood pressure; however, as shown by Keele and Neil, when the blood carbon dioxide content is raised the blood pressure is also raised (Fig. 5–6).

Elevated amounts of carbon dioxide also provide an effective shunting of blood from inactive to active tissues. During heavy work states which result in hypercapnia, the medullary pressor region elicits arteriolar constriction. In the active tissue region, however, the presence of elevated levels of carbon dioxide serves to nullify the pressor effect (vasoconstriction) and arteriole dilatation is in reality effected.

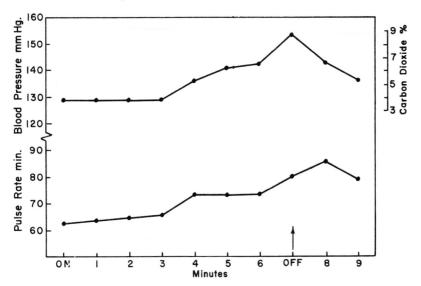

Fig. 5–6. Effect of carbon dioxide inhalation on blood pressure and pulse rate. Subject breathed a mixture of 95% O_2, 5% CO_2. After seven minutes, indicated by arrow, subject breathed ambient air. During this period, the CO_2 had increased to 8.9%. (Adapted from Keele and Neil. Courtesy of Oxford University Press.)

Hormonal Control

Increased metabolic states also result in increased secretions of many glands of the body. One such example is provided by the suprarenal, or adrenal, glands which secrete epinephrine from its medullary portion. Also produced from the adrenal medulla is the substance called norepinephrine and less commonly called levarterenol or arterenol.

TABLE 5–2.   Effect of Epinephrine and of Norepinephrine Injections on the Cardiovascular System (Adapted from Barcroft and Swan[5])

	Systolic Blood Pressure	Diastolic Blood Pressure	Cardiac Frequency	Peripheral Resistance (Arterial)	Cardiac Output
Epinephrine	I	D	I	D	I
Norepinephrine	I	I	I followed by D	I	NAE

I = increased, D = decreased
NAE = no appreciable effect

The effects upon the circulatory system by these hormones are interesting (Table 5–2).

Stress reactions to situations or conditions which disturb homeostasis, i.e., upset physiological equilibrium, would be sufficient to trigger the release of sufficient amounts of epinephrine to produce the above effects. To a degree, these effects are misleading because the epinephrine and norepinephrine were administered in separate venous injections. In reality, the secretion of the adrenal medulla contains a mixture of epinephrine and norepinephrine. Table 5–3 presents the separate and combined (natural) effects.

TABLE 5–3.   Effects of Separate Intravenous Injections of Epinephrine and Norepinephrine (Barcroft and Swan[5])

	Normal Blood Flow (ml/min)	Blood Flow Following Injection (ml/min)	
		Epinephrine	Norepinephrine
Skeletal muscles	1000	2000	1000
Liver	1500	3000	1500
Kidneys	1500	900	1200
Brain	750	900	675

From Table 5–3, one can observe that the intravenous administration of epinephrine in man causes a marked increase in blood flow through the skeletal muscle system and in the liver and brain as well, whereas norepinephrine does not produce changes of any significance. The 100% increase in blood flow through skeletal muscle (from 1 to 2 liters/min) produced by epinephrine demonstrates its role as a vasodilator, relatively speaking, rather than as a vasoconstrictor. As shown in Table 5–3, epinephrine decreases arterial peripheral resistance, thereby effecting a marked increase through skeletal muscle, i.e., a net vasodilator effect.

Histamines are known to produce arteriolar vasodilatation; however, its appearance in blood in sufficiently great concentration to effect dilatation is triggered traumatically by tissue mutilation.

Adenylic acid, formed during the chemical breakdown of adenosinetriphosphate (ATP) is conspicuous in skeletal and cardiac muscle as well as in the kidney, spleen, and brain. It also produces arteriolar dilatation while reducing cardiac frequency. The vasodilator effect of ATP was reported by Folkow to possess the potency of $\frac{1}{15}$ to $\frac{1}{5}$ the potency of acetylcholine. Like histamine, an increased presence of adenylic acid may also be triggered by trauma.

Intravenous injections of acetylcholine are also known to produce arteriolar vasodilatation while effecting a decrease in cardiac frequency and in arterial blood pressure. With reference to blood pressure, the effect of acetylcholine injection is misleading because during physiological adaptations to varying levels of metabolic activity, the net effect of acetylcholine is reduced due to its deactivation by the enzyme cholinesterase.

Valsalva Maneuver

The maneuver named for Antonio Valsalva (Italian anatomist, 1666–1723) is characterized by a voluntary attempt to exhale forcibly against a closed glottis. This effort involves shortening contraction of the diaphragm muscle, the abdominal muscle group, and the muscles which lower the rib cage. The net effect of the greatly elevated intrapulmonary pressure following sustained effort is that of impeding the return flow of blood to the heart and through the lungs. The decreased venous return results in a decreased cardiac output. The attendant drop in blood pressure is accompanied by an increase in heart frequency (reflexly increased due to a decrease in sinoaortic pressures). At the cessation of sustained effort, which is accompanied by a decrease in intrapulmonary pressure, the venous return, now unimpeded, surges into the left heart and results in a sudden but brief increase in blood volume ejected into the aortic vessels. The brief attendant increase in arterial blood pressure* is accompanied by a decrease in cardiac frequency (also reflexly elicited from proprioceptive involvement). The strain imposed upon the cardiopulmonary system is sufficiently great to cause embarrassment to a debilitated heart or may result in temporary loss of consciousness due to black-out.

Individuals possessing a perverted sense of humor have been known to utilize this technique on a permissive, unsuspecting person. By exerting (from behind) a "bear hug" to the abdominal region, while the unsuspecting person cooperates by practicing breath holding for a few seconds, a prolonged black-out will result. Accidental deaths, due to secondary causes, may result from such examples of distorted humor.

The Valsalva maneuver is practiced to varying degrees of intensity during such essential acts as defecation and micturition as well as in the performance of such feats as weight lifting.

---

* The secondary increase in arterial pressure during the Valsalva maneuver was shown by Price and Conner to bear a positive relationship to venous pressure increment (also produced by the maneuver), hence to intrathoracic pressure. By abolishing the secondary increase in arterial pressure (by drug action that partially blocks impulses through the sympathetic and parasympathetic ganglia), the authors concluded that the arterial pressure change "occurs as the result of a reflex hemodynamic adjustment to increased intrathoracic pressure."[33]

Venous Blood Pressure

During any given period, at least half the total blood volume is to be found within the venous system. Pressures within this system, being sufficiently low, necessitate the use of water columns, or of pressure transducers for accuracy of measurement rather than mercury. (Mercury is 13.6 times as dense as water.)

By comparison with arteries, veins are thinner walled, markedly less muscular, and more distensible. Venous flow is highly dependent upon a low positive, but significant, pressure. During elevated work states, the beneficial assist of the *muscle pump*, i.e., the actions of the overlying skeletal muscles* and of the intrathoracic pressures play an extremely important role in the maintenance of circulatory equilibrium.

Measurement of venous pressure may be obtained by direct or indirect means and all readings must be corrected to heart level. Because of the effect of hydrostatic pressure in the immobile standing position, the venous pressure at ankle level is on the order of 90 mm Hg (122.4 cm H_2O). To reduce as much as is possible the influence of gravity, venous pressures are taken from the recumbent position with values corrected to heart level. Normal pressures within the vena cava, at heart level, approximate 61.2 mm H_2O (4.5 mm Hg).

Although there are marked differences in function and structure of the arterial and venous systems, the same physical principles and laws apply equally to both.

Changes in venous pressures are effected by changes in body position (hydrostatic), or by positive pressure breathing, or by Valsalva maneuver. Yet, irrespective of body position or respiratory influence, for systemic equilibrium to be maintained, return blood flow to the heart must equal the cardiac output into systemic circulation. During levels of increased metabolic activity, blood is returned to the heart by pressure and by *muscle pump*.

Increased rates of blood flow, associated with exercise which is challenging to the cardiovascular-pulmonary system, are also under increased pressure since elevated levels of systolic blood pressure are reflected in an increased mean arterial blood pressure. It is this (elevated) pressure gradient which drives the blood through the capillary bed and into the venules and veins. From venules to right auricle, the resistance to blood flow offered by the veins is comparatively negligible due to several factors. The first relates to structure. Venous blood vessels possess increasingly larger diameters in relation to their proximity to the heart and thus offer decreasing resistance to flow (Fig. 5–7).

---

* The veins in the arms and legs possess valves, which permit flow only in the direction of the heart. Veins in the abdominal and thoracic region lack valves.

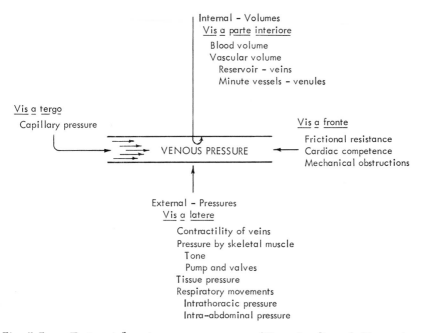

Fig. 5–7. Factors influencing venous pressure. (From Landis and Hortenstine. Courtesy of American Physiological Society.)

The second relates to a significant reduction in peripheral resistance through vasodilatation* which is the resultant of decreased sympathetic venoconstrictor impulses. The third relates to the force of the blood acting from behind, the *vis a tergo,* in relation to the impending force, the *vis a fronte,* of the blood within the venous channel. Within the venous system the *vis a tergo* exceeds the *vis a fronte.*

A pressure gradient favorable to venous flow remains at all levels of the body. As an example, the venous blood pressure, taken in the standing, inactive position largely reflects the hydrostatic pressure of the blood (from right auricle to ankle) but incorporates the low pressure within the venules. Likewise, the arterial blood pressure at ankle level is also raised and also reflects the hydrostatic pressure. A fourth consideration is the external force provided by the *muscle pump* (Fig. 5–8). Blood pressure in the ankle region, taken from the standing, inactive position, is approximately 90 mm Hg which largely reflects the hydrostatic pressure of the blood but incorporates the low level of pressure within the venules. During walking, for example, the pressure may be

---

* There is widespread disagreement among physiologists concerning the absence of dilator nerve fibers in veins.

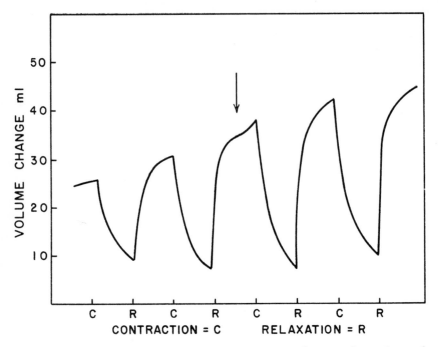

Fig. 5–8.   Schematic representation of plethysmographic recording of muscle pump. Volume changes induced by milking action of calf muscle group. Despite inflation to 90 mm Hg of pneumatic cuff placed above knee (indicated by arrow) effectiveness of muscle pump was maintained. (Adapted from Barcroft and Swan. Courtesy of E. Arnold & Co.)

considerably reduced to approximately 20 mm Hg solely through the milking action of muscle (*muscle pump*).

Still another consideration is the dominant role of the changing intra-thoracic pressures induced by breathing. During resting states, the intrathoracic pressure remains negative to atmospheric pressure, i.e., below atmospheric pressure. In the inspiratory phase, the pressure within the thorax falls to approximately −6 mm Hg and during the expiratory phase it rises to approximately −2 mm Hg. The pressure upon the blood within the thin-walled central venous system which traverses the thoracic cavity is directly influenced by the negative intra-thoracic pressure changes: the *vis a latere*.

In summary, the ultimate accelerating force, that of cardiac ventricu-lar contraction (the *vis a tergo*) is progressively spent along the arterial, arteriolar, and capillary pathways. An effective combination of reduced resistance to flow and of valves which permit unidirectional flow (the *vis a fronte*) and of such external factors as the muscle pump, and of the respiratory movements (the *vis a latere*) propel the blood toward the heart. During work or exercise states of high metabolic intensity, i.e., challenging to the cardiovascular-pulmonary systems, arterial and venous pressures remain relative. Increased circulation is met by increased muscle pump action as well as by direct action of the breathing movements. For great feats of strength and power, during which time the Valsalva maneuver may be employed, or during grueling running events, the intrathoracic pressures may vary from −40 mm Hg in inhalation to +40 mm Hg in exhalation. These pronounced *vires a latere* provide but another example of the ever present attempt of the human organism to maintain physiologic equilibrium.

Measurement of Cardiac Output

Quantitative determination of cardiac output may be accomplished by direct or indirect means. Irrespective of method, the technique requires the services of specialized experts.

Flow meters, placed in the aorta of laboratory animals, have been used as a means of directly measuring the output of the heart. This direct method has been used with varying degrees of success. Due largely to the sophistication of this technique, cardiac output data have been limited to anesthetized animals or restrained animals.

Indirect methods are more varied. Although the present indirect methods are also sophisticated, many are based on the Fick principle which was introduced in 1870 by the German physician Adolph Fick (1829–1901).[11] Through the employment of the Fick principle, which is based on the respiratory exchange, oxygen uptake is equal to the product of blood flow times the difference in the oxygen content of arterial and mixed venous blood. By rearrangement, this is expressed in the formula:

$$Q = \frac{VO_2}{AVO_2 \text{ diff}}$$

Q = cardiac output
VO_2 = oxygen uptake
AVO_2 diff = arterial-venous oxygen difference

Thus, cardiac output in ml/min is determined from the amount of oxygen consumed per minute and the amount of oxygen taken up by each milliliter of blood within the lungs.

The determination of oxygen uptake is easily accomplished by either closed or open circuit indirect calorimetry techniques (see Chapters 8 and 11). Far more complicated is the collection of the arterial and the mixed venous blood sample; the analysis of the blood samples for oxygen content is time consuming and tedious.

Collection of arterial blood is relatively easily accomplished through brachial artery puncture. Because oxygen content of venous blood varies according to the extent of specific tissue involvement, the truly representative mixed venous sample must be withdrawn from the right atrium of the heart, a process which requires cardiac catheterization.*

Through the use of Table 11–4 and by assuming an oxygen uptake of 250 ml/min for a resting subject, cardiac output can be calculated. See also Chapter 11.

$$\dot{Q} = \frac{\dot{V}O_2}{AVO_2 \text{ diff}}$$

$$\dot{Q} = \frac{250 \text{ ml/min}}{0.20 \text{ ml/ml} - 0.15 \text{ ml/ml}\dagger}$$

$$\dot{Q} = \frac{250 \text{ ml/min}}{0.05 \text{ ml/ml}}$$

$$\dot{Q} = 5000 \text{ ml/min}$$

Additional methods of determining cardiac output include the introduction of stains or dyes, or isotonic solutions, or radioisotopes. For a detailed discussion of methods of determining cardiac output, refer to Gregg.[20]

The dye method of Hamilton et al. involves the intravenous injection of a known quantity of dye, e.g., Evans blue dye, and the subsequent withdrawal of arterial blood samples.[24] The dye concentration of these arterial samples is plotted as a function of time. Extrapolation of the curve to the base line is necessary due to recirculation of blood (and dye) by the heart. Thus, the time required by the heart to eject the dye is represented by the time under the curve and the average concentration of dye in the blood ejected by the heart is represented by the area under the curve. Cardiac output is calculated by the formula:

$$\dot{Q} \text{ (ml/min)} = \frac{\text{dye injected (mg)}}{\text{average arterial concentration (mg/ml} \times \text{ time in seconds)}}$$

Recently a thermodilution method of measuring cardiac output was accomplished on exercising dogs by Cerretelli et al. Essentially, the method involves the injection of a cold isotonic solution into the right

---

* Cardiac catheterization may be accomplished either by direct needle piercing (transfixing) of the right atrium or by vinyl plastic tubing of small bore which is threaded through the antecubital vein into the right atrium.

† 20 vols % = 20 ml/100 ml blood or 0.20 ml/ml blood; 15 vols % = 15 ml/100 ml blood or 0.15 ml/ml blood.

atrium and the recording of temperature variations of aortic blood.*
The advantages of this method over the dye method are that no foreign
substance is injected into the blood stream and blood samples are not
withdrawn.

Cardiac Cycle

Reduced to the simplest of terms, the *cardiac cycle* is descriptive of
each complete phase of systole and diastole. As depicted in Figure
5–9, a rhythmically occurring sequence of valve openings and closings
produces sounds, electrical potentials, and pressure and volume changes
which enable the specialist-observer to evaluate cardiac performance.

For the ensuing discussion, the reader will benefit by referring constantly to Figure 5–9. Direction of blood flow is determined by pressure
gradient and cardiac valve action. At the end of the diastolic phase
of the cardiac cycle, depicted by the clear area to the left of the shaded
area, pulmonic and aortic pressures drop, while the pressures within
the atria and ventricles rise slightly. These latter pressures are indicative
of blood flow into the atria and ventricles. During this phase of the
cardiac cycle, sounds are not detected through a stethoscope, nor are
electrical potentials recorded on an electrocardiogram.

Another phase of the cardiac cycle, the systolic phase, is depicted as
a shaded area in Figure 5–9. This phase is characterized by dramatic
changes in pressures and volumes, electric potentials, and valve action
and sounds. At the onset of systole, the combined action of atrial
contraction against a *closed* atrioventricular valve (1) results in a slight
increase in intra-atrial pressure, which is subsequently decreased during
the *opening* of the atrioventricular valves (2)† during diastole. At the
onset of ventricular contraction, the A–V valves are open; however,
the increasing pressure on the blood within the ventricular chambers
soon forces the A–V valves to close. As the pressure on the blood within
the ventricles exceeds the pressure of the blood within the aorta and
the pulmonary arteries, the aortic valves (3), as well as the pulmonic
valves (5), open, and blood flows from the right ventricle into the

---

* The cold isotonic solution (as low as 1.5° C) was injected through a polyethylene catheter, which was inserted through the external jugular vein into the
right atrium. Aortic blood temperature variations were detected by a thermistor imbedded within another polyethylene catheter, which was inserted into the aortic
arch through the carotid artery and was attached to an amplifier-recorder unit.[12]

† For purposes of simplification, the pressure curves for the atrioventricular valve
in the right heart (uppermost tracing, Fig. 5–9) were deleted. The pressure curves
for the right and left A-V valves are similar. Atrial contraction of the right heart
commences approximately 20 milliseconds before the left atrial contraction.

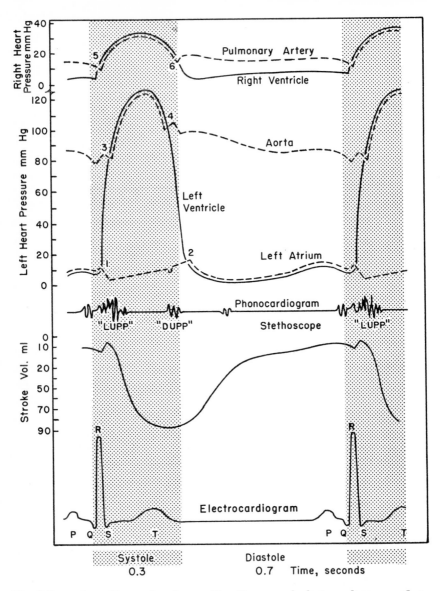

Fig. 5–9. A cardiac cycle of rest. The T wave of electrocardiogram reflects maximal ventricular contraction. Note the significantly greater force of contraction of the left ventricle in comparison to the right ventricle—peak aortic pressure is four times greater than peak pulmonic pressure (120 mm Hg vs 30 mm Hg). Note also the sequence of valve action: Mitral valve (*1* closed, *2* open); pulmonic valves (*5* open, *6* closed) open before and close after the aortic valves (*3* open, *4* closed). Pressure of blood during ventricular contraction is determined not only by force of contraction but also by volume of blood. (Adapted from Wiggers. Courtesy of Grune & Stratton.)

pulmonary arteries and from the left ventricle into the aorta. Finally, as the pressure within the ventricles falls below the pressures within the aorta and the pulmonary arteries, the aortic valve closes (4) as does the pulmonic valve (6). During this systolic phase, the familiar sounds are heard through the stethoscope, and the Q, R, S, T segments of the electrocardiogram are recorded.

The onset of diastole is marked by gradually decreasing pressures in the aorta and in the pulmonary arteries as well as within the right and left ventricles. See clear area to right of shaded area in Figure 5–9.

Tracings in the above figure depict the heart at rest. During periods of activity or stress, which are challenging to the cardiovascular and pulmonary systems, the diastolic phases are decreased and the degree of decrement of diastasis* is inversely related to intensity of cardio-vascular-pulmonary response.

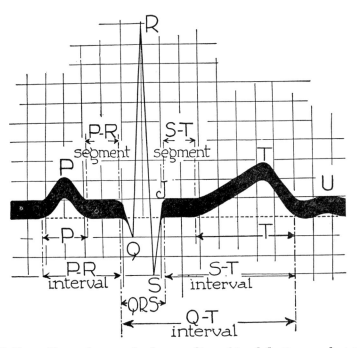

Fig. 5–10.   Nomenclature of electrocardiographic deflections and intervals. P Q R S T nomenclature was devised by Nobel Laureate Einthoven. P wave is produced by atrial activity; QRS by ventricular activation; T wave reflects ventricular recovery; (U signifies an after-potential). Deflections reflect positioning of precordial leads (see Fig. 5–11). Intervals vary inversely with heart frequency. (From Burch and Winsor, Lea & Febiger.)

---

* Diastasis describes the latter phase of diastole which is characterized by slow filling of the ventricles. As cardiac frequency increases, the diastatic phase is shortened and may disappear.

8

An electrocardiogram* is depicted in Figure 5–10. See Figure 5–11 also.

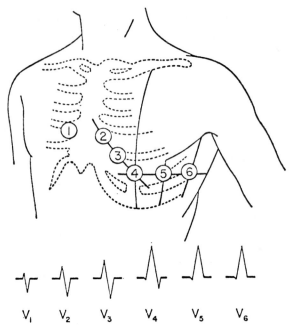

Fig. 5–11.   Positions of the chest electrodes for 6 standard precordial leads. V_1, 4th intercostal space to right of sternum. V_2, 4th intercostal space at left of sternum. V_4, 5th interspace at midclavicular line. V_3, midway between V_2 and V_4. V_5, anterior axillary line, same level as V_4. V_6, mid axillary line, same level as V_4 and V_5. Below are shown general form of QRS in normal precordial leads. V_3 represents transition zone from predominant negativity on the right to predominant positivity on left. (From Lipman and Massie. Courtesy of Year Book Medical Publishers, Inc.)

Factors Influencing Cardiac Output

As indicated in the first part of the chapter, cardiac output may range from 5.0 to 40.0 L/min. The factors which influence the cardiac output are varied but include those based on the dynamics of circulation; some factors are influenced by gravitational forces.

Cardiac output may be expressed as

$$MV_{ml} = SV_{ml} \times HR$$
$$\text{or}$$
$$\dot{Q} \, ml/min = SV_{ml} \times HR$$

---

* The electrocardiograph was invented in 1903 by Willem Einthoven (1860–1927). For this and other achievements relating to electrical activity of the heart, the distinguished professor from Leiden (The Netherlands) was awarded the Nobel prize in 1924.[11]

The events of a cardiac cycle during rest are depicted in Figure 5–9. An increased heart rate would be reflected in a decreased diastolic phase; however, the effect on ventricular filling is minimal because the greatest amount of filling is accomplished during the beginning phase of diastole. Thus, the volume of blood ejected by the ventricles during systole, the stroke volume, is not appreciably altered but the cardiac output is increased owing primarily to the increase in heart rate.

Additional factors need to be considered. Basically, the volume of blood ejected per stroke is dependent upon the blood volume within the ventricle. This amount, in turn, is dependent upon such factors as the amount of reserve volume within the heart and the rate of blood flow—which is, in turn, dependent upon the effect of gravitational forces on body positions or on level of physical activity.

A decrease in cardiac output of approximately 20% (approximately 1 L/min) was observed by Asmussen and Nielsen in a change of body position from horizontal to inactive standing.[1] This reduction in cardiac output is attributed to venous pooling, which results in a decreased blood flow to the heart. Thus, the stroke volume is decreased and, despite the increase in heart rate when the standing position is assumed, the output of the heart is reduced. Cardiac output in the standing subject can be increased through muscular activity involving the limbs, a process which insures an increased blood volume return through muscle pump action coupled with an increased heart rate associated with activity (Figs. 5–6 and 5–7). High ambient temperatures (which interfere with body heat dissipation) constitute another factor which contributes to a decreased cardiac output. Rowell et al.[35] noted a redistribution of blood in peripheral circulation resulting from the performance of moderate and severe exercise at high ambient temperature, 43.3° C. This was indicated by a decreased stroke volume and central blood volume.

Generally, increased intensity levels of physical activity are accompanied by increases in cardiac output resulting from increased venous blood return, increased force of ventricular contraction (SV), and an increased heart rate. A detailed discussion of these factors is presented under the topic of dynamics of cardiac output, neural control, chemical regulation, hormonal control, and venous blood pressure changes (pp. 88 to 97).

Effect of Exercise on Cardiac Performance

The heart is a muscular pump which confirms the biological concept that function determines structure. This is evidenced in the pronounced degree of muscularity of the ventricular walls as compared with those of the atria. Within the human, cardiovascular pulmonary training results in a more muscular, better developed, and slightly hypertrophied heart which possesses significantly greater heart volumes. This may be observed in Table 5–4.

These data of Reindell et al. corroborate the earlier data of Kjellberg et al. The significant differences between heart volumes and weights in Table 5–4 is evident. Most interesting, however, are the data pertain-

TABLE 5–4.   Comparative Cardiac Data on Untrained, Trained, and Highly Trained Individuals (From data of Reindell et al.[34])

| | Heart Vol (ml) | Heart Wgt (gm) Estimated | Heart Blood Vol (ml) | Left Heart | | Ventricular End-Systolic Vol (ml) |
				Ventricle Blood Vol (ml)	Stroke Vol (ml)	
Untrained	785	300	485	136	85	51
Trained (for a variety of athletic events)	1015	350	665	186	85	101
Highly trained (professional cyclists)	1437	500	937	262	85	177

ing to the left heart. The blood volumes of the left ventricles reflect levels of training, yet the resting stroke volumes are equal. This indicates the presence of a reserve volume* of blood, i.e., a volume of blood which remains in the heart after the completion of the systolic phase of the cardiac cycle.

The literature contains considerable data which provide a basis for clarification of the dynamics of stroke volume based on Starling's law of the heart—greater ventricular filling elicits a greater stroke volume.[2,15,26,36]. Rushmer[36] and Hyman have shown that heart volume (size) can diminish during exercise.

From the data presented in Table 5–5, the reader must conclude that the hearts are "abnormal." From a clinical viewpoint, however, only patient D, an inactive former athlete, possessed a pathologically enlarged heart.

---

* Rushmer introduced the terms systolic reserve volume and diastolic reserve volume.[36]

TABLE 5–5.   Heart Volume Changes Effected by Exercise (From data of Hyman[26])

Students	Age	Weight (kg)	Height (cm)	Heart Volume (ml)		Differ-ence (ml)	C-B Index*
				Before Exercise	After Exercise		
A. Athlete	18	100.79	190.50	942	874	−68	950
B. Athlete	21	65.83	184.15	865	636	−229	708
C. Former athlete (still active)	65	57.66	170.18	730	684	−46	715
D. Former athlete (inactive)	58	73.55	167.64	1520	1675	+155	990

*C-B index (cardio-body index) = area of heart cm^2/BSA m^2. Normal range of C-B index = 400 to 450.

Asmussen and Nielsen,[1] Donald et al., and Rushmer[36] point to the initial significance of heart *rate*, not stroke volume, as the mechanism of significantly greater importance to an increased cardiac output.* Note, in Table 5–6, as well as in Figure 5–12, the linear relationship between heart rate and cardiac output.

TABLE 5–6.   The Importance of Heart Rate in Increasing Cardiac Output (From data of Asmussen and Nielsen[1])

Work (kg/min)	VO₂ (L/min)	Heart Rate (per min)	Stroke Vol (L)	Cardiac Output (L/min)	Arterio-venous Oxygen Difference (vols %)
(Rest)	0.267	64	0.100	6.4	4.3
288	0.910	104	0.126	13.1	7.0
540	1.430	122	0.125	15.2	9.4
900	2.143	161	0.110	17.8	12.3
1260	3.007	173	0.120	20.9	14.5

* On the basis of extensive research with dogs, Rushmer was one of the first to point out the small changes in stroke volume despite the dramatic changes in cardiac output.[36] (Dr. Rushmer has also conducted extensive research on humans.) Recently the author was a member of a research team which reached similar conclusions relative to the contribution of stroke volume.[12]

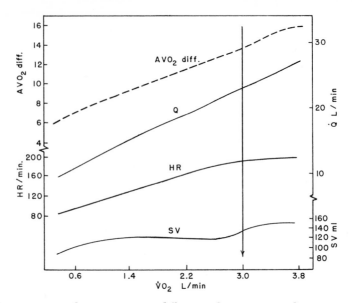

Fig. 5–12.   Arterial-venous oxygen difference, heart rate, cardiac output, stroke volume, and oxygen consumption interrelationships. Cardiac output increases linearly with oxygen consumption (i.e., up to 3.8 L/min $\dot{V}O_2$ depicted in this figure). Arrow indicates maximum oxygen consumption. Note that heart rate increased by approximately 110% while stroke volume increased by approximately 87%. Regression lines were drawn from data of ten studies performed on human subjects during exercise in the erect position. Measurement of cardiac output was based on direct Fick or Hamilton principles. (Adapted from Rushmer.[38] Courtesy of W. B. Saunders Co.)

The initial contribution of the heart rate to an increased cardiac output must not eclipse the significance of the stroke volume. During periods of activity which are challenging to the cardiovascular-pulmonary systems, greater cardiac output can result from large stroke volumes. This is evident in Figure 5–12. When oxygen uptake was above approximately 2.8 L/min, the stroke volume increased from 120 to 150 ml (an increase of 25%) while heart rate increased from 190 to 200 (an increase of approximately 5%).

The decrease in heart volume is the result of a more complete ejection of blood during systole. The systolic reserve volume, which is more than three times greater in the highly trained individual, represents an immediately available volume of blood which can be effectively utilized during any phase of exercise. This was clearly demonstrated in the study by Bock et al. and is presented in Figure 5–13. The late Clarence De Mar, a superbly conditioned marathon runner, possessed a stroke volume which was approximately twice that of a non-athlete.

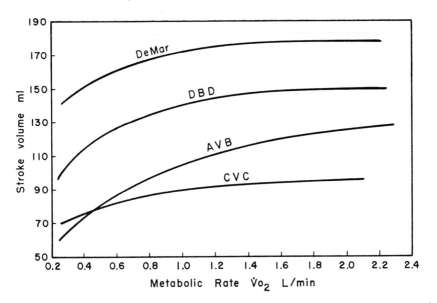

Fig. 5–13. Stroke volume as a function of metabolic rate. Stroke volume of "Mr. Marathon," the late Clarence DeMar was almost twice that of the nonathlete CVC. (Adapted from Bock et al. Courtesy of American Physiological Society.)

Individuals exhibiting good cardiovascular-pulmonary response to work not only possess larger stroke volumes, but also possess lower heart rates than their less trained counterparts. Because of its relative ease of monitoring, much data has been accumulated on maximal heart rates. Such is not the status of knowledge concerning stroke volume in humans, although much is known about dogs. Additional research on the dynamics of cardiac output, especially during heavy work, must be accomplished before the question of cardiac dynamics can be more fully answered.

REFERENCES

1. Asmussen, E., and Nielsen, M.: Cardiac output in rest and work determined simultaneously by acetylene and dye injection methods. *Acta Physiol. Scand.,* 27:217–230, 1952.

2. Asmussen, E., and Nielsen, M.: Cardiac output during muscular work and its regulation. *Physiol Rev.,* 35:778–800, 1955.

3. Astrand, P. O.: Personal communication.

4. Bainbridge, F. A.: The influence of venous filling upon the rate of the heart, *J. Physiol.,* 50:65–84, 1915.

5. Barcroft, H., and Swan, H. J. C.: *Sympathetic Control of Human Blood Vessels.* London, E. Arnold & Co., 1953.

6. Barron, D. H.: The pressure gradient and pulse in the vascular system. *In* Ruch, T. C., and Fulton, J. F. (Eds.): *Medical Physiology and Biophysics.* 18th Ed. Philadelphia, W. B. Saunders Co., 1960.

7. Bock, A. V., Vancaulaert, C., Dill, D. B., Fölling, A., and Hurxthal, L. M.: Studies in muscular activity. III. Dynamical changes in man at work. *J. Physiol., 66*:136–161, 1928.

8. Burch, G. E., and Winsor, T.: *A Primer of Electrocardiography.* 5th Ed. Philadelphia, Lea & Febiger, 1966.

9. Burton, A. C.: On the physical equilibrium of small blood vessels. *Am. J. Physiol., 164*:319–329, 1951.

10. Burton, A. C.: Relation of structure to function of the tissues of the wall of blood vessels. *Physiol. Rev., 34*:619–642, 1954.

11. Castiglioni, A.: *A History of Medicine.* 2nd Ed. Edited by E. B. Krumbhaar, New York, Alfred A. Knopf Co., 1958.

12. Cerretelli, P., Piiper, J., Mangili, F., Cuttica, F., and Ricci, B.: Circulation in exercising dogs. *J. Appl. Physiol., 19*:29–32, 1964.

13. Clark-Kennedy, A. E.: *Stephen Hales, An Eighteenth Century Biography.* Cambridge, University Press, 1929.

14. Dill, D. B.: The economy of muscular exercise. *Physiol. Rev., 16*:263–291, 1936.

15. Donald, K. W., Bishop, J. M., Cumming, G., and Wade, O. L.: The effect of exercise on the cardiac output and circulatory dynamics of normal subjects. *Clin. Sci., 14*:37–73, 1955.

16. Ertel, P. Y., Stern, A. M., Brown, R. K., and Gillespie, D. E.: Acoustic differences among stethoscopes. *J. Univ. Michigan Med. Center, 32*:35–38, 1966.

17. Folkow, B.: The vasodilator action of adenosine triphosphate. *Acta Physiol. Scand., 17*:311–316, 1949.

18. Girling, F.: Vasomotor effects of electrical stimulation. *Am. J. Physiol., 170*:131–135, 1952.

19. Green, H. D.: Circulation: physical principles. *In* Glasser, O. (Ed.): Chicago, Year Book Publishers, Inc., 1944.

20. Gregg, D. E.: Estimation of volume of blood flow, velocity of blood flow, volume of organs, vessels, cavities and regions, circulation time. *In* Best, C. H., and Taylor, N. B. (Eds.): *The Physiological Basis of Medical Practice.* 7th Ed. Baltimore, The Williams & Wilkins Co., 1961.

21. Gregg, D. E.: The heart as a pump. *In* Best, C. H., and Taylor, N. B.: *The Physiological Basis of Medical Practice.* 7th Ed. Baltimore, The Williams & Wilkins Co., 1961.

22. Hamilton, M., Pickering, G. W., Fraser Roberts, J. A., and Sowry, G. S. C.: The aetiology of essential hypertension. 1. The arterial pressure in the general population. 2. Scores for arterial blood pressures adjusted for differences in age and sex. *Clin. Sci., 13*:11–49, 1954.

23. Hamilton, W. F., and Remington, J. W.: Some factors in the regulation of stroke volume. *Am. J. Physiol., 153*:287–297, 1948.

24. Hamilton, W. F., Riley, R. L., Attyah, A. M., Cournand, A., Fowell, D. M., Himmelstein, A., Noble, R. P., Remington, J. W., Richards, D. W., Wheeler, N. C., and Witham, A. C.: Comparison of the Fick and dye injection methods of measuring the cardiac output in man. *Am. J. Physiol.*, *153*:309–321, 1948.

25. Heymans, C., and Neil, E.: *Reflexogenic Areas of the Cardiovascular System.* Boston, Little, Brown & Co., 1958.

26. Hyman, A. S.: *Practical Cardiology.* New York, McGraw-Hill Book Co., 1958.

27. Katz, L. N., and Jochim, K.: Observations on the innervation of the coronary vessels of the dog. *Am. J. Physiol.*, *126*:395–401, 1939.

28. Keele, C. A., and Neil, E. (Eds.): *Samson Wright's Applied Physiology.* 10th Ed. London, Oxford University Press, 1961.

29. Keith, A., and Flack, M.: The form and nature of the muscular connections between the primary divisions of the vertebrate heart. *J. Anat.* (London), *41*:172–189, 1907.

30. Kjellberg, S. V., Rudhe, U., and Sjöstrand, T.: The amount of hemoglobin and the blood volume in relation to the pulse rate and cardiac output during rest. *Acta Physiol. Scand.*, *19*:136–145, 1949.

31. Landis, E. M., and Hortenstine, J. C.: Functional significance of venous blood pressure. *Physiol. Rev.*, *30*:1–32, 1950.

32. Lipman, B. S., and Massie, E.: *Clinical Unipolar Electrocardiography.* 3rd Ed. Chicago, Year Book Medical Publishers, Inc., 1956.

33. Price, H. L., and Conner, E. H.: Certain aspects of the hemodynamic response to the Valsalva maneuver. *J. Appl. Physiol.*, *5*:449–455, 1953.

34. Reindell, H., Weyland, R., Klepzig, H., Schildge, E., and Musshoff, K.: Über anpassungsvorgänge un schädigungsmöglichkeiten beim sportherzen. *Schweiz. Z. Sportmed.*, *1*:97–140, 1953.

35. Rowell, L. B., Marx, H. J., Bruce, R. A., Conn, R. D., and Kusumi, F.: Reductions in cardiac output, central blood volume, and stroke volume with thermal stress in normal men during exercise. *J. Clin. Invest.*, *45*:1801–1816, 1966.

36. Rushmer, R. F.: Heart size and stroke volume. *Minn. Med.*, *37*:19–29, 1954.

37. Rushmer, R. F.: *Cardiac Diagnosis.* Philadelphia, W. B. Saunders Co., 1955.

38. Rushmer, R. F.: Control of cardiac output. *In* Ruch, T. C., and Fulton, J. F.: *Medical Physiology and Biophysics.* 18th Ed. Philadelphia, W. B. Saunders Co., 1960.

39. Sjöstrand, T.: Volume and distribution of blood and their significance in regulating the circulation. *Physiol. Rev.*, *33*:202–228, 1953.

40. Starling, E. H.: The Linacre lecture on the law of the heart. London, Longmans Green, 1918.

41. Stead, E. A., and Warren, J. V.: Cardiac output in man; analysis of mechanisms varying cardiac output based on recent clinical studies. *Arch. Int. Med.*, *80*:237–248, 1947.

42. Wiggers, C. J.: *Circulatory Dynamics.* New York, Grune & Stratton, 1952.

Chapter

6

RESPIRATION

Respiration involves an intake of oxygen and a giving-off of carbon dioxide. These considerations are still much too broad, for they suggest that breathing is synonymous with respiration. In actuality, breathing (inhalation and exhalation) is but a phase of respiration. These processes constitute the external phase of respiration. Through mechanical-chemical-neural involvement an exchange of gases between the atmosphere and the lungs is effected.

As pointed out by Claude Bernard in 1878,* man is exposed to two environments. Though he is exposed to an external environment (the atmosphere) man really lives in an internal environment. The introduction of oxygen, which is accomplished during the external phase of respiration, is of little ultimate consequence unless it can be delivered to and utilized by the cell. In order that biochemical homeostasis be maintained, such end-products of cell metabolism as carbon dioxide and water must be delivered to specific locations to become eliminated. The carbon dioxide and much of the water—in vapor form—are eliminated during exhalation.

Respiration also possesses an internal or tissue respiration phase; this phase involves the cardiovascular system.

Respiration is a mechanical-chemical-neural process which involves the delivery of oxygen via the blood stream to the cell in exchange for the end-products of cell metabolism, notably carbon dioxide and water.

---

* Specifically, Bernard referred to the constancy of tissue environment. Further, the invariable internal environment exists in all higher animals. The application of external-internal environments to a discussion of respiration represents journalistic license.

For therapeutic, diagnostic, or scientific purposes, many combinations of pressures and percentages of oxygen, carbon dioxide, helium, nitrogen, and other gases may be introduced into the pulmonary system. Unless specifically stated, the ensuing discussion will relate to the inhalation of atmospheric air which is composed of oxygen 20.93%, carbon dioxide 0.03%, and nitrogen (including trace gases) 79.04%. Biologically considered, nitrogen plays an extremely important role in plant metabolism and in the nitrogen cycle; however, for the human, under particular circumstances, this gas can produce results which span a continuum from discomfort to death. Nitrogen gas is inert (Tables 6–5 and 6–8).

The journey of the oxygen molecule to the cell begins with its introduction, through inhalation of ambient air, into the lungs. During basal states, inhalation is usually accomplished primarily through involuntary effort. As the level of metabolic activity is increased, normal inhalation, largely involuntary, may be aided by voluntary effort.

While lung tissue possesses a high degree of extensibility (elasticity), it is incapable of independent action. The movement of air into the lungs may be explained by the expansion of lung tissue which is effected by the musculo-mechanical raising of the rib cage and the accompanying effect of molecular attraction, by action of the diaphragm muscle, and by application of Boyle's law.

A moist serous membrane, the pleura, lines the inner layer of the thoracic wall. It also constitutes the outermost membrane of the lungs. Because these adjacent membranes are moist and are in extremely close proximity, conditions favorable to the occurrence of molecular attraction (surface tension) exist. During the inhalation phase, the rib cage is raised and the moist outermost layer of the lung, which adheres to the pleura, follows the course of the rib cage thus effecting an increased lung capacity. Simultaneously with rib cage elevation, the diaphragm muscle descends and increases still further the capacity of the thorax. As defined in Boyle's law an inverse relationship between gas volume and pressure exists, provided temperature remains constant. The temperature within the thorax remains close to 37° C. Thus, the setting is ideal for the observance of the law. By combined action of molecular attraction and diaphragm muscle movement, the pressure within the lungs is reduced. At peak enlargement of the thoracic cage, the pressure within the lungs is reduced to levels below those of the atmosphere. Since gas pressures seek equilibrium, the decreased pressure within the lungs results in a flow of atmospheric air through the nasal and buccal passages, pharynx, larynx, trachea, bronchi, and bronchioles into the alveoli: inhalation is accomplished.

Exhalation is usually passive. A decrease of the thorax capacity, caused by the combined effects of an ascending diaphragm muscle and rib cage depression, creates pressure gradients favorable to movement of air from the lungs to the atmosphere. The role of the diaphragm muscle is significant. In the normal adult, the surface area of the diaphragm muscle is of the order of 250 to 270 cm^2. During periods of rest associated with low levels of respiratory activity, Keith observed the diaphragm to descend through a range of approximately 1.25 cm. This lowered position may account for over one-half of the tidal volume.

Campbell[7] observed the diaphragm muscle to descend as much as 10 cm during deep breathing.

TABLE 6–1.	Intrapulmonary Volume-Pressure Relationship	
	Volume	*Pressure*
Normal inhalation	increased	−7 mm Hg
Normal exhalation	decreased	−3 mm Hg*

* An indication of lung elasticity and attributed to the fact that lung capacity is smaller than the capacity of the thorax. The heart, esophagus, and many blood vessels including the vena cava and descending aorta also occupy the thoracic space. During the Valsalva maneuver intrapulmonary pressure may be reduced to −40 mm Hg; during forced exhalation a pressure of + 40 mm Hg may be attained.

Chemical Control and Regulation of Ventilation

The role of carbon dioxide and of oxygen in the regulation of breathing was presented in the classic research of Haldane. When carbon dioxide constituted 3% of the inspired air, the rate of breathing was quickened; at 6% the rate was further increased. The effect of carbon dioxide inhalation on alveolar ventilation is presented in Figure 6–1. Note that peak ventilation response is attained when the carbon dioxide constitutes approximately 9% of the inspired air.

Factors other than carbon dioxide tension were shown to affect ventilation. In the research of Douglas and Haldane, lung ventilation was observed to increase during work, while the alveolar carbon dioxide tension decreased. Barcroft and Margaria noted the effects of moderate physical effort on total ventilation to exceed the effects produced by 7.5% CO_2 inhalation.

From additional observations relative to the effects of CO_2 inhalation, Haldane focused attention on the following point: the chemical control of breathing is dependent upon equilibrium of partial carbon dioxide pressure within the alveoli.

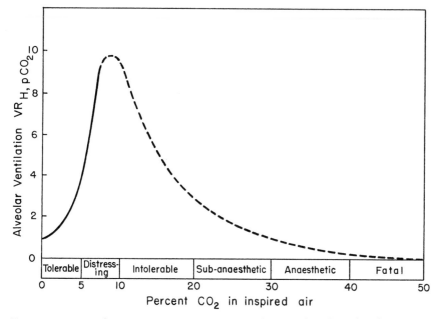

Fig. 6–1. Ventilatory response as a function of inspired carbon dioxide. (From Gray, J. S.: Pulmonary Ventilation and Its Physiological Regulation. 1950. Courtesy of Charles C Thomas, Publisher.)

The regulation of ventilation by oxygen was presented by Heymans, a Nobel Prize winner in 1938, who focused attention on the role of the carotid sinus. Chemoreceptors are located at the aortic arch and at the bifurcation of the common carotid arteries. These receptors, sensitive to the oxygen tension (as well as carbon dioxide tension) of the blood, affect ventilation.

Partial reflex control of respiration was demonstrated by Comroe and Schmidt, who observed in their subjects an average 14% increase in respiratory minute volume during active arm exercises in which the flow of blood was prevented by the inflation of a cuff.

Gray observed the effects of P_{CO_2} and P_{O_2} on ventilation and noted the effect of hydrogen ion and of reflexes arising in exercising muscles.[24] The less important effect of pressoreceptor reflexes in the arteries and veins, of the thermoreceptors from the hypothalamus, and of pain and psychogenic reflexes were also noted. By recognizing the interdependence of a number of factors, Gray proposed his *multiple factor theory* of the control of respiration. The theory incorporates three fundamental principles: the independent effects exerted by a number of factors, the interdependence factor which is a recognition of the effect of change of any one factor upon other factors, and algebraic summation. Although a number of factors exert independent and interdependent effects, the total effect on ventilation is determined by algebraic summation of the partial effects.

Grodins substantiated the theory of Gray:

> The multiple factor theory, by providing a method of analysis in which the influence of three of these factors (Pco_2, Po_2, H^+) can be quantitatively accounted for permits a more accurate evaluation of the role of additional factors.[26]

Some respiratory physiologists have maintained an attitude of partial reservation; however, it is important to point out that Gray proposed a *theory*, a formulation of principles which have in large measure been scientifically verified. The refinements of research and of mathematical expression will hasten the metamorphosis from theory to law.

Subdivisions of the Lung

In 1950, a group of eminent physiologists, under the chairmanship of J. R. Pappenheimer of Harvard University, standardized the terminology and symbols used in respiratory physiology (p. 292). Their concept of lung volumes and capacities is expressed in Figure 6–2.

Definitions of volumes and capacities are presented in Table 6–2.

TABLE 6–2.   Lung Volumes and Capacities (Adapted from Pappenheimer et al.[46])

Volume	Symbol	Definition
Tidal	V_T	Volume of gas inhaled or exhaled per breath
Inspiratory Reserve	IRV	Maximum volume inhaled from end-tidal inhaled level
Expiratory Reserve	ERV	Maximum volume exhaled from resting exhaled level
Residual	RV	Volume of gas remaining after maximum exhalation
Capacity		
Vital	VC	Maximum volume exhaled following maximum inhaled
Inspiratory	IC	Maximum volume inhaled from resting exhaled level
Functional Residual	FRC	Volume of gas remaining after resting exhaled level
Total Lung	TLC	Total volume of gas

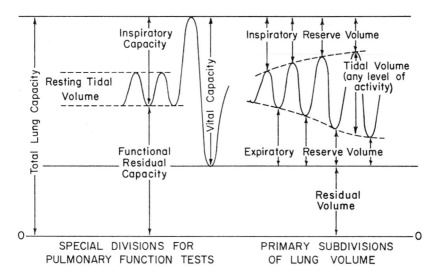

Fig. 6–2.   Subdivisions of the lung volume. (From Pappenheimer et al. Courtesy of American Physiological Society.)

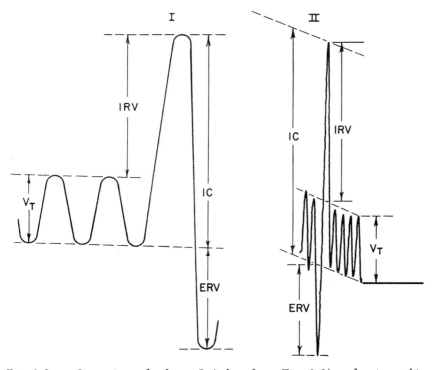

Fig. 6–3.   Comparison of schema I (taken from Fig. 6–2) and spirographic tracing II of a rested subject. V_T = tidal volume, IRV = inspiratory reserve volume, ERV = expiratory reserve volume, IC = inspiratory capacity. Vital capacity VC = IRV + V_T + ERV; or, VC = IC + ERV. (Refer to Chapter 11 for calculation methods.) Residual volume is not shown. Determination of functional residual capacity can be accomplished by a number of techniques.[11–13,17,18,35,40–42]

In order to clarify the interpretation of a spirogram, a comparison of the schematic and spirographic forms is presented in Figure 6–3.

Calculation methods for determining subdivisions of lung volume as well as other pulmonary function measurements are presented in Chapter 11.

Respiratory Dead Space

The volume of the respiratory dead space—composed of the buccal and nasal cavities, the pharynx, larynx, trachea, bronchi, and bronchioles —varies from 100 to 250 ml and is dependent upon body position and organic condition. This volume constitutes the anatomic dead space (Fig. 6–4).

Oxygen and carbon dioxide gas exchange takes place only within the alveoli; hence, if a sample consisting of approximately the first 100 ml of expired air were analyzed its composition would be equal to that of atmospheric air.

An important practical point to be emphasized is that the tubing which forms an integral part of closed circuit indirect calorimetry systems is, in fact, an extension of the subject's anatomic dead space. This should serve to underscore the necessity for reducing tubing dead space to a minimum.

ANATOMIC DEAD SPACE

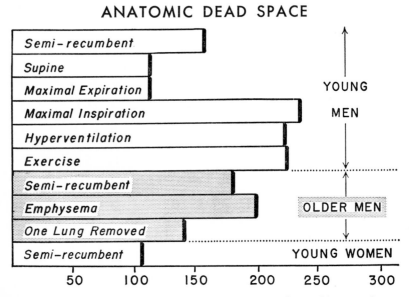

Fig. 6–4.   Anatomic dead space. (Abscissa is expressed in ml.) Note the variability in dead space volumes. (From Comroe et al.[11] Courtesy of Year Book Medical Publishers.)

Physiologic dead space and alveolar dead space, terms relating to respiratory dead space, are ambiguous. In order to simplify discussions of respiratory dead space, Comroe et al. point out the dilemma and the solution:

. . . The terms dead space, anatomic dead space and physiologic dead space are so entrenched that we shall probably continue to use them. Physiologically, it is simpler to think of a volume of inspired gas which is not useful or effective in arterializing the venous blood—in one case because it never reached alveoli, in another because it reached alveoli with no blood flow, and in a third because too much reached the alveoli in proportion to their capillary blood flow.[11]

Riley et al. reported a statistically significant increase in pulmonary dead space in the standing position over that of the supine position. Douglas and Haldane observed an increase in dead space during exercise. Young noted that dead space tends to increase with increasing lung volumes.

The pedagogy of Karpovich's hypothetical "extended walks" under the Volga River (2 m depth), equipped with weighted boots and a bamboo breathing tube (4 cm diameter, 1 m length) was highly effective. In such an example, the total dead space volume exceeded the tidal volume (which was further reduced due to water pressure). These combined effects could only result in a lack of renewal of air in the alveoli with concomitant hypoxia—and failure to cross under the Volga.

Gas Diffusion

Uninterrupted cell metabolic activity is dependent upon the diffusion of oxygen and carbon dioxide gas. This diffusion process, through solid yet porous membranes, into the circulatory system is extremely important. Assuming an effective blood gas carrying capacity, as well as an effective rate of circulation, the oxygen requirement of the cell will be met and the end-products of cell metabolism will be transported and eliminated.

The diffusion property of respiratory gases is clarified by application of Dalton's law, often called the Law of Partial Pressures: the total pressure exerted by a mixture of gases is equal to the sum of the partial pressures of the component gases. The law also may be stated: in a mixture of gases the partial pressure exerted by each gas is proportional to its volume per cent.

By focusing attention on the atmospheric gases through application of Dalton's law, one can calculate the partial pressure exerted by each of the gases at any level of the respiratory or circulatory system.

9

TABLE 6-3.   Partial Pressure Exerted by Atmospheric Gases at Sea Level

Gas	%	Partial Gas Pressure (mm Hg)	Symbol
Oxygen	20.93	158.1	P_{O_2}
Carbon dioxide	0.03	0.2	P_{CO_2}
Nitrogen	79.04	597.1	P_{N_2}
	100.00	755.4	
		P_{H_2O} 4.6	
		760.0°	

° 760 mm Hg, the atmospheric pressure at sea level, is defined as the standard pressure, i.e., it is the pressure equal to that of a column of mercury 760 mm in length.

The partial pressures exerted by each of the gases is expressed by the formula:

$$P_{gas} = \frac{Vol\%}{100} \times P_{gas\ tot}$$

$$P_{O_2} = \frac{20.93\%}{100} \times 755.4 \text{ mm Hg} = 158.1 \text{ mm Hg}$$

$$P_{CO_2} = \frac{0.03\%}{100} \times 755.4 \text{ mm Hg} = 0.2 \text{ mm Hg}$$

$$P_{N_2} = \frac{79.04\%}{100} \times 755.4 \text{ mm Hg} = 597.1 \text{ mm Hg}$$

$$755.4 \text{ mm Hg}$$

$$P_{H_2O} \quad 4.6$$

$$760.0 \text{ mm Hg}$$

Due to metabolism, the percentage of each gas comprising the alveolar air differs from that of the atmosphere. In addition, the moisture within the alveoli exerts a pressure which remains constant. Since the body temperature remains stable, the pressure exerted by the moisture also remains constant. Typical values are presented in Table 6-4.

At various levels of the respiratory and circulatory system, important changes in the percentage of each gas as well as in the total gas pressure enable one to follow the diffusion of the respiratory gases. Typical pressures are presented in Table 6-5.

Gases follow pressure gradients. The oxygen molecule will flow in the direction of the tissue—from atmosphere to alveoli to arterial blood to tissue. Carbon dioxide flows in the opposite direction—from tissue to venous blood to alveoli to atmosphere. Note the stable pressures exerted by nitrogen gas and by moisture. Pressure gradients for oxygen and carbon dioxide are depicted in Figure 6-5.

TABLE 6–4. Partial Pressures Exerted by Alveolar Gases at Sea Level

Gas	%*	Partial Gas Pressure (mm Hg)
Oxygen	14.2	P$_{O_2}$ 101
Carbon dioxide	5.5	P$_{CO_2}$ 39
Nitrogen	80.3	P$_{N_2}$ 573
	100.0	713
		P$_{H_2O}$ 47
		760

* These figures are variable but are representative.

TABLE 6–5. Typical Partial Pressures Exerted by Each of the Gases and of Moisture Within the Respiratory and Circulatory Systems and Tissues (Sea Level)

	Atmospheric	Alveolar	Arterial	Venous	Tissue
P$_{O_2}$ mm Hg	158.1	101	100	40	30
P$_{CO_2}$ mm Hg	0.2	39	40	46	50
P$_{N_2}$ mm Hg	597.1	573	573	573	573
	755.4	713	713	659	653
P$_{H_2O}$ mm Hg	4.6	47	47	47	47
TOTAL	760.0	760	760	706	700

The movement of gas molecules across membranes is also dependent upon the resistance afforded by the membrane. Lowered resistances are interpreted in terms of higher levels of membrane permeability and vice versa and are expressed in terms of pulmonary diffusion coefficients (D).

Pulmonary diffusion coefficient is defined as the minute volume of gas which passes through a membrane for each mm Hg tension differential on opposing membrane surfaces. For oxygen, the diffusion coefficient would be expressed as

$$D_{O_2} = \frac{\dot{V}_{O_2}}{\bar{P}_{A_{O_2}} - \bar{P}_{c_{CO_2}}}$$

$\dot{V}_{O_2}$ = oxygen uptake, ml/min, pulmonary blood
$\bar{P}_{c_{O_2}}$ = mean alveolar O$_2$ pressure
$\bar{P}_{A_{CO_2}}$ = mean capillary CO$_2$ pressure

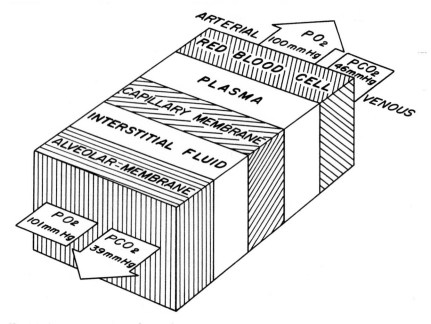

Fig. 6–5.   Pressure gradients for oxygen and carbon dioxide. Gas tension figures are taken from Table 6–5. Arrows indicate direction of diffusion.

As depicted in Figure 6–7, the diffusion coefficient for oxygen can increase from 75 to over 90 ml/min.

During elevated metabolic states, diffusion capacity follows such a course. The factor contributing to the increase is related to the increased demand placed upon the cardiopulmonary system by the elevated metabolic response to work. This results in a compensatory and beneficial increase in pulmonary capillary dilatation, an increased blood flow, as well as an increase in alveolar surface area. Mostyn et al. found a greater pulmonary diffusion capacity in champion swimmers and lesser capacities in swimmers of average ability and in sedentary individuals. In the same study, cross-country track athletes did not attain the rate of oxygen transfer across alveolar membranes exhibited by the champion swimmers.

The alveolar dead space is a dynamic concept which is dependent upon the volume of the gas entering the alveoli. Thus an increased alveolar surface reflects its functional capacity.

The estimated surface area of the lung capillary bed is amazingly extensive: of the order of 60 to 70 m². A quick glance at a body surface area table (p. 293) places most Caucasoid adults between 1.5 to 2.2 m². Thus the pulmonary capillary surface area is roughly 35 times

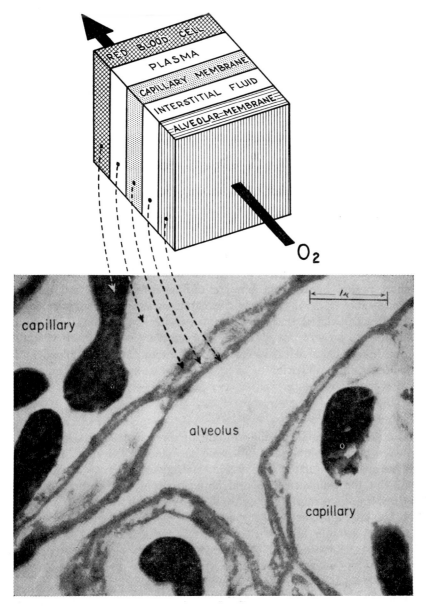

Fig. 6–6. Electron microscopy of rat lung tissue. Oxygen molecule, depicted in the schema above, must diffuse through two membranes, alveolar and capillary, before it is *taken-up*, in chemical combination, by the blood. (From Comroe et al.[11] Courtesy of Year Book Medical Publishers, Inc.; top portion from Low, F. N.: Anat. Rec., *117*:241, 1953.

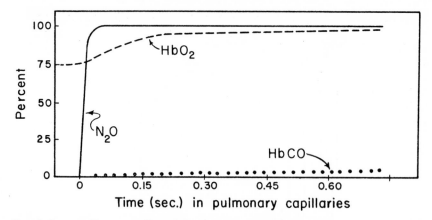

Fig. 6–7.   Diffusion coefficient for oxygen; 100% along ordinate indicates maximal blood gas content when blood is in equilibrium with alveolar gas. (From Comroe et al.[11] Courtesy of Year Book Medical Publishers, Inc.)

more extensive. Rapid and effective gas transfer is accomplished within a short period because the amount of blood in the lungs during rest is small—about 75 ml—whereas the capillary surface area is extensive. Roughton calculated the average time spent by the blood in the lung capillaries to be 0.75 ± 0.25 sec for normal men at rest and 0.34 ± 0.10 during hard work.[49] He also calculated the total volume of blood in the expanded lung capillaries to average 60 ml at rest and 95 ml during hard work.

Pulmonary Ventilation

Ventilation, defined as the volume of air which is drawn into and expelled from the lungs per unit time, is influenced by psychological as well as metabolic factors. The classic experiments of Krogh and Lindhard point out the influence of neural impulses from the cerebral cortex on the respiratory center. This is exemplified by the anticipatory increase in breathing before exercise or competition, which precedes the increased metabolic demand of physical work. During work states, the ventilation rate is increased and is attributed to the demand for oxygen imposed by the elevated metabolic state. Typical values are given in Table 6–6. See also the discussion of airway resistance (p. 125).

Lindhard,[36] and Comroe et al.[11] indicate the adequacy of lung ventilation in maintaining normal pulmonary blood saturation.

To steady-state level, a linear relationship has been shown to exist between ventilation and oxygen consumption. Bock and Dill, using Lindhard's data, depict a ventilation of approximately 70 L/min to be directly related to an oxygen uptake up to 3.5 L/min.[36] These relationships are also expressed by Grodins in Figure 6–9.

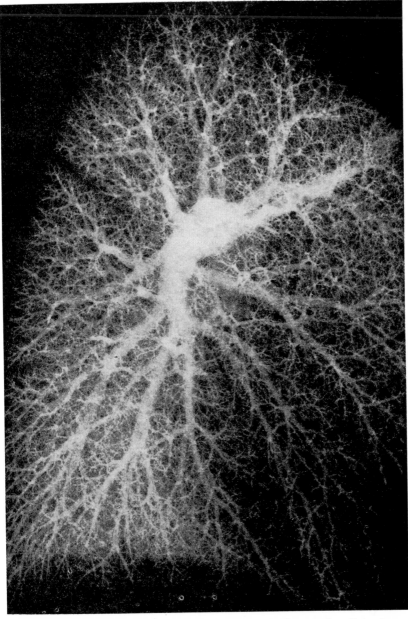

Fig. 6–8.   Lung vascular bed revealed through x-ray photography. Extensiveness of the vascular bed, which surrounds approximately 300 million alveoli, is more fully appreciated with the realization that a large portion of the capillary bed is invisible to the naked eye and too extremely fine to be recorded on film. (From Comroe.[9] Courtesy of Scientific American, Inc.)

In heavy work states a curvilinear relationship exists between ventilation and oxygen consumption. While the arterial blood is adequately oxygenated, the oxygen demand at cell level can only be met by an increase in cardiac output and in blood circulation rate. The rate of blood circulation, then, is the primary cause of the inability of the human to perform sustained work of high metabolic intensity.

TABLE 6–6.   Approximate Range of Values of Respiration Rate, Tidal Volume, and Minute Volume

	At Rest	During Vigorous Work
Respiration rate/min	7 — 12	40 — 60
Tidal volume (L)	0.4 — 0.6	2.5°
Minute volume (L)	2.8 — 7.2	100 — 150

° A typical, low value. Tidal volume is decreased during vigorous work.

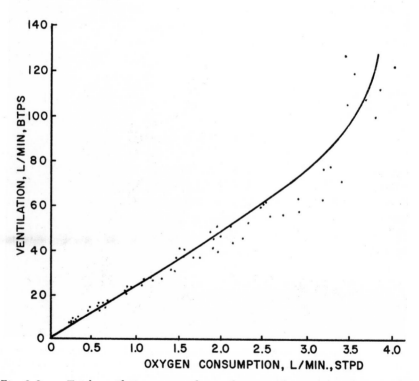

Fig. 6–9.   Total ventilation expressed as a function of oxygen consumption during walking, running, and bicycling. Data represent 611 observations on 86 subjects. (From Grodins. Courtesy of American Physiological Society.)

Ventilation is the product of depth and rate of respiration $MV = V_T \times f$; however, the attainment of particular levels of ventilation is also affected by two types of resistance to air flow within the pulmonary system.

The first type of resistance, the airway resistance, is basically dependent upon gas pressure and rate of gas flow and is expressed through rearrangement of Poiseuille's law (pp. 82–83, 88, 284).

$$R = \frac{P}{F}$$

Upon closer analysis of the situation, resistance to gas flow through the bronchi and bronchioles is seen to be dependent upon the nature* of the gas flow as well as the dimensions of the bronchi and bronchioles. Comroe et al. have noted airway resistance to be variable: it varies inversely with lung volume. Airway resistance also increases toward the end of maximal exhalation.

The second type of resistance is related to the elasticity of lung tissue and muscle tissue during any phase of ventilation. This elastic resistance is also variable and tends to increase during deep breathing and with increased ventilation.

The question of the merit of shallow, rapid breathing during athletic competition or sustained work is often raised. There are two points to consider. As pointed out by Agostoni and Fenn, rapid contractions of respiratory muscles result in a reduced force of contraction, hence a reduced tidal volume. The prospect of experiencing discomfort is increased and is attributable to a reduced depth of breathing which is coupled with an increased rate of respiration. The musculature surrounding the chest wall, especially those muscles which aid in forced inhalation, becomes fatigued and contributes to discomfort. Secondly, as pointed out by Comroe et al.,[11] shallow breathing results in a smaller fraction of the tidal volume entering the alveoli. Since the important oxygen-carbon dioxide exchange occurs only within the alveoli, a smaller fraction of air signifies that lesser volumes of blood can become arterialized.

Voluntary Hyperventilation

The term refers to a voluntary increase in ventilation. Usually, the stated purpose of engaging in such a maneuver produces little meaning. Many individuals, especially athletes, practice this technique. What is intended is that during these maneuvers, a substantial amount of

---

* Comroe et al. recognize the presence of turbulent flow at many locations within the tracheobronchial tree.[11]

carbon dioxide will be eliminated and an improvement in blood oxygenation will result. As pointed out by Comroe et al. and presented in Table 6–7, hyperventilation produces respiratory alkalosis but, unless the alveoli are initially hypoventilated, adds little to the oxygenation of the blood.

TABLE 6–7.   Effect of Normal, Increased, and Decreased Alveolar Ventilation on Arterial Blood (From Comroe et al.[11])

| Type of Ventilation | Alveolar Ventilation (L/min) | Alveolar & Arterial Gas Tensions | | Arterial Blood Gas Contents | | Arterial pH (Units) |
		O_2 (mm Hg)	CO_2 (mm Hg)	O_2 (% sat.)	CO_2 (mM/L)	
Hypoventilation	2.50	67	69	88.5	27.2	7.24
Normal	4.27	104	40	97.4	21.9	7.40
Hyperventilation	7.50	122	23	98.8	17.5	7.56

Note from Table 6–7 the lowered blood carbon dioxide tension and content. It is this carbon dioxide content which stimulates the respiratory center; an apneic response usually accompanies the cessation of voluntary effort.

As reported by Haldane, breath holding ability is increased by hyperventilation. Lewis and Morton noted a decrease in maximal breathing capacity resulting from prior hyperventilation. Since maximal breathing capacity is a measure of the maximal volume of air which can be inhaled and exhaled per unit of time, a reduction in this capacity is considered detrimental to pulmonary endurance. See Chapter 11, Calculation Methods.

Respiratory Gymnastics

Perhaps no other exercise form is so subtly or extensively practiced as respiratory gymnastics. The pendulum has swung from deep breathing exercises to breath holding to voluntary overbreathing. One must not discount the gain in psychological benefit to the adherents of such practices.

The effect of posture on ventilation is generally less dramatic than is the effect of posture on lung volumes. Postures requiring greater muscular involvement generally require greater ventilatory effort as well as greater oxygen consumption. The involvement of accessory muscles of inhalation, resulting from an arms-overhead position, contributes to the greatest increases in minute volume and tidal volume yet the ventilation equivalent for oxygen* for such a position is low (see Chapter 11).

The mechanical advantage of such a position is apparent. Moreno and Lyons reported a decreased total lung and vital capacity to result from a change of postures from sitting to supine and prone. The effect of hemostatic pressure within the thoracic cage coupled with the decreased musculo-mechanical advantage no doubt accounts for such decreases.

The merit of practicing belly breathing is often questioned. (Belly breathing is variously called diaphragm or abdominal breathing; the term is general and ambiguous.) The diaphragm is a principal muscle of respiration; the abdominals are accessory. Further, through electromyographic monitoring, Campbell noted that abdominal muscles aided in exhalation only when a pulmonary ventilation rate of 40 to 60 L/min was attained.[6] The abdominal muscle group and the rib elevators can produce significant increases in breathing effectiveness; however, their effect can only be acquired through voluntary control and as such requires constant attention.

Breath holding is urged upon swimmers and track athletes specializing in the sprint events. The physiological basis of breath holding is related to chemical-neural control of respiration; the respiratory center within the medulla oblongata is sensitive to increases in carbon dioxide levels. Craig[14] and Craig et al.[15,16] have reported the *break point*, i.e., the inability to continue breath holding, to occur when the alveolar air P_{CO_2} reaches approximately 50 mm Hg. In sprint swimming, at least, the gain in mechanical advantage resulting from breath holding is apparent; the necessity of rotating the head in order to "gulp-in" air is obviated. A *break point* does exist; however, the ability to endure discomfort is variable.

The practice of breath holding in underwater swimming is hazardous. As indicated by Craig,[14] a reduction in alveolar P_{O_2} levels to 25 mm Hg affects cerebral function including loss of consciousness. Reduction of alveolar P_{O_2} levels is hastened by the metabolic requirement of underwater swimming. The loss of consciousness is gradual; the environment becomes inimical and unforgiving of carelessness.

Vital Capacity

From the standpoint of logic, the oft-uttered statement that vital capacity bears no relationship to physiological fitness is false. A reduced vital capacity, attributed for example to respiratory pathway obstruc-

---

* Ventilation equivalent for oxygen VE_{O_2} is a rough indicator of ventilation efficiency.

tion or to emphysema or tuberculosis will be reflected in a reduced response of pulmonary function to elevated work-states, hence to reduced capability for physical performance. At the other extreme, a large vital capacity may precipitate the erroneous conclusion which relates large vital capacities to high levels of cardiopulmonary fitness.

At least two considerations must be kept in mind when discussing vital capacity. As an index per se it is quite meaningless. Vital capacity must be related to body size—to body weight or to body surface area—to become a meaningful index. Or, in order to provide a more meaningful reliable index of ventilatory capacity, vital capacity must be timed, i.e., measured during a specified time interval, usually 0.5 or 1.0 second (see Chap. 11). By this procedure, a common time basis is established thus making comparisons valid.

Dreyer established the relationship between vital capacity and body weight as:

$$VC_{cc} = \frac{\text{Body Wgt}_{gm} \times 0.72}{0.69}$$

West, reporting vital capacity per centimeter of height and vital capacity per square meter of body surface area, found the greatest ratios in athletes and the smallest ratios in sedentary women. Holmes also observed that total capacity increased with height and with body surface area. Stuart and Collings, comparing the vital capacity and maximum breathing capacity of physically active with physically inactive male students, found the active group to possess a significantly greater mean vital capacity. This was attributed "to increased development of respiratory musculature incidental to regular physical training." The groups did not differ with respect to maximum breathing capacity or to the *capacity ratio*—maximum breathing capacity expressed as a function of vital capacity (MBC/VC). In this study, all students were matched in age, height, weight, and body surface area. Gordon et al. observed a nonsignificant relationship between size of vital capacity and the order of finish of Boston marathoners.

Increased physical performance results in an increase in P_{CO_2}, a decrease in tissue P_{O_2}, an increase in blood and tissue temperature, and a decrease in blood pH. These changes are beneficial in that they favor the dissociation of oxygen from the blood (Fig. 6–10).

In the final analysis, the inadequacy of the delivery system (blood) sets a limit to the intensity and duration of physiologic and physical effort. Prolonged effort may be limited by depletion of blood glucose or the accumulation of lactic acid; however, this is secondary to an inadequate delivery system.

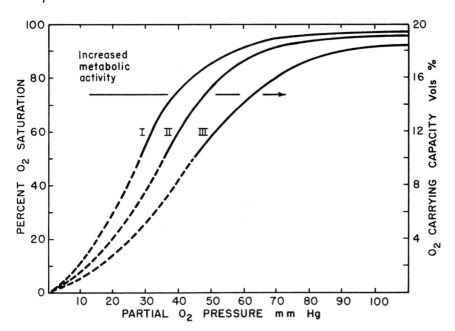

Fig. 6–10. Oxygen disassociation curve. Blood pH and Pco₂ values for each of the curves are: I, pH 7.60, Pco₂ 20 mm Hg; II, pH 7.40, Pco₂ 40 mm Hg; III, pH 6.90, Pco₂ 80 mm Hg. Increased physical activity effects a lowering of muscle tissue Po₂ and blood pH and an increase of tissue Pco₂ and blood and tissue temperature. These factors cause a "flattening" or sifting of the curve to the right and favor oxygen disassociation. Arterial blood is depicted by solid line; venous blood by broken line. (Adapted from data of Margaria.[37,38])

Oxygen and Carbon Dioxide Transport: Tissue Respiration

The role of pulmonary ventilation in the oxygen uptake process has been presented. This constitutes the external phase of respiration. Attention will now be focused on the chemical attraction of oxygen into the blood and the delivery of oxygen to the tissues. This constitutes the internal phase of respiration.

Several terms may be used interchangeably to describe the consumption of oxygen by the cells and tissues: oxygen uptake, oxygen intake, or oxygen consumption. At least to minimize the possibility of ambiguity, it would be ideal to engage one term exclusively; however, the probability of using the terms interchangeably remains high. Such is not the case with carbon dioxide. It is an end-product of tissue metabolism and is "taken up" and carried by the blood; hence, the term carbon dioxide uptake is used.

TABLE 6–8.   Chemical Combination and Physical Solution of Respiratory Gases Expressed in Vol%

| | Chemical Combination | | Physical Solution | |
	Arterial	Mixed Venous	Arterial	Mixed Venous
O_2	20.0	15.0	0.23	0.12
CO_2	46.0	50.0	2.62	3.00
N_2	0.0	0.0	0.98	0.98

As depicted in Table 6–8, the amount of oxygen which is carried in physical solution is 0.23 vol%.* Assuming a $\dot{V}O_2$ of 225 ml/min and a cardiac output of 4000 ml/min for standing rest, the total tissue oxygen volume, i.e., the oxygen available to the tissues, would be:

$$\text{Tissue } \dot{V}O_2 = O_2 \text{ vol\%} \times \text{ cardiac output } {}_{ml/min}$$
$$= 0.23 \quad \times 4000 \div 100^*$$
$$= 0.23 \quad \times 40$$
$$= 9.20 \text{ ml/min}$$

*Note: O_2 vol% = ml O_2/100 ml blood $\therefore$ 4000 ÷ 1000
(Or 0.23 ml/100 ml blood = 2.3 ml/1000 ml blood $\therefore$ 4000 ÷ 1000 = 4L   2.3 × 4 = 9.20 ml/min)

Quite obviously this tissue oxygen availability, 9.20 ml/min, falls far short of the 225 ml/min which is necessary to maintain the person in the standing position. In fact, 9.20 ml/min falls far short of the minimal oxygen requirement to sustain life.† Since the amount of

---

* vol% (volumes per cent) is an expression of the volume of a gas per 100 ml blood; thus, O_2 0.23 vol% indicates 0.23 ml O_2/100 ml blood.

† There exists another mechanism which turns out to be physiologically impossible. Tissue $\dot{V}O_2$ requirements for standing rest could be met, at least theoretically, by a cardiac output of 97.8 L/min.

$$\text{Cardiac output} = \frac{\dot{V}O_2 \text{ L}}{\text{Arterial } O_2} \times 100$$
$$\text{(in physical solution)}$$
$$= \frac{0.225}{0.23} \times 100$$
$$= 97.8 \text{ L/min}$$

The above calculation is based upon two assumptions not corroborated by scientific data: (a) Tissue $\dot{V}O_2$ is 100%, thereby resulting in a PO_2 of zero. (In actuality, mixed venous blood would probably not fall below approximately 25% saturation.) (b) Even assuming a stroke volume of 200 ml (close to 180 ml was reported by Bock et al.), coupled with a heart frequency of 200 beats/minute, would result in a cardiac output of 40 L/minute which represents a discrepancy of 145%.

oxygen which is carried in physical solution in the blood is totally inadequate to even sustain life, attention must be turned to the gas carrying capacity of the blood and in particular to hemoglobin, Hb. Hemoglobin is composed mainly of globin, a protein substance, and of a small amount of ferrous iron, Fe^{+++}. Each ferrous atom is capable of binding one molecule of oxygen. Because each molecule of hemoglobin contains four atoms of iron, it is capable of carrying four molecules of oxygen. (Incidentally, since carbon monoxide, CO, is bound in the same relationship, this noxious gas can compete on equal terms with oxygen.)

Each gram of hemoglobin is capable of combining with 1.34 ml of oxygen at standard temperature and pressure (STP).[47] Normal values for hemoglobin concentration for healthy adults differ slightly between the sexes. For the male, the hemoglobin-to-blood ratio is about 15 gm/100 ml; for females the ratio is slightly lower, being approximately 13 gm/100 ml blood. Because each gram of hemoglobin is capable of combining with 1.34 ml oxygen and the normal hemoglobin content for males is 15 gm/100 ml blood, the *oxygen carrying capacity* of the blood may be calculated and is depicted along the right ordinate of Figure 6–10.

$$15 \text{ gm Hb} \times 1.34 \text{ ml } O_2 = 20.1 \text{ ml/100 ml blood or } 20.1 \text{ vol\%.}$$

Due in part to the amount of hemoglobin, there exists a maximum oxygen carrying capacity of blood. Saturation of blood with oxygen* is expressed as a ratio of the oxygen content to the oxygen capacity:

$$\text{Hb \% saturation} = \frac{\text{Total blood } O_2 \text{ content} - \text{physically dissolved } O_2}{O_2 \text{ capacity of blood}} \times 100$$

In actuality the blood might carry less oxygen than it is capable of carrying; however, the amount of oxygen carried in chemical combination is approximately 20 vol% arterial and 15 vol% mixed venous.

Oxygen Transfer at Tissue Level

The ability of hemoglobin to attract oxygen from the lung capillaries is as remarkable as its ability to unload the oxygen to the cell. The unloading of oxygen to the cell is accomplished when the pressure gradient is favorable.

---

* Determination of oxygen saturation of whole blood may be accomplished by the manometric technique of Van Slyke.[47] In recent years a photoelectric method of oxygen saturation determination has been developed by Millikan. Spectrophotometric methods are described by Gordy and Drabkin and by Lambertsen et al.

When plotted graphically, the relationship between the partial pressure of oxygen and the percentage of saturation of hemoglobin with oxygen exhibits an "S" shaped curve called the *oxygen disassociation curve.** Construction of the curve is carried out with the aid of an apparatus consisting of a series of tonometers (glass chambers sealed off to prevent air contamination). Blood samples which are introduced into the tonometers are kept in a water bath for a sufficient time interval to assure equilibrium between gas and blood. By application of Henry's law the partial pressures of the gases, which are determined by the pressure of the blood gases, are plotted and produce a figure similar to that of Figure 6–10.

TABLE 6–9.   Typical Partial Pressures Exerted by Oxygen and Carbon Dioxide

	Alveolar	Arterial	Venous	Tissue
P_{O_2}	101	100	40	30 (40–20?)
P_{CO_2}	39	40	46	50

Changes in hydrogen ion concentration of blood, the pH, to levels of increased acidity are reflected in a shifting of the curve to the right. The "flattening" influence of carbon dioxide, an observation by the Danish physicist Neils Bohr, is commonly referred to as the Bohr effect. The observations of W. E. Brown and A. V. Hill point out a similar shifting influence created by blood temperature increases.[5] In summary, the shifting, or "flattening," of the oxygen disassociation curve is influenced by changes in blood pH, which is in turn influenced by carbon dioxide, by lactic acid, and by blood temperature.

A shifting of the curve to the right is interpreted as a reduction in the affinity of hemoglobin for oxygen. Notice, however, in Figure 6–10, that a reduction in oxygen tension† from 100 mm Hg to approximately 75 mm Hg results in a very slight decrease in oxygen saturation levels. Thus, should alveolar oxygen tension (Pa_{O_2}) fluctuate to this great extent, the oxygen saturation level of arterial blood (Pa_{O_2}) would be but slightly influenced.

Much physiologic significance is attached to the "S" shaped asymptotic curve, hence an understanding of oxygen disassociation is essential. In order to assure thorough understanding, the reader is urged to refer to Table 6–9 as well as to Figure 6–10.

---

* The words disassociation and dissociation are used interchangeably.

† Gas tension implies pressure, hence the word tension may be used interchangeably with the term pressure.

An example will be drawn from a constant pH of 7.60 (line I, Fig. 6–10). At pulmonary capillary level, PA_{O_2} 101 mm Hg, PA_{CO_2} 39 mm Hg, arterial hemoglobin is approximately 98% saturated with oxygen. Assuming, the presence of a normal quantity of hemoglobin, the oxygen content of the arterial blood would be:

δ 15 gm Hb/100 ml blood $\times$ 1.34 ml O_2 $\times$ 0.98 (% saturation) = 19.70 vol%.

At tissue capillary level assuming these values, Pc_{O_2} 40 mm Hg, Pc_{CO_2} 50 mm Hg, a disassociation occurs, as evidenced by the fact that the hemoglobin is now approximately 75% saturated with oxygen. Thus a great amount of oxygen carried in chemical combination in the arterial blood is transferred to the tissues. At tissue level, again assuming the presence of a normal quantity of hemoglobin, the oxygen content of the venous blood would be:

δ 15 gm Hb/100 ml blood $\times$ 1.34 ml O_2 $\times$ 0.75 (% saturation) = 15.07 vol%.

From the arteries to the veins, in the above example, the blood has given up 19.70 vol% −15.07 vol% = 4.63 vol% of oxygen to the tissues, i.e., for every 100 ml blood which flowed to and through the tissues, 4.63 ml O_2 was surrendered to the tissues. A *utilization coefficient*, the percentage of the total oxygen amount utilized by the tissues, may be determined by the formula:

$$\text{utilization coefficient} = \frac{O_2 \text{ uptake tissues}}{O_2 \text{ content arterial blood}} \times 100$$

For the above example, the utilization coefficient is calculated to be:

$$\frac{4.63}{19.70} \times 100 = 23.5\%$$

During elevated metabolic states an even greater amount of oxygen is rapidly surrendered to the tissues. The Po_2 at tissue level during elevated activity states may be decreased to 30 mm Hg and the extent of hemoglobin saturation with oxygen reduced to 60%.

δ 15 gm Hb/100 ml blood $\times$ 1.34 ml O_2 $\times$ .60 (% saturation) = 12.06 vol%.

Note, however, that the utilization coefficient is increased
19.70 − 12.06 = 7.64 vol% of oxygen made available to the tissues.

$$\text{utilization coefficient} = \frac{7.64}{19.70} \times 100 = 38.8\%$$

These calculations are based on the assumption that the Pco_2 remained at a set level. In acuality such is not the case, for during increased work or exercise states the curve becomes "flattened," as exemplified by

10

curves II and III in Figure 6–10, thus even greater amounts of oxygen are made available to the more active tissues, which are constantly adjusting to elevated work states. The carbon dioxide role in oxygen availability to active tissues is evident. Even without a lowering of the partial pressure of oxygen at active tissue level, increased oxygen availability is assured.

During work states of high metabolic intensity, the concomitant increases in carbon dioxide tension, in blood lactate and other acid metabolites (which lower the pH), and in blood temperature, all exert a beneficial influence on oxygen availability to active tissues. In addition, an increased rate of blood circulation and pulmonary activity are reflected in an increased utilization coefficient of oxygen at tissue level. During extremely heavy work states the coefficient of oxygen utilization may increase to over 75%. At this level of work, the tissue oxygen requirement is provided by a reduction in blood oxygen tension and by the attendant increases just cited. The importance of the circulatory system is evident; however, the significance of the changes in the capillary bed must not be overlooked. The capillary bed is responsive to levels of metabolic activity. Krogh[30] observed capillary involvement in a stimulated muscle to greatly exceed the degree of involvement in the same muscle under rested conditions: 190 capillaries/mm vs 5 capillaries/mm². The increased capillary bed, evident during increased levels of metabolic activity, assures an increased rate of blood flow (pp. 88–89)* and oxygen delivery to the active tissues. An increase in muscle oxygen consumption to well over 15 times the resting state is to be expected. In superbly conditioned individuals, i.e., in individuals possessing excellent cardiovascular-pulmonary response, the muscle oxygen uptake may be increased up to 24 times that of resting.

Influence of Myoglobin

Although found in all muscles, myoglobin is present in relatively greater amounts in such muscles as the heart, diaphragm, and soleus and generally in lesser amounts in the flexor muscles. This protein sub-

---

* From Hagen's mathematical expression of Poiseuille's law, blood flow rate is proportional to blood vessel dimensions:

$$F = P_1 - P_2 \times \frac{(\pi r^4)}{(8L)} \frac{(1)}{(v)}$$

Factors which increase the power of the numerator aid blood flow. Degree of capillary involvement is analogous to lumen or radius change. Of particular physiological significance is r^4. At constant pressure and viscosity, doubling the radius will result in a 16-fold increase in blood flow. This assures more time for oxygen disassociation. Likewise a decrease by one-half of the blood vessel radius results in a flow reduction of one-sixteenth of the initial value.

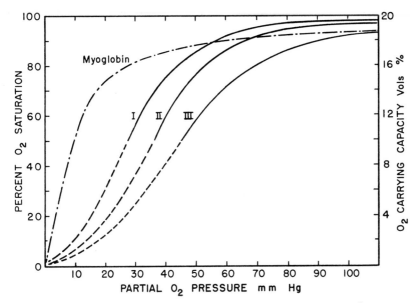

Fig. 6–11. Oxygen disassociation curve for myoglobin superimposed on curves for blood at varying pH levels. Arterial blood depicted by solid line; venous blood by broken line. (From data of Roughton.[50])

stance rapidly attracts the oxygen molecule, is affected by increased carbon dioxide tension (Bohr effect), and generally presents a hyperbolic curve (Fig. 6–11).

By being bound to the oxygen molecule, myoglobin serves as a source for muscle oxygen which is utilized especially during periods of temporary ischemia. The local anemia produced by isometric muscular contraction is countered in small measure by the oxygen bound with myoglobin.

Carbon Dioxide Uptake

Transport and delivery of the oxygen molecule to the tissues have been discussed. Attention will now be focused on the mechanism of removal of one of the end-products of tissue metabolism: carbon dioxide. (The removal of some of the acid metabolites is discussed in Chapter 2.)

Carbon dioxide removal is dependent upon its high diffusion coefficient, its transport as a bicarbonate, and its chemical union with hemoglobin.

From the data of Krogh[32] and of Foster the diffusion coefficient of carbon dioxide Dco_2 is calculated to be 20 times greater than the diffusion coefficient of oxygen Do_2. ($Dco_2 = 24.6$ ml/min/mm Hg; $Do_2 = 1.23$ ml/min/mm Hg).

In chemical union with hemoglobin, carbon dioxide combines specifically with the globin content of hemoglobin to form the carbamino compound. (Carbamino acid is frequently called carbhemoglobin, carbaminohemoglobin, or hemoglobo-carbamic acid.)

Upon entering the blood stream from the tissues, carbon dioxide is transformed by chemical combination with plasma into weak carbonic acid. This relatively slow chemical reaction favors a similar but greatly speeded reaction to take place in the erythrocyte. Due to the presence of great amounts of carbon dioxide and, more important, to the presence of a catalyst, carbonic anhydrase, which serves to accelerate the reaction, the compound carbonic acid is formed. Brinkman and Margaria were among the first to measure the speed of reaction of carbon dioxide uptake.

Because it possesses the remarkable ability of quickly altering its acidity level* with its degree of oxygenation, hemoglobin plays an important role in carbon dioxide elimination in the form of carbonic acid. As an example, the hemoglobin, being oxygenated in the lungs, becomes a stronger acid thus hastening carbon dioxide elimination. In the venous blood it is less oxygenated, is therefore a weaker acid and is capable of attracting carbon dioxide in bicarbonate form. Of the carbon dioxide eliminated from the lungs, approximately one-fourth is carried in direct combination with hemoglobin; the remaining three-fourths is carried in bicarbonate form.

Far greater amounts of bicarbonate are formed in the erythrocytes, hence the diffusion process is through the erythrocyte membrane into the plasma. Because the erythrocyte membrane is impermeable to sodium (Na^+) and potassium (K^+), base ions, chloride ions (Cl^-) move in to establish ionic equilibrium (homeostasis). This exchange of chloride ions (Cl^-) between plasma and cells—appropriately termed the chloride shift and often called the Hamberger phenomenon—allows for large amounts of carbon dioxide to be carried chemically without altering blood pH.

Carbon Dioxide Disassociation Curves

Christiansen, Douglas, and Haldane plotted carbon dioxide disassociation curves. The essential differences in the ordinates of the graphs are attributed to the fact that hemoglobin is attracted to each of the respiratory gases, oxygen and carbon dioxide in different ways. Almost all the oxygen is carried in chemical combination with hemoglobin;

---

* Assuming a normal blood pH of 7.4, relative degrees of acidity and alkalinity are recognized. A pH of 7.3 or less identifies acidosis; in excess of pH 7.4 alkalosis. These changes may be metabolically induced or may result from respiratory alterations.

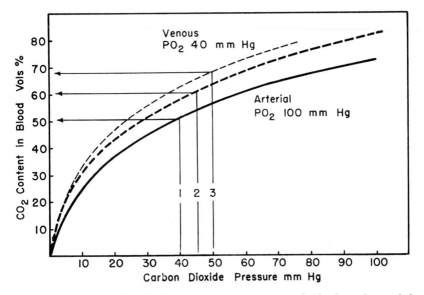

Fig. 6–12. Carbon dioxide disassociation curve. Arterial blood is depicted by solid line; venous blood by heavy, broken line. Typical Po_2 values are noted on the slopes. Corresponding Po_2, Pco_2 values, taken from Table 6–5, are depicted by numbered arrows for arterial blood (1) and for venous blood (2). At increased levels of metabolic activity, characterized by decreased Po_2 and increased Pco_2, greater CO_2 uptake and elimination will be effected. This is depicted by broken, uppermost line (indicating Po_2 decrease) and by line 3 (indicating Pco_2 increase). Increased CO_2 production results in increased CO_2 elimination; carbon dioxide provides for its own removal. (Adapted from data of Christensen, Douglas, and Haldane.)

therefore, the degree of oxygen saturation of hemoglobin is in fact a true reflection of the oxygen carried. Such is not the relationship of hemoglobin with carbon dioxide. The carbon dioxide–hemoglobin attraction is representative of a minor part of the total carbon dioxide uptake (Fig. 6–12).

During rest states, arterial blood (Pa_{O_2} 100 mm Hg, Pa_{CO_2} 40 mm Hg) reflects an amount of carbon dioxide of the order of 50 ml/100 ml blood, whereas venous blood (Pv_{O_2} 40 mm Hg, Pv_{CO_2} 46 mm Hg) may possess a carbon dioxide content of 60 ml/100 ml blood. An essentially positive, linear relationship exists between the carbon dioxide tension and uptake, thus an increased production of carbon dioxide will be effectively transported by the venous system. The adequacy of the transport and elimination mechanism is practically assured because carbon dioxide gas is readily soluble and highly diffusive.

A mutually beneficial arrangement exists between blood gases. Increased demands for oxygen at tissue level results in a decreased oxygen tension which, in turn, effects an even greater carbon dioxide uptake.

Respiration, an invariable characteristic of living beings, is accomplished at low energy cost. As pointed out by Margaria et al., the energy cost of respiration even during exercise states represents not more than 3% of the total energy expended.

REFERENCES

1. Agostoni, E., and Fenn, W. O.: Velocity of muscle shortening as a limiting factor in respiratory air flow. *J. Appl. Physiol.*, 15:349–353, 1960.

2. Barcroft, J., and Margaria, R.: Some effects of carbonic acid on the character of human respiration. *J. Physiol.*, 72:174–185, 1931.

3. Bock, A. V., Van Caulaert, C., Dill, D. B., Fölling, A., and Hurxthal, L. M.: Studies in muscular activity. III. Dynamical changes in man at work. *J. Physiol.*, 66:136–161, 1928.

4. Brinkman, R., and Margaria, R.: The influence of haemoglobin on the hydration and dehydration velocities of CO_2. *J. Physiol.*, 72:6P–7P, 1931.

5. Brown, W. E., and Hill, A. V.: The oxygen-dissociation curve of blood and its thermodynamical basis. *Proc. Royal Soc.*, s.B 94:297–334, 1923.

6. Campbell, E. J. M.: An electromyographic study of the role of the abdominal muscles in breathing. *J. Physiol.*, 117:222–233, 1952.

7. Campbell, E. J. M.: *The Respiratory Muscles and the Mechanics of Breathing.* London, Lloyd-Luke, 1958.

8. Christiansen, J., Douglas, C. G., and Haldane, J. S.: The absorption and dissociation of carbon dioxide in human blood. *J. Physiol.*, 48:244–271, 1914.

9. Comroe, J. H.: The Lung. *Scientific Am.*, 214:56–68, 1966.

10. Comroe, J. H., and Schmidt, C. F.: Reflexes from the limbs as a factor in the hyperpnea of muscular exercise. *Am. J. Physiol.*, 138:536–547, 1943.

11. Comroe, J. H., Forster, R. E., DuBois, A. B., Briscoe, W. A., and Carlsen, E.: *The Lung, Clinical Physiology and Pulmonary Function Tests*, 2nd Ed. Chicago, Year Book Medical Publishers, Inc., 1962.

12. Consolazio, C. F., Johnson, R. E., and Pecora, L. J.: *Physiological Measurements of Metabolic Functions in Man.* New York, McGraw-Hill Book Company, 1963.

13. Cournand, A., Baldwin, E. deF., Darling, R. C., and Richards, D. W.: Studies on intrapulmonary mixtures of gases. IV. The significance of the pulmonary emptying rate and a simplified open circuit measurement of residual air. *J. Clin. Invest.*, 20:681–689, 1941.

14. Craig, A. B., Jr.: Causes of loss of consciousness during underwater swimming. *J. Appl. Physiol.*, 16:583–586, 1961.

15. Craig, A. B., Jr., and Babcock, S. A.: Alveolar CO_2 during breath-holding and exercise. *J. Appl. Physiol.*, 17:874–876, 1962.

16. Craig, A. B., Jr., Halstead, L. S., Schmidt, G. H., and Schnier, B. R.: Influences of exercise and oxygen on breath-holding. *J. Appl. Physiol.*, 17:225–227, 1962.

17. Darling, R. C., Cournand, A., and Richards, D. W.: An open circuit method for measuring residual air. *J. Clin. Invest.*, 19:609–618, 1940.

18. DiSalvo, R. J., and Goto, U.: The helium closed circuit method for measuring the functional residual capacity. *Dis. Chest.*, 36:624–630, 1959.

19. Douglas, C. G., and Haldane, J. S.: The capacity of the air passages under varying physiological conditions. *J. Physiol.*, 45:235–238, 1912.

20. Dreyer, G.: *The Assessment of Physical Fitness.* New York, P. B. Hoeber Co., 1920.

21. Foster, R. E.: Exchange of gases between alveolar air and pulmonary capillary blood: pulmonary diffusing capacity. *Physiol. Rev.*, 37:391–452, 1957.

22. Gordon, B., Levine, S. A., and Wilmaers, A.: Observations on a group of marathon runners. *Arch. Int. Med.*, 33:425–434, 1924.

23. Gordy, E., and Drabkin, D. L.: Spectrophotometric Studies. XVI. Determination of the oxygen saturation of blood by a simplified technique, applicable to standard equipment. *J. Biol. Chem.*, 227:285–299, 1957.

24. Gray, J. S.: The multiple factor theory of the control of respiratory ventilation. *Science*, 103:739–744, 1946.

25. Gray, J. S.: *Pulmonary Ventilation and Its Physiological Regulation.* Springfield, Charles C Thomas, 1950.

26. Grodins, F. S.: Analysis of factors concerned in regulation of breathing in exercise. *Physiol. Rev.*, 30:220–239, 1950.

27. Haldane, J. S.: *Respiration.* New Haven, Yale University Press, 1922.

28. Holmes, E. L.: Pulmonary function in the normal male. *J. Appl. Physiol.*, 14:493–495, 1959.

29. Keith, A.: *The Mechanism of Respiration in Man; Further Advances in Physiology.* London, Edw. Arnold Co., 1909.

30. Krogh, A.: *The Anatomy and Physiology of Capillaries.* New Haven, Yale University Press, 1929.

31. Krogh, A., and Lindhard, J.: A comparison between voluntary and electrically induced muscular work in man. *J. Physiol.*, 51:182–201, 1917.

32. Krogh, M.: The diffusion of gases through the lungs of man. *J. Physiol.*, 49:271–300, 1915.

33. Lambertsen, C. J., Bunce, B. L., Drabkin, D. L., and Schmidt, C. F.: Relationship of oxygen tension to hemoglobin oxygen saturation in the arterial blood of normal men. *J. Appl. Physiol.*, 4:873–885, 1952.

34. Lewis, B. M., and Morton, J. W.: Effects of inhalation of CO_2, muscular exercise and epinephrine on maximal breathing capacity. *J. Appl. Physiol.*, 7:309–312, 1954.

35. Lilly, C. J., and Anderson, T. F.: Preliminary studies on respiratory gas mixing with nitrogen and a tracer gas. *Am. J. Med. Sci.*, 208:136–137, 1944.

36. Lindhard, J.: *In* Bock, A. V., and Dill, D. B.: Bainbridge's, *The Physiology of Muscular Activity.* London, Longmans, Green & Co., 1931.

37. Margaria, R.: *Principi di Chimica e Fisico-Chimica Fisiologica.* 8th Ed. Milano, Casa Editrice Ambrosiana, 1958.

38. Margaria, R.: A mathematical treatment of the blood dissociation curve for oxygen. *J. Clin. Chem.*, 9:745–762, 1963.

39. Margaria, R., Milic-Emili, G., Petit, J. M., and Cavagna, G.: Mechanical work of breathing during muscular exercise. *J. Appl. Physiol.*, 15:354–358, 1960.

40. Meneely, G. R., and Kaltreider, N. L.: Use of helium for determination of pulmonary capacity. *Proc. Soc. Exper. Biol. and Med.*, 46:266-269, 1941.

41. Meneely, G. R., and Kaltreider, N. L.: Volume of lung determined by helium dilution; description of method and comparison with other procedures. *J. Clin. Invest.*, 28:129–139, 1949.

42. Meneely, G. R., Ball, C. O. T., Kory, R. C., Callaway, J. J., Mabe, R. E., Merrill, J. M., Roehm, D. C., and Kaltreider, N. L.: A simplified closed circuit helium dilution method for the determination of the residual volume of the lungs. *Am. J. Med.*, 28:824–831, 1960.

43. Millikan, G. A.: The oximeter, an instrument for measuring continuously the oxygen saturation of arterial blood in man. *Rev. Scientific Inst.*, 13:434–444, 1942.

44. Moreno, F., and Lyons, H. A.: Effect of body posture on lung volumes. *J. Appl. Physiol.*, 16:27–29, 1961.

45. Mostyn, E. M., Helle, S., Gee, J. B. L., Bentivoglio, L. G., and Bates, D. V.: Pulmonary diffusing capacity of athletes. *J. Appl. Physiol.*, 18:687–695, 1963.

46. Pappenheimer, J. R., Comroe, J. H., Cournand, A., Ferguson, J. K. W., Filley, G. F., Fowler, W. S., Gray, J. S., Helmholtz, H. F., Otis, A. B., Rahn, H., and Riley, R. L.: Standardization of definitions and symbols in respiratory physiology. *Fed. Proc.*, 9:602–605, 1950.

47. Peters, J. P., and Van Slyke, D. D.: *Quantitative Clinical Chemistry.* Baltimore, The Williams & Wilkins Co., 1931.

48. Riley, R. L., Permutt, S., Said, S., Godfrey, M., Cheng, T. O., Howell, J. B. L., and Shepard, R. H.: Effect of posture on pulmonary dead space in man. *J. Appl. Physiol.*, 14:339–344, 1959.

49. Roughton, F. J. W.: The average time spent by the blood in the human lung capillary and its relation to the rates of CO uptake and elimination in man. *Am. J. Physiol.*, 143:621–633, 1945.

50. Roughton, F. J. W.: Respiratory functions of blood. *In* Boothby, W. M. (Ed.): *Handbook of Respiratory Physiology.* Randolph Field, Texas, U.S.A.F. School of Aviation Medicine, 1954.

51. Stuart, D. G., and Collings, W. D.: Comparison of vital capacity and maximum breathing capacity of athletes and non-athletes. *J. Appl. Physiol.*, 14:507–509, 1959.

52. West, H.: Clinical studies on the respiration. VI. A comparison of various standards for the normal vital capacity of the lungs. *Arch. Int. Med.*, 25:306–316, 1920.

53. Young, A. C.: Dead space at rest and during exercise. *J. Appl. Physiol.*, 8:91–94, 1955.

C h a p t e r

7

HEAT REGULATION

MAN is homeothermal. His metabolic processes exhibit narrow fluctuations of core temperature. Sustained elevated core temperatures, i.e., above 41.6° C,* result in irreversible damage to the neurons of the central nervous system. Enzymatic activity, essential to metabolic activity, ceases at this febrile level as well as at slightly reduced core temperatures. In order to maintain normal metabolic activity, heat gain must eventually be balanced by heat loss and vice versa. Man cannot withstand the debilitating effects of pyrexia, yet in strenuous physical activity he is in a febrile state.

Temperature regulation is essentially involuntary and automatic. By enveloping himself in an ambient temperature which prevents excessive heat losses or gains, man has demonstrated an ability to survive anywhere on the surface of earth, at numerous locations beneath the sea, and in the immediate outer space.

He often becomes concerned with oral temperature readings which exhibit the slightest change. Perhaps he equates so-called normal temperature with a fixed figure, 37° C, rather than as an interval. Perhaps he is conditioned by the small indicating arrow which appears on the vast majority of clinical thermometers. At any rate, in relation to core temperature, Ivy[21] raised the question of normal and normality. The mean temperature of 276 medical students, obtained between 8 a.m. and 9 a.m. was found to be 36.7° C (Fig. 7–1).

Core temperatures also exhibit a diurnal rhythm which varies from a low reading, recorded between 3 a.m. and 6 a.m., to a high reading which is recorded some twelve hours later. This diurnal rhythm is depicted in Figure 7–2.

---

* To convert C to F: $\times 9 \div 5 + 32$

141

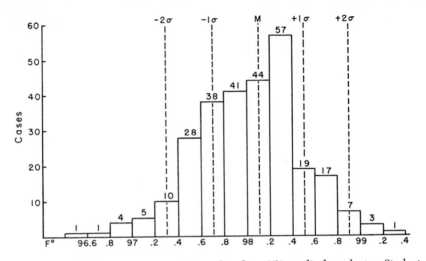

Fig. 7–1.   Oral temperature variations found in 276 medical students. Students were seated; temperatures were taken between 8 and 9 a.m. Mean 98.1°F (36.7°C). (From Ivy. Courtesy of Northwestern University Medical School.)

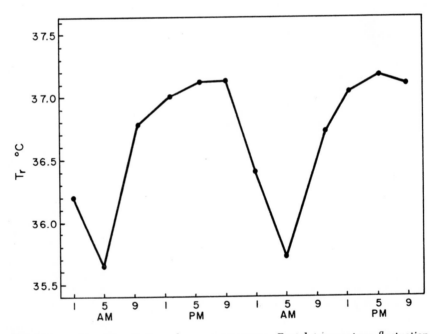

Fig. 7–2.   Diurnal variation of core temperature. Rectal temperature fluctuation during two-day period of relative physical inactivity. Probe inserted to depth of 15.5 cm (a 43-year-old man).

Within this text, the term body temperature is synonymous with core temperature as opposed to shell temperature. *Core temperature* is the temperature of the deep underlying structures: the brain, the thoracic and abdominal regions, and the deep muscle tissue in the limbs. *Shell temperature* includes the skin surface temperature as well as temperature of the more superficial tissues. Due to the insulating quality of epithelial,

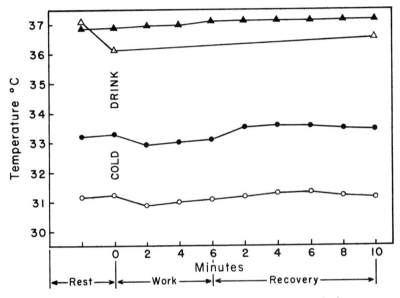

Fig. 7–3. Effect of work performed on bicycle ergometer on body temperatures. Immediately before work, young male subject drank 1 liter of cold orange juice (1°C). Even after 11,271 kg work and recovery, oral temperature did not return to pre-work levels. Note stability of rectal temperature. Higher temperature of left thigh was due to thermal insulation provided by one-legged "sweat pants." Lower temperature of exposed right thigh was attributed to more effective radiation loss. (triangle, oral; solid triangle, rectal; solid dot, left thigh; circle, right thigh).

connective and muscle tissue, core temperature (especially rectal) exhibits a high degree of constancy. Skin temperatures not only vary greatly between differing anatomical locations, but also change rapidly in response to work of even short duration, whereas rectal temperature remains fairly stable. If properly taken, oral temperature may reflect core temperature; however, this reading is subject to pronounced fluctuations (Fig. 7–3). Smoking one cigarette may influence oral temperature.

Reliability of rectal temperature readings was shown by Mead and Bonmarito to be related to depth of insertion of measuring instrument. They observed temperature variation to be a function of the depth of insertion.

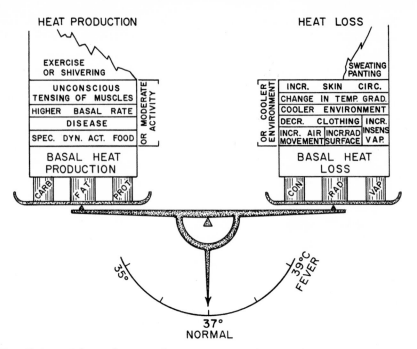

Fig. 7–4. Balance between factors increasing heat production and heat loss. (From DuBois. Courtesy of New York Academy of Medicine.)

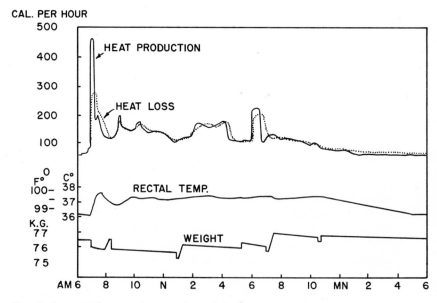

Fig. 7–5. Daily variations in heat balance, temperature, and weight. (From DuBois. Courtesy of New York Academy of Medicine.)

Body temperature is a resultant of the balance between body heat production and loss (Fig. 7-4).

As might be imagined, temperature balance is not a fixed concept (Fig. 7-5). It is an ever changing concept which is related to changing levels of metabolic activity. During basal states, disequilibrium is of a temporary nature and of short duration; however, during markedly elevated metabolic states heat production outstrips heat loss and the imbalance may be of long duration. Hot, humid afternoons in late summer and early fall pose a particular problem for the unacclimatized football player whose protective padding and snug-fitting helmet further reduce heat loss.

Perspiration

For general usage, the words *sweat* and *perspiration* may be used interchangeably. More precisely, perspiration is the excretion of fluids by the sweat glands. Through vaporization (evaporation) perspiration exerts an extremely important influence in the maintenance of fairly stable body core temperatures.

While it was Galen who described respiration through the skin (he characterized it as having the form of a light vapor),[9] it remained for Santorio Santorio (1561–1636) to evaluate this form of respiration— to discover metabolism. His studies of "the insensible perspiration," i.e., through the skin, focused on a form of respiration which lent itself to exact measurement. He placed his bed, desk, food, and provisions in a room which was suspended on a specially constructed balance. He investigated alterations in body weight; he also pioneered the use of a thermometer to record body temperatures.[9]

More than two and a half centuries later, in 1847, Helmholtz gave general application to J. R. Mayer's law of conservation of energy. The law now is recognized as the *first law of thermodynamics:* all kinds of energy can be transformed from one form to another but cannot be destroyed or created.

Insensible perspiration is the term applied to the process of perspiration evaporation which is neither observable nor felt. Tissue fluid is constantly escaping through the epidermis—irrespective of sweat gland activity—and readily evaporates. Fluid also escapes via exhalation of respiratory gases. By contrast, *sensible perspiration* is perceived as moisture on the skin and is indicative of sweat gland involvement. *Sweat* is generally used to describe sensible perspiration. Atmospheric conditions, e.g., ambient temperature, movement of air, and relative humidity, exert great influence on the rate of evaporation. Sweating patterns were observed by Hertzman to be related to total sweat output and unrelated to skin and oral temperatures.

Chemical Composition of Sweat

Sweat is composed chiefly of sodium chloride, 300 mg%, and in addition contains in approximate quantity: nitrogenous urea, 21 mg%; glucose equivalents including small amounts of lactic acid, 20 mg%; amino acids, 6.5 mg%; and nitrogenous ammonia, 6 mg%. Its pH may vary from 4.2 to 7.0 with an approximate, so-called average value of 6.0. Specific gravity of sweat may vary from 1.001 to 1.006.

Sweat Glands

Eccrine sweat glands are widely distributed over the body surface and secrete a dilute solution composed chiefly of sodium chloride, urea, and lactic acid. These glands are distributed throughout the body but are found in greater abundance in the soles of the feet, the palms, the axillae, and on the head. They are under the control of the sympathetic nervous system and are particularly effective in dissipating body heat. *Apocrine* sweat glands are located mainly in the axillary and pubic regions.

Freshly formed perspiration from the apocrine glands is odorless. As a result of bacterial action, *bromhidrosis,* perspiration with an offensive odor, may develop unless proper personal hygiene is practiced and antisudoral agents used. The fetid odor which can emanate from the axillae carries the descriptive word *tragomaschalia.* (Of Greek derivation, *tragos* means goat.)

Heat Loss

Heat losses from the body may take one or all of the following forms: radiation, evaporation (vaporization), convection, or conduction.

Radiant heat is thermal energy. In an environment which is cooler than the body, an exchange will take the form of heat waves being emitted (radiated) from the body surface into the surrounding medium (Fig. 7–3). The magnitude of the loss is dependent upon such factors as the temperature gradient between the body surface and the surrounding medium, the amount of body surface exposure, and such atmospheric considerations as air temperature, air movement, and relative humidity. As reported by DuBois, body surface area exposure can be reduced from 80% in erect standing to 55% of total surface in the knees-to-chest tuck position.

Although the amount of heat loss through radiation is inversely related to ambient temperature, the amount lost through *vaporization* is directly related to it. At air temperature higher than body temperature, the effective heat loss mechanism is through *evaporation* of perspiration. It is generally held that approximately one fourth of the heat production in resting metabolism is dissipated in the unnoticed evaporative way (insensible perspiration). The rate of heat loss is dependent upon such considerations as ambient temperature and relative humidity. Relative humidity is expressed as a ratio of the water vapor saturation of a given volume of air to its maximum saturation capacity and is reported as a percentage. An increase in ambient temperature is directly related to an increase in water vapor retention.

During a hot day, as the relative humidity is increased, the effectiveness of the heat loss through vaporization is decreased. As the relative humidity decreases, man's comfort index increases. The combined effect of an increase in ambient temperature and relative humidity requires increased cardiac effort to maintain heat balance (Fig. 7–6). For individuals with poor cardiac response, the combined effects of heat and humidity may trigger cardiac embarrassment.

Heat loss through *convection* constitutes still another mechanism of temperature regulation. Heat of metabolism is generally transferred throughout the body via the blood stream; however, as temporary heat imbalances occur, as in elevated work states, more blood is directed to

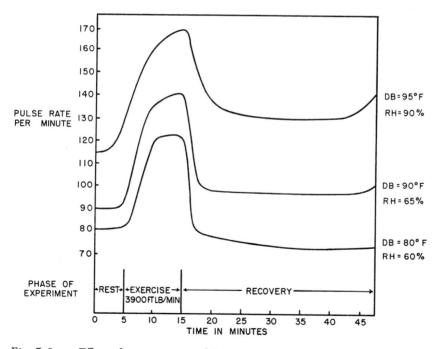

Fig. 7–6. Effect of temperature and humidity upon heart rate. (From Brouha.[6] Courtesy of Industrial Hygiene Foundation.)

the superficial vascular beds. Because of the proximity of the blood to the body surface, subdermal temperatures may attain a temperature level equal to that of the core. The exchange of heat occurs between the skin surface and the ambient air. In the above example, it is assumed that the insulating effect of clothing is reduced by loosely fitted or ventilated clothing or clothing which is light in texture.

Heat loss through *conduction* represents the least effective avenue for heat loss primarily because physical contact is required for heat transfer to be effected. Nonetheless, resting against a tile wall as opposed to a wooden wall will result in a greater heat transfer due to the fact that tile is a better heat conductor, i.e., its conductivity is greater.

A small heat loss is also incurred in the excretion of urine and feces.

Water (Fluid) Loss

Water is continually being lost. Body heat dissipation through evaporation of perspiration represents a water loss. Also, the moisture content of the exhaled air is indicative of an escape of body fluids. The amount of water loss is variable and is dependent upon such factors as level of metabolic activity and such weather considerations as ambient temperature, wind velocity, and relative humidity.

In conditions of low relative humidity and low ambient temperature, i.e., relative to body temperature, water loss is not noticeable to the eye. Most noticeable perhaps is the condensation of the exhaled air during a cold day. (Incidentally, this predictable and observable change in state of exhaled air, from gaseous to liquid, serves to ascertain the effectiveness of a nose clip worn during indirect calorimetry or respirometry work. Because of high thermal conductivity, a glass or metallic mirror placed beneath the nose clip would abstract heat from the escaping air and the condensation would be visible.)

It might also be pointed out that the water loss via the pulmonary pathway is a function of the minute volume of respiration.

Copious amounts of body water may be lost through profuse sweating. Here again, the degree of loss is related to ambient temperature, relative humidity, degree of acclimatization, type and fit of clothing, and level of physiological fitness.

Dill[11] reported a maximal rate of water evaporation of 1600 ml/hr during work performed in a hot, dry environment. This represents an expenditure of $1600 \times 0.58 = 928$ kcal/hr. If projected over an eight-hour work day, this would represent the expenditure of 7424 kcal. Sedentary subjects exposed to desert simulated conditions (120° to 130° F, 10 to 20% relative humidity) were found by Kanter[22] to exhibit the typical patterns of weight loss (mainly water loss), fatigue, decreased urine flow, and an increased heart rate. The fall in urine pH was supported by arterial blood pH which fell from 7.46 to 7.41 in four hours. Snellen calculated sweating rates of 6.59 g/min/°C and 8.56 g/min/°C for two young male subjects during exercise. The sweating rates were directly proportional to changes in mean body temperature.

Heat Gain

Metabolism is synonymous with heat production. Heat is a resultant of the oxidation of food; heat is also a by-product of tissue metabolism. During quiescent states, heat production is decreased due to reduced levels of metabolic activity. For several reasons, heat production is lowest during deep sleep. First, the metabolic activity is at its lowest level. Second, assuming a fast of approximately ten hours' duration, oxidation of food is practically completed, hence, the heat of oxidation is greatly reduced. (During this postprandial state, heat results mainly from the oxidation of stored lipids.) Third, the reduced levels of cardiac, liver, kidney, and muscle activity, are reflected in a low level of heat production and oxygen consumption.

During the time interval between awakening and going to sleep, heat production is increased due to the introduction of food (which must be oxidized) and to the increase in metabolic activity of the visceral, cardiac, and muscle mass of the body. A gradual temperature fluctuation, the diurnal rhythm, is exhibited (Fig. 7–2).

Of particular interest is the research of Iampietro et al. The effects of a cold environment on oxygen consumption and rectal temperature were studied in sedentary male subjects. A diurnal rhythm was observed in both of the above parameters; however, the first recorded resting oxygen consumption (8 a.m.) was found to be elevated by as much as 20% above values obtained during comparable time periods in warm environments. The increased oxygen consumption was indicative of increased metabolic activity, which was reflected in significantly elevated rectal temperatures.

Heat production is also the resultant of certain endocrine gland activity—the thyroids and adrenals in particular. The relative thermogenic influence of the thyroid gland has long been recognized. Basal metabolic rates are markedly elevated in hyperthyroidism and markedly lowered in hypothyroidism; however, these changes are of a gradual and sustained nature. The thyroid gland does not influence immediate changes in heat regulation.

By contrast, through adrenal medulla secretion, epinephrine plays an immediate role in heat production by stimulating metabolic responses.

The most profound, normal increase in heat production is provided by the extensive muscular system. Heat is formed during muscle contraction and during recovery from contraction. Voluntarily, then, man is capable of increasing his heat production merely by contracting and relaxing his muscles. Since all activity incorporates involuntary muscle and cardiac muscle activity, heat production is further increased. In frigid temperatures, the commuter at the train stop may soon engage in the involuntary act of shivering. By this manner, heat production is increased slightly, but more important, shivering compels one to move about voluntarily, thereby increasing heat production further.

Heat gain may result from a number of causes in addition to an increased level of metabolic activity—from the ingestion of hot foods and beverages to radiated heat which confronts certain occupational groups. Direct or reflected radiation from the sun is yet another source of heat gain.

To some extent, the wearing of loosely fitted clothing of light color and texture proves to be effective in the reduction of heat gain. The availability of a shaded area is also effective in reducing the heat gain from solar rays (Fig. 7–7).

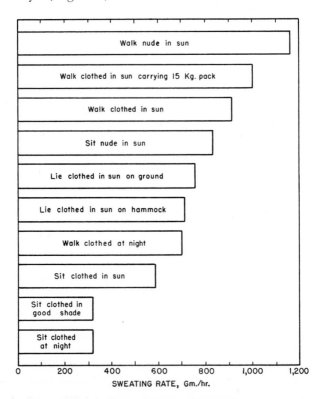

Fig. 7–7. Sweating rates under varying conditions of exposure to hot desert air, 37.7°C. (From Gosselin. Courtesy of Interscience Publishers.)

Neural Thermoregulation

The animal research of Clark et al. established the location of the thermoregulatory center within the hypothalamus. The anterior portion of the hypothalamus exerts control over sweat gland function, dilatation of the cutaneous blood vessels, and pulmonary activity. Within the posterior hypothalamus lies the control of heat maintenance. Destruction of this posterior region results in a loss of power to adapt to cold environments. Keller and Hare located the hypothalamic site which controls the involuntary act of shivering.

Pyrexia

Metabolic function, whether anabolic or catabolic, not only requires energy but also produces heat. Provided the physical task is of sufficient duration and challenge, an elevation of core temperature is associated with an elevated level of metabolic activity. During heavy work, core temperatures of 40° C are not uncommon. A number of factors may contribute to such a rise in rectal temperature. Heat gain in heavy work is obviously hastened by high atmospheric temperatures, high relative humidity, low degree of acclimatization, low level of cardiopulmonary fitness and by the texture, fit, and color of clothing.

In the superbly conditioned athlete, i.e., one who possesses a good cardiovascular-pulmonary response, a rectal temperature of 40° C is not uncommon. Yet, by comparison with accepted standards, the individual is in a febrile state.

Generally, as a safeguard to life, a temperature of 40° C must signal the cessation of experimental work or athletic participation. In physical work, there is usually a noticeable lag in heat loss with respect to heat gain. This is especially true during the late summer and early fall and should have meaning for the coaches of fall sports such as football and soccer. The initial practice sessions should be conducted carefully, for it is during this time of year when atmospheric temperatures are high, when levels of physiological and physical conditioning are inclined to be low, and when, as in football, players are required to wear much gear which is protective yet lessens heat loss. Not only are water imbalances created but, more important, salt losses might be experienced and might produce the deleterious effects of heat illnesses.

Water Intake

The data of Pitts et al. should be sufficiently convincing to those coaches who hold the scientifically unfounded "Spartan" view that water ingestion must not be tolerated during practice sessions or games (Fig. 7–8).

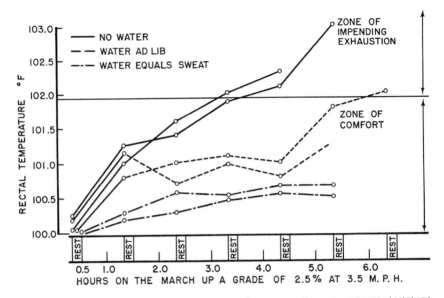

Fig. 7–8. Effect of water ingestion on subjects marching in 100°F (37.7°C) temperature with relative humidity 35 to 40%. (From Pitts et al. Courtesy of American Physiological Society.)

It should also be noted that sweat evaporation, an important avenue for heat loss, is reduced following a reduction in water intake. Pearcy et al. found that when male subjects were deliberately dehydrated, sweat rates were also significantly reduced even though skin and rectal temperatures were elevated. Further, Robinson et al. reported a reduced salt loss in men who were permitted to replace water loss during work periods.[32] Blyth and Burt observed that athletes performed better on all-out treadmill running in a hot environment, 48.8° C, when allowed to drink 2 liters of water before running. Water denial contributed to poor endurance.

Salt Balance

During increased muscular activity the sodium chloride and potassium content of sweat increases and may represent a significant loss. Further, salt loss in sweating varies between individuals and was shown by Adolph and by Robinson et al.[30,31] to be dependent upon the degree of acclimatization. The amount of salt loss increases as the rate of sweating increases; however, as was shown by Pitts et al. and by Taylor et al., the rate of sweating decreases after salt replacement. A lowering of the salt concentration of sweat is inversely related to the degree of acclimatization.

The question of the supplemental feeding of salt tablets to athletes is often raised. Based on the data of Taylor et al., a daily average salt intake of 20 gm is considered adequate. Unless salt-free diets are prepared, the intake of 20 gm is easily attained with the ingestion of three adequately planned and prepared meals. Scott also advocates approximately 20 gm per day according to the following formula: 2 gm salt for each hour of exercise; 0.5 gm salt for each hour of inactivity. Assuming a five-hour work or exercise period, the twenty-four hour requirement of 20 gm salt would be met.

In certain occupational groups, work is required to be performed in a hot environment. For these individuals, a supplementary salt intake is necessary to maintain salt balance.

There are other considerations. First, the ingestion of an uncoated salt tablet without a fluid chaser may result in nausea. If salt tablets are indicated, they should be taken with a cupful of water as a chaser. Or, enteric coated salt tablets may be ingested; these tablets would be dissolved in the small intestine rather than the stomach.

Thirst

The mechanism of thirst is not clearly understood. In many studies, an inverse relation between salivary flow and the sensation of thirst has been established.

The role of the hypothalamus has been established.[3,4,17,27]

Observations of Wolf[41] center on the role of cellular dehydration in eliciting the thirst response.

In particular, the research of Andersson and McCann is of great interest.[4] Goats responded to electrical stimulation of the lateral portion of the hypothalamus by drinking and ceased drinking when the stimulus was removed. Drinking induced by stimulation appeared to be independent of the rate of salivary flow.

There is general agreement that thirst is triggered by uncomfortable sensations resulting from dryness of the oral mucosa. Yet, in terms of maintaining water balance, the thirst mechanism is not dependable.

Heat Disorders

With adequate precautions physical and physiological incapacities will become minimal. Thorough medical examinations, progression in physiological and physical conditioning, allowance of sufficient time for acclimatizing to heat, sufficient water and salt to maintain balance, dress appropriate to weather conditions, staggered practice sessions to avoid early exposure to hot, sunny, humid weather, and sufficiently lengthy periods of rest constitute adequate precautions.

On occasion, however, disorders will occur and each disorder must be brought to the attention of a physician. Although each disorder is an unpleasant experience, one is of an extremely serious nature which requires immediate medical attention: *heat stroke* (*sun stroke*).

The onset of *heat stroke* may be characterized by headache and vertigo only. In severe cases, a febrile state, 43° C, may be reached. The skin is *hot* and *dry* and the cardiac frequency is *rapid* (tachycardia). These are symptomatic of a complete breakdown in the heat balance mechanism.

Heat cramp is characterized by muscle spasm and pain (which is often severe). The pupils become dilated and the pulse is weak.

Heat exhaustion is characterized by weakness and collapse. The skin becomes hot and is moist, sweating may be profuse and the pulse is rapid.

Cold Environment

Man has adapted to cold climates by maintaining a comfortable microclimate about his skin. This is accomplished through the wearing of clothing which assures a protective, comfortable insulating layer of air. Often work productivity in cold climates is reduced, due especially to discomfort of the hands and feet. Foot warmth is more readily achieved; however, hand warmth, aided by wearing of gloves or mittens, is often achieved at the expense of digital dexterity.

The importance of finger and hand temperature to fine digital manipulation is clearly established. Gaydos[15] observed that body temperature could be reduced to uncomfortable levels yet fine manipulations were preserved provided hand surface temperatures were maintained at normal levels. Gaydos and Dusek found finger temperature to be the primary determinant of digital manipulative performance.

The fact that natives of arctic regions exhibit, in cold environments, greater digital dexterity than do non-natives was borne out by Carlson et al. Brown and Page observed differences in digital blood flow of natives, Eskimos, and non-natives. These blood flow differences are depicted in Figure 7–9.

Rodahl's review of earlier literature contains references to higher basal metabolic rates of Eskimos. He attributed these elevated basal metabolic rates to apprehension states and to diet. He further showed that, when carefully taken, basal metabolic rates were equal in natives and non-natives.

In comparison with the non-native, the native may be said to possess a higher degree of acclimatization to cold. Scholander et al.[34] observed that Lapps possess the same levels of "physiological insulation" as men living in temperate climates.

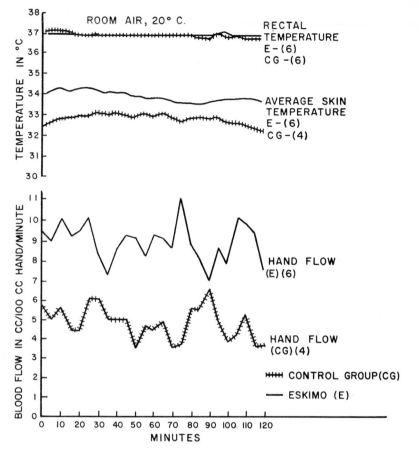

Fig. 7–9. Temperature and blood flow in Eskimo (E) and control group (CG) monitored over a two-hour period. Indoor ambient temperature was 20°C. Skin temperatures represent averages from five surface sites. (From Brown and Page. Courtesy of American Physiological Society.)

In the experiments conducted by Meehan, Eskimos demonstrated a greater capacity for heat production through the involuntary act of shivering. This observation is in keeping with the earlier observation of Carlson et al. that in comparison with unacclimatized subjects, acclimatized individuals maintain higher foot and hand temperatures through greater loss of total body heat.

In cold climates the use of headgear which provides insulation for the head is essential to maintenance of heat balance. Nonevaporative heat loss from the unprotected head was shown by Froese and Burton to be substantial. From their calculations, one can easily discern the practical importance of covering the head. With an uncovered head, heat steady-state could be achieved by increasing the insulation provided by clothing by 4 clo units,* i.e., from 5 to 9, whereas head covering alone, 2.4 clo units, provides the same heat balance.

That shivering is effective as a heat producing mechanism was borne out by Horvath et al.[19] who estimate that this act was 11% efficient in protecting against total heat loss. Later, Spurr et al. found the shivering mechanism to be more effective with decreasing temperature in protecting body heat loss (5.9% effective at 10° C; 11.6% at −3° C).

Racial Differences

Racial differences as well as differences within culture groups have been observed relative to stresses imposed by heat and cold. Kuno describes racial differences relative to numbers of sweat glands: Negroes possess 3 to 4 million glands, fully a million more than the non-Negroes. Adams and Covino[1] concluded that physiological differences between racial groups increase the probability of cold injury to Negroes exposed to stresses of cold. Scholander et al.[36] observed the superior cooling adaptation of Australian aborigines. Caucasians (Norwegians) required approximately six weeks to become acclimatized to cold, according to Scholander et al.[35]

By altering his microclimate and his rate of work by maintaining fluid and salt balance, man displays an amazing ability to perform physical and mental tasks in all natural environments on this planet. His ability to take a bit of his atmosphere and microclimate along with him enables him to endure in hostile ambient environments.

---

* Clo unit was introduced by Gagge et al. and is defined as the thermal insulation required to maintain heat balance in a resting subject sitting in an ambient temperature of 21.1°C and relative humidity less than 50%.

REFERENCES

1. Adams, T., and Covino, B. G.: Racial variations to a standardized cold stress. J. Appl. Physiol., 12:9–12, 1958.

2. Adolph, E. F.: Physiological fitness for the desert, Fed. Proc., 2:158–164, 1943.

3. Andersson, B.: The effect of injections of hypertonic NaCl solutions into different parts of the hypothalamus of goats. Acta Physiol. Scand., 28:188–201, 1953.

4. Andersson, B., and McCann, S. M.: A further study of polydipsia evoked by hypothalamic stimulation in the goat. Acta Physiol. Scand., 33:333–346, 1955.

5. Blyth, C. S., and Burt, J. J.: Effect of water balance on ability to perform in high ambient temperatures. Res. Quart., 32:301–307, 1961.

6. Brouha, L. A.: Protecting the worker in "Hot Environments." Industrial Hygiene Foundation Bull., 29:207–216, 1955.

7. Brown, G. M., and Page, J.:   Effect of chronic exposure to cold on temperature and blood flow of the hand. *J. Appl. Physiol.*, 5:221–227, 1952.

8. Carlson, L. D., Burns, H. L., Holmes, T. H., and Webb, P. P.:   Adaptive changes during exposure to cold. *J. Appl. Physiol.*, 5:672–676, 1953.

9. Castiglioni, A.:   *A History of Medicine,* 2nd Ed. Edited by E. B. Krumbhaar, New York, Alfred A. Knopf Co., 1958.

10. Clark, G., Magoun, H. W., and Ranson, S. W.:   Hypothalamic regulation of body temperature. *J. Neurophysiol.*, 2:61–80, 1939.

11. Dill, D. B.:   *Life, Heat, and Altitude.* Cambridge, Harvard University Press, 1938.

12. DuBois, E. F.:   Heat loss from the human body. *Bull. N. Y. Acad. Med.*, 15:143–173, 1939.

13. Froese, G., and Burton, A. C.:   Heat losses from the human head. *J. Appl. Physiol.*, 10:235–241, 1957.

14. Gagge, A. P., Burton, A. C., and Bazett, H. C.:   A practical system of units for the description of the heat exchange of man with his environment. *Science,* 94:428–430, 1941.

15. Gaydos, H. F.:   Effect of complex manual performance of cooling the body while maintaining the hands at normal temperatures. *J. Appl. Physiol.*, 12:373–376, 1958.

16. Gaydos, H. F., and Dusek, E. R.:   Effects of localized hand cooling versus total body cooling in manual performance, *J. Appl. Physiol.*, 12:377–380, 1958.

16a. Gosselin, R. E.:   Rates of sweating in the desert. *In* Adolph, E. F., et al.: *Physiology of Man in the Desert.* New York, Interscience Publishers, Inc., 1947.

17. Greer, M. A.:   Suggestive evidence of a primary "drinking center" in hypothalamus of the rat. *Proc. Soc. Exper. Biol. and Med.*, 89:59–62, 1955.

18. Hertzman, A. B.:   Individual differences in regional sweating. *J. Appl. Physiol.*, 10:242–274, 1957.

19. Horvath, S., Spurr, G. B., Hutt, B. K., and Hamilton, L. H.:   Metabolic cost of shivering. *J. Appl. Physiol.*, 8:596–602, 1956.

20. Iampietro, P. F., Bass, D. E., and Buskirk, E. R.:   Diurnal oxygen consumption and rectal temperature of man during continuous cold exposure. *J. Appl. Physiol.*, 10:398–400, 1957.

21. Ivy, A. C.:   What is normal or normality? *Quart. Bull. Northwestern Univ. Med. School,* 18:22–32, 1944.

22. Kanter, G. S.:   Heat and excretion in man. *J. Appl. Physiol.*, 7:533–536, 1955.

23. Keller, A. D., and Hare, W. K.:   The hypothalamus and heat regulation. *Proc. Soc. Exper. Biol. and Med.*, 29:1069–1070, 1931.

24. Kuno, Y.:   *The Physiology of Human Perspiration.* London, J. & A. Churchill, 1934.

25. Mead, J., and Bonmarito, C. L.:   Reliability of rectal temperatures as an index of internal body temperature. *J. Appl. Physiol.*, 2:97–109, 1949.

26. Meehan, J. P.:   Body heat production and surface temperatures in response to a cold stimulus. *J. Appl. Physiol.*, 7:537–541, 1955.

27. Morrison, S. D., and Mayer, J.: Adipsia and aphagia in rats after lateral sub-thalamic lesions. *Am. J. Physiol., 191*:248–254, 1957.

28. Pearcy, M., Robinson, S., Miller, D. I., Thomas, J. T., and DeBrota, J.: Effects of dehydration, salt depletion, and Pitressin on sweat rate and urine flow. *J. Appl. Physiol., 8*:621–626, 1956.

29. Pitts, G. C., Johnson, R. E., and Consolazio, F. C.: Work in the heat as affected by the intake of water, salt and glucose. *Am. J. Physiol., 142*:253–259, 1944.

30. Robinson, S., Gerking, S. D., Turrell, E. S., and Kincaid, R. K.: Effect of skin temperature on salt concentration of sweat, *J. Appl. Physiol., 2*:654–662, 1950.

31. Robinson, S., Kincaid, R. F., and Rhamy, R. K.: Effects of desoxycorticosterone acetate on acclimatization of men to heat. *J. Appl. Physiol., 2*:399–406, 1950.

32. Robinson, S., Maletich, R. T., Robinson, W. S., Rohrer, B. B., and Kunz, A. L.: Output of NaCl by sweat glands and kidneys in relation to dehydration and to salt depletion. *J. Appl. Physiol., 8*:615–620, 1956.

33. Rodahl, K.: Basal metabolism of the Eskimo. *J. Nutrition, 48*:359–368, 1952.

34. Scholander, P. F., Andersen, K. L., Krog, J., Lorentzen, F. V., and Steen, J.: Critical temperature in Lapps. *J. Appl. Physiol., 10*:231–234, 1957.

35. Scholander, P. F., Hammel, H. T., Andersen, K. L., and Loyning, Y.: Metabolic acclimation to cold in man. *J. Appl. Physiol., 12*:1–8, 1958.

36. Scholander, P. F., Hammel, H. T., Hart, J. S., Le Messurier, D. H., and Steen, J.: Cold adaptation in Australian aborigines. *J. Appl. Physiol., 13*:211–218, 1958.

37. Scott, J. W.: The body temperature. *In* Taylor, N. B.: *The Physiological Basis of Medical Practice.* 7th Ed. Baltimore, The Williams & Wilkins Co., 1961.

38. Snellen, J. W.: Mean body temperature and the control of thermal sweating. *Acta Physiol. Pharmacol. Neerl., 14*:99–174, 1966.

39. Spurr, G. B., Hutt, B. K., and Horvath, S. M.: Shivering, oxygen consumption and body temperatures in acute exposure of men to two different cold climates. *J. Appl. Physiol., 11*:58–64, 1957.

40. Taylor, H. L., Henschel, A., Mickelsen, O., and Keys, A.: The effect of sodium chloride intake on the work performance of man during exposure to dry heat and experimental heat exhaustion. *Am. J. Physiol., 140*:439–451, 1943.

41. Wolf, A. V.: Osmometric analysis of thirst in man and dog. *Am. J. Physiol., 161*:75–86, 1950.

C h a p t e r

8

METABOLISM

GENERALLY defined, metabolism is the sum of multiple and complex biochemical reactions. Specifically, there are as many kinds of metabolism as there are tissues of the body, or foodstuffs, or vital processes. For example, one might speak specifically of carbohydrate, protein, or fat metabolism. Since basal or resting metabolism reflects the sum of liver metabolism, muscle metabolism, and many other types, it represents collective metabolism. Thus, a basal oxygen consumption of 200 ml/min represents all the metabolic processes of the body. The rate of metabolism may be determined by direct measurement of the heat that is liberated as a result of biochemical action. Since heat production involves an oxidative process, it is reflected in the oxygen uptake and usually is expressed as a rate of oxygen consumption per minute, hence rate of metabolism may be determined by an indirect measurement.

History

Approximately four centuries ago, the discovery of metabolism was made by Santorio Santorio.[14] Through his studies of "the insensible perspiration," i.e., through the skin, he developed a method of measurement. Santorio placed his bed, desk, food, and provisions in a room that was suspended on a specially constructed balance. He investigated alterations in body weight and temperature. The results of his investigations, conducted for over thirty years, are described in his *De Statica Medicina* (Venice, 1614).[14]

Antoine Lavoisier, the discoverer of oxygen, was the first to recognize the similarity between respiration and combustion processes, but believed that the "decomposition" of the inspired air took place in the lungs.[14]

It remained for Gustav Magnus to infer that the oxygen-carbon dioxide exchange occurred in the tissues (1837, 1845).[14] Confirmation of Magnus's inference was presented in the discovery by Carlo Matteucci (1856) that isolated muscles consume oxygen and give off heat.[14]

During the latter part of the nineteenth century, Karl Voit and Max von Pettenkofer constructed a calorimeter and measured oxygen consumption and heat production in man. Their direct calorimetric assessment of metabolism caused them to conclude that "the oxygen requirement was the result, not the cause of metabolism."[14] The pronouncement of Carl von Voit, though issued in 1881, has withstood the test of time:

> The mass and capacity of the cells of the body determine the height of the total metabolism . . . the requirement of protein is dependent on the organized mass of the tissues, that of fat and carbohydrate is dependent on the amount of mechanical work performed.[14]

A bomb calorimeter, a steel container lined with platinum surrounded by a water jacket and filled with pure oxygen, is an apparatus used in the determination of potential energy of food. The food is ignited electrically and the resulting heat is calculated from the rise in water temperature. The unit of heat is the calorie (small), which is defined as the quantity of heat that is required to raise the temperature of one gram of water one degree centigrade, i.e., from 15° C to 16° C. A large calorie, or kcal, is 1000 times larger.

TABLE 8–1.   Caloric Value of Food per Gram

	Carbohydrate	Fat	Protein
In bomb calorimeter	4.3	9.5	5.3
In digestive tract	4.1	9.3	4.3

The results which are obtained by placing food in a bomb calorimeter are similar to those occurring biochemically. Quantitatively, the heat and end-products produced are remarkably identical. Comparisons are given in Table 8–1.

The discrepancy in the caloric values of protein (Table 8–1) is traceable to an incomplete oxidation of this complex food within the body.

Heat production within the body, the resultant of many biochemical reactions (many kinds of metabolism) may be measured by one of two basic techniques: direct calorimetry or indirect calorimetry.

Direct Calorimetry

Apparatuses are available for the measurement of the caloric value of the sum of all kinds of tissue metabolism of the body. These apparatuses are essentially complex chambers which are insulated by a water jacket (Fig. 8–1). By direct measurement, reflected in heat absorption by water and chamber air, the total heat production of a subject is ascertained.

Direct calorimetry apparatus is highly accurate but, despite this asset, the subject must be studied within the chamber. Thus, such studies as energy cost of lawn mowing or of skiing cannot be conducted by direct means. This method has been eclipsed by indirect calorimetric techniques.

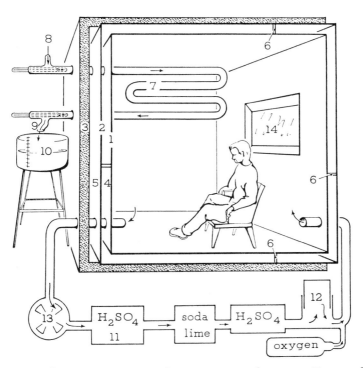

Fig. 8–1. The Atwater-Rosa-Benedict respiration calorimeter. Heat production as well as gaseous exchange of subject can be measured. The air-tight room has copper walls (*1* and *2*) surrounded by a cork wall (*3*). Dead air spaces are depicted by *4* and *5*. Thermocouples (*6*) detect temperature differences between copper walls. Cold water flows through tubing (*7*), past thermometers (*8* and *9*), into collecting apparatus (*10*). Respiratory gases are pulled through fan (*13*) into sulfuric acid absorber (*11*) followed by soda lime absorber and second acid absorber, then through spirometer (*12*). (From Lucas and Ridout. Courtesy of The Williams & Wilkins Co.)

Indirect Calorimetry

Contrasting with the direct measurement method, i.e., measurement of actual heat production, is an indirect calorimetry technique which is based on the role of oxygen in the production of heat. Because the production of heat involves an oxidative process, calorimetry can be accomplished indirectly by measuring oxygen consumption. Further, this indirect measurement method can be accomplished by either of two methods or systems: the closed circuit system or the open circuit system.

As implied in the title, the *closed circuit* system incorporates a gas source within a system which does not interact with the atmosphere. The gas is inhaled on a demand basis. If a face mask is used, the exhaled

Fig. 8–2.   Collins 13.5 L recording spirometer. Carbon dioxide in exhaled air is absorbed by soda lime crystals, which are contained within canister shown in "cut." (Courtesy of Warren E. Collins, Inc., Boston, Massachusetts.)

air from the buccal and nasal passages is directed into the return line to the source. If a mask is not used, a nose clip prevents the escape of air from the nose. In either case, the exhaled air is returned to the source through a return line which incorporates an absorber for the carbon dioxide which is an end-product of metabolism (Fig. 8–2). One-way valves permit only unidirectional flow. Over a given time period, the oxygen uptake is represented by a reduction in volume of the gas in the bell (see Chap. 11).

During inhalation, gas volume withdrawn from the bell is recorded as an upward stroke of the pen on the recording drum. Since drums revolve at one of several speeds, it becomes possible to determine the interval of elapsed time.

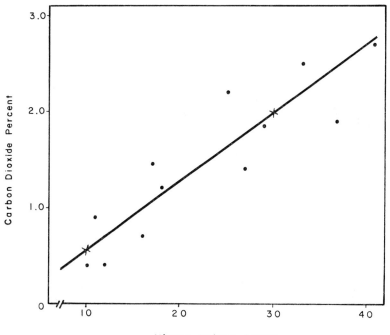

Minute Volume Liters

Fig. 8–3. Carbon dioxide contamination as a function of flow rate. Regression line is depicted. Above data were collected from a 120 L spirometer with soda lime ($CaCO_3$) absorber. All values for tidal volume and minute volume were corrected to BTPS. Data were collected on subjects during 5 min recovery phase only. $\dot{V}O_2$ values ranged from 0.500 L to 0.900 L/min corrected to STPD. Respiration rate ranged from 7 to 19/min. Initial volume of pure O_2 in bell was established at either 20L or 50L. Analysis for carbon dioxide was accomplished with Beckman CO_2 analyzer, model LB-1. Contamination of gas in bell with CO_2 is clearly a function of flow rate. Commercial spirometers were designed for basal or resting metabolism determination. Because of CO_2 contamination of gas source, these apparatuses must not be used for energy cost studies. (From Laboratory of Applied Physiology, Boyden Gymnasium, University of Massachusetts, Amherst.)

Soda lime (Ca CO_3) is commonly used as an absorber for carbon dioxide. A potassium hydroxide solution (KOH) also may be used. An efficient absorber of this latter type was described by Margaria et al.[50]

There is an appealing simplicity in the closed circuit system. It is essentially a one-man operation and oxygen consumption as well as other measurements are easily calculated.

One precaution must be observed. Closed circuit systems which incorporate a soda lime absorber must not be used in energy cost studies principally because of the ineffectiveness of soda lime in absorbing carbon dioxide at differing flow rates (Fig. 8–3).

Commercial spirometers were not designed for energy cost studies. Even presuming fresh reagents (and a change in canister placement from horizontal to vertical), carbon dioxide contamination and back-pressure of exhaled air would introduce additional problems such as an elevated cardiac frequency and an elevated ventilation rate.

Greater versatility and accuracy is assured through the use of the *open circuit* system of indirect calorimetry. This system contrasts rather sharply with the closed circuit system. The subject breathes ambient air (Fig. 8–4). The exhaled respiratory gases are directed through a tubing and valve arrangement into collapsible bags typified by the Douglas bag, which is made of canvas covered rubber. Plastic bags are also available and are less expensive than the canvas-rubber type. Bag sizes may range from 50 to 200 L.

Exhaled gases, collected for specified time periods in numbered bags (to reduce possibility of error), are directed through a gas meter in order that volume be ascertained. Dependent upon the characteristics of gas analysis apparatus, small samples may be directed through an arrangement depicted in Figure 8–5.

Or, small samples can be aspirated from the self-sealing rubber tubing connected to the small outlet located at the neck of the bag into 10 ml syringes* fitted with a No. 22 needle. The numbering or lettering of syringes reduces the possibility of errors. Collected gas samples are kept in syringes temporarily sealed by a size 00 rubber stopper† until analysis can be accomplished. Transfer of collected samples to gas analysis apparatus, e.g., Scholander apparatus, is accomplished according to the technique advanced by Van Liew.[68]

Through the use of the nomogram of Dill and Fölling, or the constant 0.265 (the ratio of % of atmospheric O_2 and N_2), the oxygen consumption is easily calculated (Chap. 11).

---

* A 10 ml sample of gas allows double determinations of gas analysis.

† The needle is thrust into the rubber stopper.

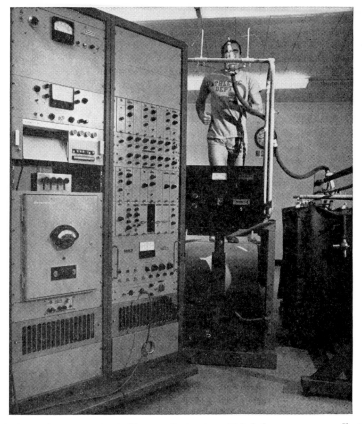

Fig. 8–4. Open circuit indirect calorimetry. Exhaled gases are collected in Douglas bags (suspended on rack) for specified intervals and later directed through an arrangement depicted in Figure 8–5. Oxygen and carbon dioxide analyzers are contained in Honeywell console shown at left. Data from this subject are contained in Table 11–4. (From Laboratory of Applied Physiology, Boyden Gymnasium, University of Massachusetts, Amherst.)

Advantages of the open circuit technique are: (1) it is more precise (assuming of course that the O_2 and CO_2 analyzers are reliable apparatuses); (2) it will allow for the collection of important data during work states of any metabolic intensity (provided of course that low resistance valves are used); (3) it affords far greater comfort to the subject; and (4) the respiratory exchange ratio can be calculated.

A disadvantage of the open circuit system is that it is not a one-man operation, but requires the combined efforts of a smooth quartet or the strained efforts of a trio. (With the aid of an electromedical monitoring system a duet can perform, but the tempo is allegro.)

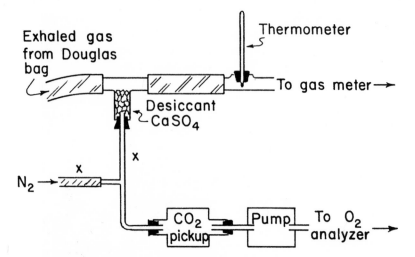

Fig. 8–5. Gas flow pattern. Exhaled gas from Douglas bag is directed to gas meter for volumetric determination. Note thermometer in the line. A small sample of the gas (100 to 150 ml) is diverted through desiccant and carbon dioxide pickup into oxygen analyzer. X indicates position of tubing clamps. Nitrogen gas is used to "wash" CO_2 and O_2 apparatuses between analyses. (From Laboratory of Applied Physiology, Boyden Gymnasium, University of Massachusetts, Amherst.)

Irrespective of the system employed, tubing dead air space must be kept to a minimum in order to ensure reliability of sampling results. It is not uncommon to have a 500 ml tubing dead air space necessitated by the physical distance from subject (on treadmill or bicycle ergometer) to bag system or gas source.

Thermogenesis

The technique of indirect calorimetry is predicated on the principle of heat production as an indicator of increased metabolism. This increased metabolic level is evidenced by an increased oxidation rate and measured by increased oxygen consumption. Thus, oxygen uptake reflects the thermogenetic nature of body metabolism resulting from an increased food intake or an increased rate of work production.

Interrelationships between the four variables of energy exchange, based on the first Law of Thermodynamics,* is discussed by Brobeck:[6]

food intake = heat loss + work output + energy storage.

---

* In 1847, Ludwig von Helmholtz (1821–1894) formulated the first Law of Thermodynamics—*energy, though capable of becoming transformed from one form to another, can be neither created nor destroyed*—which was based on the Law of Energy Conservation formulated by Robert Mayer in 1842.[14]

Basal metabolism must reflect the lowest possible level of cell chemistry. In order to ensure this, conditions are standardized by reducing to a minimum those factors which would increase thermogenesis: work output, food intake, and ambient temperature. Mental states also play an important role in metabolic rate; however, this factor is neither easily nor assuredly controlled.

Basal metabolism determinations are made on individuals who are in a fasting or post absorptive state,* and who are in a physically rested condition. Morning represents an ideal time for these conditions to exist. When an individual is required to ambulate from bedroom to laboratory, an additional sixty minutes of supine rest must be imposed. Eating, drinking, and smoking must be denied and room temperature should be maintained at 20° C.

Under these standardized conditions (see Brobeck formula), food intake and work output are controlled, and heat loss reflects the level of energy storage and, in turn, the level of cell biochemical activity. Even under the most ideal conditions, the so-called basal metabolism is approximately 10% higher than the lowest possible level of biochemical activity which occurs during deep sleep. A substantial portion of the decrease in basal metabolism is attributed to the decrease in muscle tonus during deep sleep.

Interpretation of metabolic rates is usually accomplished by expressing the thermogenous process as a function of body surface area, e.g., kcals BSA/m^2/hr. Such a procedure, however, is not without fault. Brobeck points out that the dissipation of heat is not necessarily a function of the skin surface area.[7] Changes in radiating surface area, affected by posture as well as by microclimate, serve to justify his claim.

The recognition of the relatively inactive role of depot fat tissue in energy exchange has led to the practice of expressing metabolism as a function of lean body mass. This is discussed in an editorial by Lim and Luft.

At times the term basal rate is used to denote oxygen consumption during pre-work intervals. In this case, the term *basal rate* is misleading and should be replaced with *resting rate*. Furthermore, since oxygen consumption rates differ appreciably for varying postures, e.g., lying, sitting, and standing, the body position should be clearly noted.

Comparison of values of basal metabolic rates obtained by closed circuit and open circuit systems reveals differences ranging from 5 to 12% of open circuit values: Lewis et al. reported 5%, Fowler et al. and

---

* Food intake causes an elevation of heat which is indicative of an increased metabolism and observed as an increased oxygen consumption. This phenomenon is termed the *specific dynamic action* of food.

Harmon reported 7%, Willard and Wolf reported 10% and Hunt reported 12%.

Sources of error in closed circuit calorimetry have been identified by Fowler et al. Harmon, in 1953, and Fowler et al., in 1957, reported identical standard errors of estimate of 2.28 kcal/m²/hr. As pointed out by Consolazio et al., this is equivalent to the inter-individual variability of the normal population (S. D. 2.5 kcal/m²/hr). The possibility of leakage at various sites is easily determined and rectified. More serious, however, is the assumption of complete absorption of carbon dioxide from the expired air (Fig. 8–3).

Carbohydrate Metabolism

Since up to 75% of the energy requirements of the body is supplied through carbohydrate metabolism, a discussion of it will be presented first followed by protein and fat metabolism discussions.

Depending upon their molecular structure, carbohydrates are classified as either mono-, di-, or polysaccharides, which are exemplified by glucose, sucrose, and glycogen respectively. The latter two carbohydrate forms, disaccharides and polysaccharides, are normally converted during the digestive process into monosaccharides. In this form, the carbohydrates are readily and almost completely absorbed into the small intestine.

Glucose, a monosaccharide, is singled out for discussion because it represents the principal form in which carbohydrates are transported by the blood, and constitutes an immediate energy source. Blood-glucose values reflect carbohydrate ingestion; thus, snacks or mixed diets will be discernible in the immediate postprandial increase in blood glucose. The relative quickness of this discernible result serves as the basis for the important clinical determination of glucose tolerance (Fig. 8–6).

TABLE 8–2.   Approximate Carbohydrate Distribution (%) in the Human at Rest

	Glycogen*	Glucose	Lactic Acid
Liver	0.2–10.0	0.05–0.15	0.01
Muscle	0.2– 1.5	0.02–0.04	0.01
Blood	trace	0.08–0.11	0.01

* Note: Glycogen is in greater concentration in liver than in muscle. Since the total muscle mass constitutes approximately 50% of the total body weight, vs 3% for the liver, a far greater quantity of glycogen is carried in the muscles and represents an immediate energy source. Blood constitutes 7% of the total body weight.

Even prolonged periods of low or moderate metabolic intensity present small physiological challenge and the glycogen requirements of the muscle are adequately met (Table 8–2).

The earlier discussion of the Cori cycle was principally related to lactic acid conversion; however, as was indicated, the liver glycogenetic and gluconeogenic functions assure the adequate formation of liver glycogen. Physiological equilibrium is easily maintained during such periods; a steady-state is said to exist. Periods of high metabolic intensity present yet another problem for they involve the reserve form of energy. During such periods physiological equilibrium is not attained, and the discernible evidence is available in the reduced blood glucose and liver glycogen levels and the elevated lactic acid levels.

Energy liberation through carbohydrate oxidation is accomplished directly through oxidation of glucose, as well as indirectly through conversion into glycogen and pyruvic acid and through the oxidation of pyruvate. Vass suggests that the usual energy liberation source is provided mainly by the latter reaction.[63]

A charitable, sympathetic approach to the particular fate of individuals who regularly ingest excess carbohydrates incorporates the viewpoint that fat represents stored potential chemical energy. Stated in

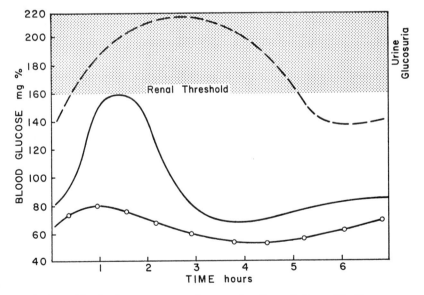

Fig. 8–6. Blood glucose expressed as a function of time. Healthy response represented by solid line. Abnormal response of diabetic individual depicted as broken line (mostly in shaded area). Insulinogenic effect represented by lowermost line. In healthy individuals, blood glucose level varies with diet, but renal threshold maintains upper limit at 160 mg%.

lenient terms, some fellow humans display great reservoirs of potential energy. In some societies, e.g., the Khoisans (Hottentots) of Southwest Africa, excessive gluteal adiposity (steatopygia) in the female symbolizes beauty and holds an irresistible appeal for the male.[62]

In view of the statistics, which are alarmingly convincing, an effort must be directed to the conversion process which allows the stored chemical potential energy to become transformed into kinetic energy thus reducing the obesity level. This topic is discussed at greater length under the topic of positive energy balance (pp. 188–196).

Excessive carbohydrates are converted first to pyruvate, then to fatty acids and stored. *Fat formation is essentially a constructive process.*

Insulation afforded by the fat cells serves to maintain a relatively constant body temperature. In addition these cells provide protection against physical trauma. The formation of such important constituents as nucleic acids and cerebrosides must also be recognized. (Nucleic acid controls enzyme patterns of the cells in which the acid is present. It also combines with proteins to form nucleoproteins. Cerebrosides, also called glycolipids, are lipoids which contain galactose or glucose and are essential for brain and nervous tissue metabolism.)

Blood-glucose levels may vary considerably; however, upper limits display amazingly little variation. Blood glucose levels which exceed 160 mg% elicit an increased kidney involvement which is detectable as glucose in the urine. Sugar is regarded as an abnormal constituent. The blood glucose tolerance test serves as an important clinical procedure. Raised glucose levels appear in the blood between one-half and one-and-one-half hours following the deliberate administration of glucose at the rate of 1 gm per kilogram of body weight (Fig. 8–6).

Normally, control of blood glucose level is accomplished by the liver through a variety of mechanisms. Glucose may be converted into glycogen and stored. Glucose also may be reduced through glycogenic and gluconeogenic processes. Pancreatic involvement, through insulin formation, produces a hypoglycemic effect in that insulin hastens glucose metabolism.

Insulin, a hormone secreted by the pancreas, serves the important function of regulating carbohydrate metabolism. The cells that manufacture insulin were first described in 1869 by the German physiologist Paul Langerhans. (These cells are fittingly called the Islands of Langerhans and insulin is occasionally referred to as the Langerhansian hormone. The name *insulin,* however, was coined by J. J. R. Macleod in the early 1920's.) Through surgical pancreatectomy in dogs, physiologists J. von Mering and Oscar Minkowski definitely established the connection between the cells and the secretions; it remained for Eugene

Opie at Johns Hopkins University, in 1900, to relate through microscopic studies the degeneration of the Islands of Langerhans with human diabetes mellitus. The discovery and clinical use of insulin earned for the Canadian physicians Frederick G. Banting and John J. R. Macleod the Nobel Prize for Medicine in 1923.

Specifically, insulin promotes tissue glucose oxidation, inhibits gluconeogenesis and ketosis,* aids the formation of glycogen in liver and muscles, and perhaps best known to all, regulates blood glucose levels.

Protein Metabolism

In common with carbohydrates, protein and fats consist of carbon, hydrogen, and oxygen; however, protein is distinguished by the presence of nitrogen (a few carbohydrates also contain nitrogen). Some proteins also contain sulfur, phosphorus, and iron. In addition to its direct involvement in tissue growth and repair and in enzyme formation, protein constitutes a source of energy.

In amino acid form, protein is readily absorbed into the upper intestinal tract and is reflected as amino nitrogen in the blood in the concentration of approximately 6 mg%. As an amino acid, protein can provide energy through oxidation or it can be converted to carbohydrates or into more complex protein form. It can be transformed into fat or be stored in the liver. Amino acid is excreted at the rate of approximately 1 gm per day; however, the amount excreted also increases with high protein ingestion. Amino acid is also utilized in the process of enzyme† and hormone‡ formation. Energy liberation from amino acid sources involves the liver and, to a lesser extent, the kidneys. Within the liver, deamination§ of the amino acids occurs as an oxidative process which yields energy and releases the ammonia group from the amino compounds. Some of the deaminated residues of amino acid are capable of being converted through glucogenic action into glucose or glycogen. In actuality approximately 50% of the amino acids are converted within

---

* Ketosis is a condition resulting from incomplete combustion of fatty acids. Etiologic factors include high fat diet or inadequate utilization of carbohydrates. The presence of ketosis is established through urine analysis for ketone bodies (ketonuria).

† A tissue secretion which acts as a catalyst, i.e., induces intermolecular action yet remains unchanged by the chemical interaction.

‡ A tissue secretion which is carried from its site of formation (usually the ductless glands) by the blood stream and stimulates specific tissues or organs to increased functional activity.

§ Deamination, or deaminization, is produced through enzymatic reaction within the liver principally and in the kidney.

the liver into carbohydrate form. The glucose can be burned, stored as glycogen, or become transformed into fat. Other residues are reaminated to form amino acids. Still other residues are transformed, before oxidation, via the complex Krebs cycle into a major energy source. The liver is also capable of storing amino acids.

The conversion of amino acids through glucogenic action into carbohydrates (glucose) which can be oxidized, stored as glycogen, or transformed into fat suggests less necessity for tissue protein in furnishing energy. Salter refers to carbohydrates and fats as "protein sparers."* Salter also points out the futility of protein as a supplier of the daily energy requirement of man.†

The presence of nitrogen in the urine (as urea, creatinine, ammonium salts and uric acid) is indicative of the metabolic level of protein metabolism and more especially of amino acid catabolism. Thus, urine analysis sheds light on the status of nitrogen equilibrium.‡

Positive nitrogen balance is evidenced during periods of muscle development, during convalescence following traumatism, and during growth periods. Negative nitrogen balance is reflected during periods of fasting and starvation and may accompany protein intake of low nutritive value.

Protein sources bear a similarity to carbohydrate sources in that both possess approximately equal caloric value and both can become converted to fat. Conversion of protein to fat is accomplished through the amino acid to fatty acid to fat production route. The conversion is enhanced during positive energy balance. The term *energy balance* implies caloric equilibrium in terms of nutritional intake vs energy expenditure. Any discrepancy in this balance is reflected as positive with an increase or negative with a decrease in the biochemically converted foodstuff reserve§ (see p. 88, Energy Balance and Weight Control).

---

* The concept of the protein-sparing effect of carbohydrate was introduced by Graham Lusk in 1890.[14]

† A daily caloric expenditure of 3000 kcal would require the ingestion of about eight pounds of meat; 8 lbs. meat (3600 gm) which is 20% protein has a caloric value of 20/100 × 3600 × 4.1 or 2900 kcal.

‡ The term *nitrogen equilibrium* was introduced by Carl von Voit in 1857.[14] It is expressed as the difference between nitrogen intake (food) and nitrogen excretion in urine (urea, creatinine, ammonium salts, uric acid) and feces. Nitrogen excretion is much greater in urine than in feces, approximately 13 gm vs 1.5 gm daily.

§ The basis of the energy balance concept is embodied within the studies of Voit and Pettenkofer who first established the concept of nutritional (caloric) equilibrium.

Fat Metabolism

As used in the subtitle, fat is an adjective. In order to lessen the likelihood of ambiguity, the noun lipid is substituted. At any rate, lipid denotes those compounds which are insoluble in water. Fats and oils serve as common examples as do compound lipids.

In addition to its important role as an insulator against body heat loss, fat tissue serves to protect subdermic tissues and organs against mechanically induced trauma. (Simple lipids may be converted into compound forms.) Fat deposits in glyceride form are abundant even in persons of lean somatotype. These deposits represent a large store of potential chemical energy.

Fat sources are gained by ingestion as well as through lipogenesis by conversion from carbohydrate* and protein form. Conflicting viewpoints are expressed relative to the conversion of carbohydrate into fat. Brobeck presents the long-held view that food in excess of the metabolic demands is stored in the adipose tissue as fat.[6] Campbell, however, citing the results of research with isotopes, presents the conversion of carbohydrate into fat as a continuous process and not one which occurs only during periods of excessive carbohydrate intake.

Fat, an excellent source of energy, is stored in deposits in particular body areas such as the abdominal and gluteal regions. The influence of hormones on fat metabolism is noteworthy: injected insulin promotes the conversion of carbohydrate into fat yet prevents the loss of depot fat; Thyroxin promotes a rise in metabolic level which is accompanied by a diminution of fat and glycogen; and estrogenic hormonal influences on female fat metabolism is specific and results in fat deposition in thighs, buttocks, hips, and breasts.

Thermal Equivalent of Oxygen

The accountable role of oxygen in the liberation of heat of metabolism serves as the basis for indirect calorimetry. As shown in Table 8–3, however, each class of foodstuffs possesses differing caloric values. Common to each class, though at differing rates of formation, are such end-products of metabolism as carbon dioxide and water. Further, the amount of oxygen which is required in the combustion process differs markedly among foodstuffs. From Table 8–3 one can observe that carbohydrates require the least amount of oxygen for combustion while the fats require the greatest amount.

---

* The formation of fat from carbohydrates was established in 1852 by the pioneer in physiological chemistry, Justus von Liebig.[14]

TABLE 8–3.   Thermal Equivalents of Oxygen for Each Class
of Foodstuff*

	O_2 Required (kcal/gm)	(L/gm)	CO_2 Produced (L/gm)	(RQ)	Thermal (caloric) equivalent (kcal/L O_2)
Carbohydrates	4.1	0.81	0.81	1.00	5.061
Fats	9.3	1.98	1.40	0.70	4.696
Proteins	4.3	0.97	0.78	0.80	4.432

* Values for each of the above foodstuffs are representative: for carbohydrates, starches; for fats, mixed fats; for proteins, amino acids. For a mixed diet of all three foodstuffs the thermal equivalent is 4.825.

The figures within the body of Table 8–3 are also representative of each class of foodstuff. For example, kcal/gm of carbohydrates may range from 3.7 to 4.3; the O_2 requirement/gm may range from 0.75 to 0.83 as will the CO_2 produced/gm. These values are dependent upon the molecular structure of the carbohydrate. Thus, one gram of glycogen, which liberates more heat than one gram of glucose, also requires proportionately greater amounts of oxygen for combustion thus causing the respiratory quotient (RQ) to remain constant. Such is also the case with the fats and proteins.

The derivation of the above values is based upon Avogadro's law: equal volumes of different gases under the same temperature and pressure contain the same number of molecules. Thus, the molecular-weight of one gram of such a carbohydrate substance as glucose is 180 gm-mole. According to the above stated law, 1 gram molecular weight* of any gas occupies 1 gram molecular volume 22.4 L at STP.†

The oxidation of glucose is represented by the following equation:

$$C_6H_{12}O_6 + 6O_2 \rightarrow 6CO_2 + 6H_2O$$

Calculation of thermal equivalent of oxygen:

Avogadro's law: 1 gm-mole = 6 × 22.4 or 134.4 L O_2

$$= \frac{134.4 \text{ L } O_2}{180 \text{ gm glucose}}$$

= 0.74 L O_2 react/gm glucose

$$\frac{3.74 \text{ kcal (heat liberated by the reaction)}}{0.74 \text{ L } O_2 \text{ react/gm glucose}}$$

= 5.054 kcal/L O_2

---

* Abbreviated as GMW or as gm-mole or simply as mole.
† STP, Standard temperature and pressure or 0°C at 760 mm Hg.

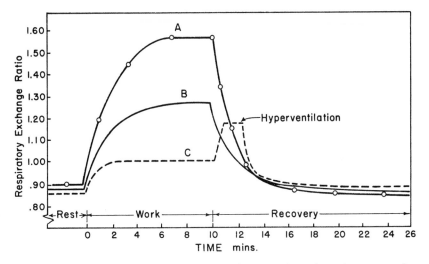

Fig. 8–7. Respiratory exchange ratio R of rest and work and recovery from treadmill running: *A, B.* A, heavy work course; *B,* moderate. Mild exercise of treadmill walking, *C.* Hyperventilation in recovery accounted for increase in R.

Respiratory Quotient

The respiratory quotient, or RQ, is expressed as a ratio of carbon dioxide produced to oxygen consumed.* The value of such computation is limited to broad interpretations of the types of foodstuffs which are being metabolized. As can be observed in Table 8–3, an RQ of approximately 1.00 indicates that mainly carbohydrate foodstuffs are being metabolized. Fats yield an RQ of 0.70; proteins, 0.80; and mixed diets 0.85.

Since the relative proportions of carbon dioxide and oxygen may be readily altered through a multiplicity of factors, the RQ will quickly reflect these alterations. Whereas oxygen consumption values are increased through stress, carbon dioxide values may be increased voluntarily through hyperventilation. Thus, blowing off carbon dioxide will alter the ratio and result in an increased respiratory exchange ratio.

Similarly, raised blood lactic acid levels, which are associated with demanding work, also account for an increased carbon dioxide percentage in the expired air. (During prolonged periods of elevated metabolic activity, the increased amount of exhaled carbon dioxide re-

---

* In respiratory physiology, *respiratory exchange ratio* R was proposed as a replacement for the term *respiratory quotient* RQ. Its acceptance has been slow as evidenced by the continued use of RQ in texts and articles. The method of calculation remains unchanged.

flects a change in blood pH. The raised blood lactic acid levels result in the liberation of some carbon dioxide which is stored in the blood in bicarbonate form.) In each instance just cited the R can exceed 1.00, but the causative factors are diametric in nature: the former is respiratory while the latter is metabolic.

Respiratory quotients must be interpreted with care. Citing the complex biochemical nature of metabolism, Cathcart and Markowitz long ago cautioned against placing excessive reliance on RQ values as precise indicators of particular foodstuff metabolism. A. V. Hill also pointed out the more precise nature of the RQ value of steady-state.

Generally the respiratory exchange ratio reflects the intensity of bodily effort (Fig. 8–7). Since the ratio is subject to biochemically caused fluctuations, the R must always be interpreted with great care.

Classification of Metabolic Activity

A number of factors—including speed and duration of physical performance, degree of bodily effort, level of proficiency, and level of cardiovascular-pulmonary-somatic response—influence the energy cost of activity. Added to these factors are such environmental factors as climatic conditions (including temperature, wind velocity, and relative humidity) as well as composition and grade of terrain, or, if in water, temperature and turbulence of water. The list of factors is not exhaustive, but it is developed sufficiently to focus attention on the myriad of factors influencing intensity of metabolic effort. However, irrespective of causative factors, metabolic intensity is in need of classification.

Basically because oxygen consumption is conveniently yet accurately measured and reflects levels of metabolic intensity, this parameter readily lends itself to a classification scheme. Further, classification schemes usually incorporate comparisons in the form of increases above basal values or resting values. Such a scheme was proposed by Dill. Moderate work was characterized by oxygen uptakes up to three times the resting oxygen uptake. Hard work resulted in an oxygen uptake between four and eight times the resting level. Oxygen uptakes in excess of eight times the resting level characterize maximal work. What must be borne in mind is that these values—applicable to factory workers —are based on an eight-hour work day (Fig. 8–8).

Obviously, individuals who perform over shorter time periods can perform at high metabolic intensity. Athletes possessing good cardiovascular-pulmonary response perform at exercise metabolic levels which exceed basal metabolic levels by a factor of twenty.

Weiss and Karpovich used the ratio of work metabolic rate/resting metabolic rate as a basis for their prescription of exercise to convalescent patients. This technique is of great significance because it represents one of the earliest attempts at establishing a pharmacopeia of exercise. More recently, Kottke et al. have classified physical activities according to the work imposed on the myocardium.

On numerous occasions, thermal equivalents of oxygen are used to classify work. Such was the technique of Christensen, which appears in Table 8–4.

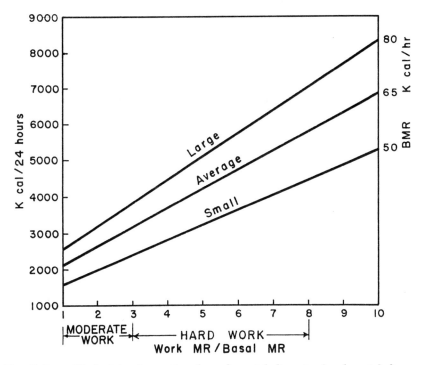

Fig. 8–8. Work intensity—ratio of work metabolism to basal metabolism—expressed as a function of kilocaloric production. Lines correspond to kilocaloric production of small, average, and large men. Assumptions: (1) metabolic rate was basal for eight hours of sleep; (2) metabolic rate was elevated to twice basal rate for nonworking, waking hours; (3) working period was of eight hours duration. (Adapted from Dill.[23])

TABLE 8–4. Classification of Work in Gross Kilocalories

Work Classification	Kcal/hr
Sedentary	below 150
Light	150–300
Moderate	300–450
Heavy	450–600
Very heavy	above 600

Still another work classification scheme, shown in Figure 8–9, compares favorably with that of Christensen in Table 8–4. For purposes of rough calculation and comparison, an R of 1.00 is assumed $\therefore \dot{V}_{O_2}$ of 1 L/min = 5 kcal. From Figure 8–9, moderate work classification: 0.8 − 1.6 L/min $\dot{V}_{O_2}$

$\dot{V}_{O_2}$ = 1.2 L/min (note 1.2 L = midpoint of interval)
    = 1.2 L/min × 5 kcal = 6.0 kcal/min = 360 kcal/hr.

There is agreement in all work classifications except the classification for severe work. Christensen, 600 kcal/hr vs Committee on Aviation Medicine, 720 kcal/hr.

Additional work classification schemes have been presented on the basis of biochemical analyses, e.g., blood lactic acid concentration, or on the basis of ventilation or pulse rates. A detailed summary of such methods of work classification was accomplished by Wells, Balke, and Van Fossan[70] (Table 8–5). Wells et al. also proposed their own work classification scheme (Table 8–6).[71]

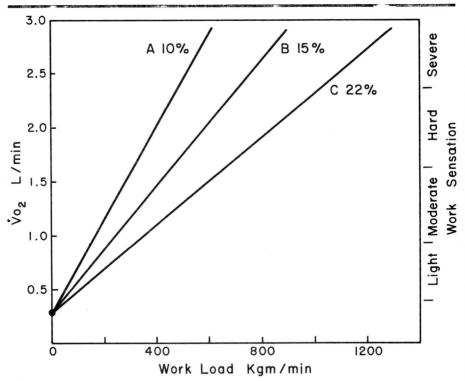

Fig. 8–9. Comparisons of work. A, Weight lifting at 10/min cadence; B, treadmill walking at 3.5 miles/hr (5.6 km/h); C, bicycle ergometer at 70 rev/min. Subjective evaluation of work sensation (right ordinate) was related to oxygen consumption rather than work accomplished. (Adapted from Handbook of Respiratory Data in Aviation.[81])

TABLE 8-5. Summary of Physical Work Capacity (From Wells et al.[70])

Classification of Work	Oxygen Consumption (cc/min)	Caloric Expenditure (Cal/min)	Pulse Rate	Ventilation BTPS (liters/min)	Lactic Acid (mg %)	Treadmill Data (speed, grade, duration)
Light	500–1,000 (13) 2,000 (16)	2.5– 5 (13)	Resting value + 20 to 30 beats (16)			
Mild	500/m.² (17)				57 (19) 20–25 (20)	
Moderate	1,000–1,500 (13)	5 – 7.5 (13) 4 (18) 6 – 7 (24)		50 (21)	No increase (25)	4 mph, 12.5%, 7 min (22) 10 mph, level, 20 min (23)
Moderate hard		4 –10 (18)				1.73 mph, 10%, 3–5 min (24)
Hard		7.5–10 (13)				
Heavy	1,500–2,000 (13)	10 –12.5 (13)				
Very heavy	2,000–2,500 (13)	12.5+ (13)				
Unduly heavy	2,500+ (13)					
Vigorous	2,400 (26)			63 (26)	300 (7)	
Strenuous	2,200 (6)				140 (6)	14 km/hr (6) 5 mph, 10%, 15 min (27)
Severe				120 (21)	188 (19)	10 mph, 17.5%, 4 min (23)
Maximal		10 (18)				
Exhausting			180–200 (28)			

TABLE 8-6. Classification of Physical Work by Work Capacity Test (From Wells et al.[71])

Classification of Work	Pulse Rate/ min	M.R. O_2 cc/min	M.R. Cal/min	Ventilation Vol. 1/min	Ventilation Rate/ min	RQ	Lactic Acid in Multiples of Rest. Val.	Duration of Time Work Can Be Sustained
I Light								
1. Mild	<100	<750	<4	<20	<14	.85	Normal	Indefinite
2. Moderate	<120	<1500	<7.5	<35	<15	.85	Within normal limits	Eight hours daily
II Heavy								
3. Optimal	<140	<2000	<10	<50	<16	.9	1.5 ×	Eight hours daily for few weeks (seasonal work, military maneuvers, etc.)
4. Strenuous	<160	<2500	<12.5	<60	<20	.95	2 ×	Four hours 2 or 3 times a week for few weeks (special physical training)
III Severe								
5. Maximal	<180	<3000	<15	<80	<25	<1.0	5–6 ×	One to 2 hr occasionally (usually in competitive sports)
6. Exhausting	>180	>3000	>15	<120	<30	>1.0	>6 ×	Few minutes, rarely

Despite the number of contributors, there is good general agreement relative to work classification through physiological assessment. Considerably greater variation is provided through subjective assessment of work severity.

Oxygen Debt

The term, introduced in 1927 by A. V. Hill, is defined as the quantity of oxygen required by the contracting muscles over and above the quantity actually supplied to them during their activity. The debt is represented graphically by an elevated oxygen consumption (in excess of resting values) during the period of recovery from physical effort. Further, this elevated rate during recovery reflects a deficit incurred during the performance of the task. In other words, the oxygen debt reflects the discrepancy between the oxygen requirement of the task and the oxygen uptake during the performance of the task (Fig. 8–10).

According to A. V. Hill's concept, oxygen debts are constantly being incurred and repaid. For example, a change of body position from supine to standing results in an increase in metabolic activity as reflected

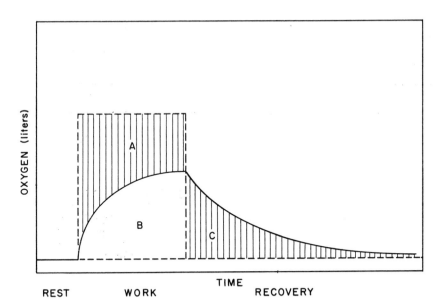

Fig. 8–10. Oxygen debt. Area *B* represents the actual *oxygen uptake* and *A* the *oxygen deficit.* Area *C*, the *net recovery oxygen* is the *oxygen debt.* Combined areas *B+C*, net work oxygen plus net recovery oxygen is equal to the combined area *A+B*, the *oxygen requirement.* The rapid decrease in oxygen consumption, most pronounced during the first few minutes of the recovery period, indicates that the major portion of the oxygen debt is being repaid. (Adapted from Hill.[34])

13

in an elevated oxygen consumption. The oxygen deficit incurred in the change of body position will be small, but a debt is contracted none-the-less.

At face value, the calculation of oxygen debt appears to be a simple procedure: one need merely total the net recovery oxygen. Yet, most interesting, and confusing, is the wide variation in maximum oxygen debt values. Karpovich dubiously noted a 22.8 L O_2 debt which had been reported by Krestovnikoff. Winton and Bayliss report that from 15 to 20 liter debts may be incurred. Margaria defends, biochemically, a maximum debt of approximately 8 liters. Such wide variation in oxygen debt values suggests errors in method of measurement. Generally, higher debts will be incurred after all-out effort of short duration.

Calculating the oxygen debt leaves much room for variation (and error) since recovery may have many meanings. Recovery values within 50 ml of rest values may be accepted by some as evidence of complete recovery. Other researchers may establish a 25 ml variation before adjudging recovery to be complete. Should post-work oxygen consumption values remain elevated for many hours, oxygen debt values would increase greatly. In Table 8–7 is presented one calculated (actual)

TABLE 8–7. Variability in Oxygen Debt Values (All values in liters)

	20 min	1 hr	2 hr	4 hr	6 hr
Recovery O_2 (gross)	13.7	30.1	54.7	103.9	153.1
O_2 uptake (based on 0.374 L/min rest value for comparable recovery time period	7.5	22.5	45.0	90.0	135.0
Oxygen debt	6.2*	8.6	9.7	13.9	18.1

* Actual O_2 debt following an 8 min treadmill run at 10 km/h + 6%; see Table 11–4 and p. 264. All recovery values to right of vertical line were elevated by 36 ml/min. Passmore and Johnson noted recovery O_2 to remain elevated by approximately 36 ml/min six hours after a hike of 16.1 km at the rate of 6.4 km/h.

Measurement	Subjects	Basal	Walk (mean values)	Recovery	Elevated Recovery Values (from basal)
$\dot{V}O_2$ ml/min	R.P.	226	1212	267	41
	B.N.	254	1521	289	35
	T.S.L.	195	1005	231	36
	7 young adults	236	1478	272	36

oxygen debt value and four additional values which were based on an assumed recovery oxygen value which remained elevated by 36 ml/min or within approximately 9% of pre-work, rest values.

The immediate thought which comes to mind is that of establishing limits of variability of recovery to pre-work rest oxygen values. Rapid determination of blood lactic acid levels might some day provide an objective basis for complete recovery. Post-work, rest oxygen uptake values, which may be elevated by 20% from pre-work rest values *even after a restful night of sleep* reflects an oxidative process which apparently does not provide energy for the resynthesis of the products formed from the muscular contraction of work. Determination of blood lactic acid levels cannot be accomplished within minutes; the process requires several hours. Until rapid techniques can be developed the necessity of establishing intraindividual variability limits must be agreed upon. Post-work rest values within 5% of pre-work rest values represent a generous allowable limit.

A. V. Hill also proposed another method of measuring oxygen debt. In order to clear up the uncertainty of the return of recovery oxygen to a base line of resting oxygen uptake, Hill suggested to Cowan and Solandt the use of a base line of oxygen uptake in steady yet mild exercise.[20] The Cowan and Solandt study is interesting in that it eliminates the uncertainty which can plague the researcher. By their technique, recovery was adjudged to be complete, i.e., to an initial steady-state base line, in approximately one fourth of the recovery time when compared to the usual method which compares recovery oxygen uptake to resting oxygen uptake.

Some exercise physiologists question the term *oxygen debt*. As Karpovich and Consolazio et al. point out, the term implies that the excess oxygen has been borrowed from the body stores of oxygen. Between 2 and 2.5 liters of oxygen is present in lung residual volume, dead space, and in molecules carried in chemical union with hemoglobin (blood).

An added consideration is that the physiological utilization of the stored oxygen is significantly less than complete. During moderate and heavy work states the circulatory rate does not prove sufficient and active muscles are denied adequate amounts of oxygen. The result is an increase in blood lactate levels.

Another group of physiologists questions the oxygen debt theory, which holds that recovery oxygen is equal to the initial lag in oxygen uptake. Asmussen reported an oxygen repayment in recovery to be between 160 and 190% of the oxygen deficit in work. Later, Christensen and Hogberg reported an oxygen repayment which was approximately twice greater than the oxygen deficit. Still later, Henry and DeMoor presented similar results: that the total recovery oxygen exceeded the initial oxygen deficit. Lukin and Ralston reported mathematical ratios of oxygen repayment to oxygen deficit of 0.6 to 3.6.

Lactic Acid

Margaria et al. were among the first to relate oxygen debt to above-normal blood lactic acid levels.[49] The elevated oxygen consumption during the first part of recovery was evident, but there was a relatively stable amount of lactate present in the plasma and in the muscles. Because it appeared to Margaria that levels of metabolites other than lactic acid were being reduced, he categorized the oxygen debt into an alactic acid or alactacid component and a lactic acid or lactacid component. This view is supported by Grollman and Phillips and by Henry and DeMoor (Fig. 8–11).

As may be seen in Figure 8–11, the alactacid mechanism of oxygen debt repayment is much faster. Within approximately 30 seconds, 50% of the alactacid portion is repaid and within 3 minutes repayment is practically complete. The lactacid component is much slower.

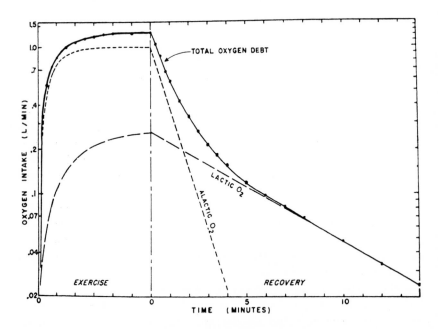

Fig. 8–11.   Alactacid and lactacid components of the oxygen debt. (From Henry and DeMoor.[38] Courtesy of American Physiological Society.)

Margaria et al. also presented the oxygen-lactic acid relationship depicted in Figure 8–12,[49] in which one can observe that above-normal lactic acid levels in blood become apparent when the oxygen debt is above 3.5 L. Margaria explains the lactic acid accumulation to be a resultant of an oxygen debt increase beyond the iimit determined by depletion of creatine phosphate stores. Beyond an oxygen debt of 4.0 L the blood lactate concentration rises in direct proportion to increasing oxygen debt ievels. With oxygen uptakes of less than 2.5 L/min, blood lactic acid levels do not change, but oxygen debts are incurred.

Blood lactic acid concentration at rest-state has been reported by Bock et al. at 10.5 mg%; Edwards 9.4 mg%; Dill et al. 12.6 mg% and Ricci 7 to 10.5 mg%.[58] Differing methods of analysis account for the slight variations. Blood lactate levels during work states may be elevated to over 150 mg%. Crescitelli and Taylor reported a value of 300 mg%.

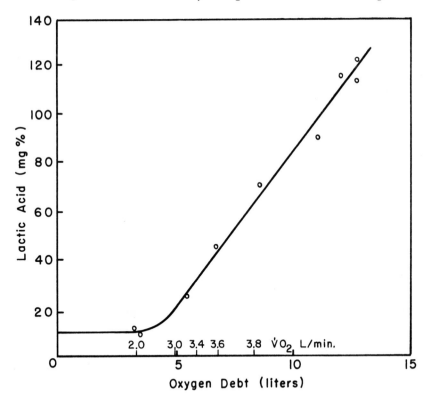

Fig. 8–12.   Blood lactic acid concentration expressed as a function of oxygen uptake and oxygen debt at steady-state. Blood lactic acid levels remain unchanged with oxygen debts up to approximately 4L and oxygen uptakes of approximately 2.5L/min. Beyond this debt and uptake level the relationship is linear. (From Margaria et al.[49] Courtesy of American Physiological Society.)

Hill and Lupton calculated a 7-gm increase in blood lactic acid for each additional liter of oxygen debt. Conversely, each liter of oxygen consumed during the recovery phase signals the disappearance of 7 gm of lactic acid.

Margaria et al. observed no additional blood lactic acid production when the energy cost of work fell below 220 cal/kg/min for a non-athletic subject.[48] Ricci observed an elevated blood lactic acid concentration when the energy cost of work increased beyond 162 cal/kg/min for an obese subject (110 kg, 30% body fat) and 238 cal/kg/min for an individual of diametric somatotype (60 kg, 14% body fat).[58] See Figure 8–13.

Karpovich describes the presence of lactic acid and other work by-products as promissory notes, as collateral, which assure prompt payment of the oxygen debt. The reader may rightfully conclude that lactic acid is a beneficial by-product of an increased metabolic demand placed upon the organism of an individual who is unable to experience an adequate oxygen uptake. The human organism is superior to a sophisticated, internal-combustion engine in that it is capable of overcoming

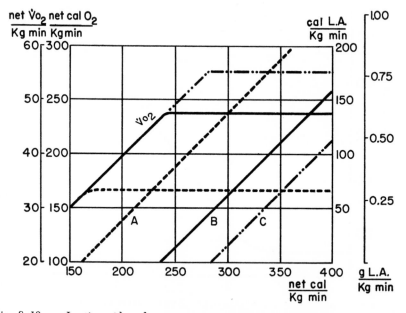

Fig. 8–13.   Lactic acid and net oxygen consumption—comparisons of capacity for aerobic work. Blood lactic acid and net oxygen consumption of endomorph (*A*) represented by broken lines, of ectomorph (*B*), by solid line, and of athlete (*C*), by a combination of solid and dotted lines. (From Ricci.[57] Courtesy of Taylor and Francis Ltd.) Robinson and Harmon reported a decline in blood lactic acid levels as a result of training.

the discrepancy between oxygen requirement and oxygen availability by incurring an oxygen debt.

Steady State

Interrelationships exist between the oxygen requirement of a given task, the rate of oxygen utilization by the organism, and the amount of lactic acid which is formed.

The oxygen requirement for exercise may be described as a continuum extending from extremely light to extremely severe. Somewhere along this continuum there exists an oxygen requirement which allows for a balance between lactic acid formation and removal (Fig. 8–14).

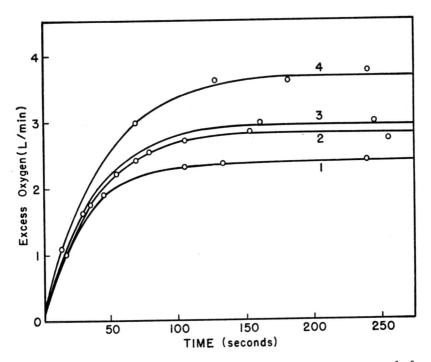

Fig. 8–14. Steady state: apparent and genuine. Steady state was attained after an initial lag of approximately 1½ mins. During this time, oxygen expenditure exceeded oxygen intake and a small oxygen debt was contracted. Beyond this time interval, oxygen intake was sufficient to meet the oxygen requirement of the work. Performance depicted by curve 4, which can be maintained for relatively short periods of time, is termed the apparent steady state. By comparison, performance depicted by curves 1, 2, and 3, which can be maintained for an extended period of time, is termed the genuine steady state. Steady state, for most individuals, can be maintained if the work oxygen requirement does not exceed approximately 2.5 L/min. (Adapted from Hill.)

For most individuals, a steady state is attained when the oxygen requirement for activity is less than approximately 2.5 liters per minute. At this level, anaerobic and aerobic biochemical processes are likely to be in balance; lactic acid removal keeps pace with lactic acid production, and oxygen expenditure is in balance with oxygen intake. The result is that an incurred oxygen debt is stabilized, i.e., no additional oxygen debt is incurred. Biochemically, the system is on a "pay-as-you-go" basis. An observation of some other parameters will reveal that heart frequency and respiratory frequency are also maintained at fairly steady levels.

Maximum Oxygen Uptake

In 1927, A. V. Hill calculated the theoretical limit of maximal oxygen uptake to be 5.50 liters per minute.[34] In actuality, Hill observed an uptake of 4.4 liters per minute on research involving oarsmen at Cornell. The famed 2-miler of the 1936 Olympic games, Don Lash, enjoyed a 5.35 liter per minute oxygen uptake. Astrand reported a maximum oxygen uptake of 5.88 liters per minute for a Swedish skiing champion. In resting states, oxygen uptake may vary between 0.200 and 0.350 liters per minute. As an example, for the 100 meter dash, the oxygen requirement may be approximately 4.5 liters per minute. To perform this event, an individual with a resting rate of 0.200 L/min will require an increase of oxygen uptake by a factor of 22.5.

The oxygen requirement for this event is challengingly high. The duration of time required to complete the event is short (approximately 9.5 to 12.0 seconds). The normal rate of oxygen utilization is appreciably lower than the requirement; therefore, an oxygen debt will be incurred and lactic acid will be present in blood in above-normal amounts. The elevated rate of oxygen consumption in recovery (the oxygen debt) is necessary to combat the results of the elevated metabolic processes and is used in the reconversion of lactic acid to glucose and the reconstitution of adenosinetriphosphate and creatine phosphate to their pre-exercise levels.

Energy Balance and Weight Control

The Brobeck formula (p. 166) provides the basis for yet another discussion—that of energy balance and weight control. Further, since obesity constitutes a major national health problem* which can become ameliorated by practicing physical activity and caloric restriction, this discussion will be centered on obesity and its etiology.[51]

---

* Obesity and Health, U. S. Dept. of Health, Education, and Welfare, 1966.

Obesity is characterized by an abnormal increase of fat within the subcutaneous connective tissues. Other words or terms which describe obesity are corpulence, general adiposis, and general liposis. Yet, such imprecise words as *abnormal* and *general* cater to ambiguity. In an attempt to provide a reference point many authors regard obesity as pronounced when the body weight is 25% or more above normal. This procedure is still general and not without fault primarily because it is based on height-weight tables which were drawn up many years ago and are in dire need of revision. More precise determination of body fat can be accomplished through the use of a number of anthropometric, densiometric, mathematic, and nomographic techniques.[40] Several representative types require minimal equipment,[3,4,9,10,21,56] but more detailed techniques of determining body composition have been reported.[19] See discussion of somatotypology in Chapter 11.

The etiology of obesity is varied. It might be precipitated and maintained by abnormal endocrinological function, a primary, widespread contributing factor to obesity by virtue of lay diagnosis and pronouncement. However, *few* cases of endocrinologically caused obesity in humans are supported by endocrinological researchers. Since credibility is not necessarily viewed as a function of numbers, two quotations from competent endocrinologists are presented in the hope of eradicating this feeble crutch for obesity.

Talbot et al. are quoted as follows relative to the secondary role of functional hyperpituitarism to caloric hypernutrition (simple dietary obesity):

The clinical histories of such obese children may yield interesting information. If due care is taken, it is almost always possible to elicit a story of overeating. Sometimes this is told spontaneously; at others, it is vigorously denied. When denied, skillful questioning may be needed to obtain a clear picture of past and present food habits.

The exact sources of excess calories vary somewhat. Most commonly the greatest excesses are accounted for by carbohydrates, especially sweets and starchy foods (potatoes, rice, macaroni, spaghetti, cereals, breads, pastries, candies, and the like). High-fat foods (butter, cream, salad oils, etc.) frequently play a role, the tendency being to combine them with starches (butter on bread, cream on cereal, and so forth).

The reasons for overeating are legion. In certain instances, eating simply constitutes a major family pleasure. In certain others, there has developed the idea that a good appetite insures good health. This belief often grows in the minds of parents who have suffered the loss of another child through illness or accident. Psychiatric studies reveal that a good many obese children result from an unplanned and unwanted pregnancy. This can culminate in emotional rejection of the child by the parents. In such cases the mother and father may have an unconscious sense of guilt because of their inability to feel affection. In an effort to salve their conscience, parents may give such children excessive physical attention in the form of food. Children who are insecure, worried, overprotected or bored tend spontaneously to eat for the comfort, pleasure and satisfaction which derives from the taste of food and the sensation of a full stomach.

These factors have been mentioned to suggest that it is usually possible to find some reasonably acceptable cause for obesity other than a mysterious "glandular disturbance." To be sure, there are rare patients who develop a morbid appetite because of a hypothalamic lesion involving neurologic centers which control appetite. Likewise, there are rare patients whose obesity is due in part to a reduction in energy output secondary to thyroid hormone deficiency and there are the very rare patients who show excess weight gain as a manifestation of Cushing's syndrome or chronic hyperinsulinism. The incidence of these conditions relative to simple dietary obesity is, however, extremely low.

Taylor states:

In many cases of simple obesity there appears to be a genetic element, a conclusion borne out by statistical studies. In surveys of a large number of obese persons, one or both parents were obese, whereas the incidence of obesity in persons both of whose parents are of normal weight is only about 10 percent. . . . An inherent tendency to fatness seems to be illustrated by the common observation that of two persons who appear to eat about the same amount of food, and exercise to the same extent, one may remain thin or of normal weight while the other grows fat. Furthermore, the "spare" person may have a large appetite and remain underweight while the obese may diet himself and still be fat. In order to explain such cases it has been suggested that they are due to an inherited endocrine characteristic. Yet, if this were so, some evidence of it should be forthcoming from metabolic studies. On the contrary, the basal metabolic rate per unit of body surface of the subject of the common or simple type of obesity is within normal limits—that is, his energy expenditure at rest is not less than normal. Nor is work performed more economically than usual by the obese; the reverse is probably true on account of the greater amount of inert adipose tissue. His greater storage of energy cannot therefore be explained upon this basis.

Other possibilities have been explored, namely, that the obese person may absorb his food more efficiently, that there exists an inborn peculiarity of the tissue cells, whereby they accumulate fat in excess, or that they release the fat less freely into the circulation for use as fuel. None of these factors has been found to play a significant part.

It is probable that a hereditary or constitutional factor, in the great majority of instances of ordinary obesity, is more apparent than real, and that a careful investigation of these cases with respect to food intake and muscular activity would reveal a positive energy balance. It is therefore likely that, when obesity shows a familiar tendency, the inclination of members of the same family to follow similar habits with respect to diet and exercise, rather than that some inherited endocrine peculiarity, is responsible. Or again, traits which lead to obesity—overindulgence of the appetite, or a distaste for muscular exertion may be inherited. Also, the obese person often, though not a "big eater," indulges in highly concentrated food.

The possibility of a hypothalamic or an endocrine element in the development of obesity is very difficult to prove or disprove. From what is known of the role played by the hypothalamus and the endocrines in the control of food intake and in fat metabolism, it is tempting to look in this direction for an explanation of obesity. Obesity might conceivably be due to some hypothalamic or endocrine idiosyncrasy. There is experimental evidence that the hypothalamus exerts an influence upon the hunger sensation, but endocrine effects are more often exerted upon the distribution of fat rather than the total body weight. There is no substantial evidence that obesity is due to any other cause than overindulgence in food in relation to the body's energy requirements.

The thorough yet concise treatment of energy balance by Tepperman contains a discussion of factors which influence balance (Fig. 8–15). Conspicuously (and significantly) absent from this excellent treatise is the contribution of endocrine glands in the etiology of obesity.

Energy balance has been expressed in a variety of ways. Brobeck's formula establishes an energy intake and an energy expenditure but in addition allows for imbalances in the form of energy storage (positive energy balance) or utilization of body energy stores (negative energy balance).

Johnson describes the components of energy balance in terms of potential and kinetic sources (Table 8–8).[38]

Irrespective of the mode of expression, energy balance, reduced to simplest terms, implies an expenditure which is equal to intake (Fig. 8–15).

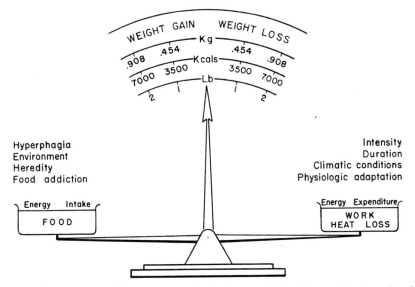

Fig. 8–15. Energy balance: some of the factors which influence it. A multitude of psychological factors can influence food intake. Energy balance can be maintained only if expenditure equals intake. 3500 represents calorific value of 0.454 kg (1 lb) of human fat after allowances for body water and connective tissue have been made.

TABLE 8–8.   Components of Human Energy Balance

	Energy Gain	Energy Loss
Potential	Food	Excreta
	Synthesis of high energy bonds	Useful work in the physical definition
		Degradation of high energy bonds
Kinetic	Metabolic heat	
	Heat gained from environment	Heat lost to the environment

Simple obesity is the direct result of positive energy balance; weight reduction is the outcome of negative energy balance. This suggests three basic possibilities in weight reduction programs:

1. A reduction of caloric intake to a level *below* that of caloric expenditure.

2. An increased caloric expenditure to a level *above* that of intake.

3. A combination of the above two.

Quite widespread is the view that participation in physical activity, as a means of weight control, is self-defeating since the end result of such participation is an increased appetite. Provided the physical activity level is at least moderate, an increased caloric intake can be tolerated and weight balance maintained (Fig. 8–16).

Each autumn tens of thousands of examples of successful management of weight control through physical activity are provided. Despite the fact that American football players regularly ingest 5000 to 6000 calories daily,* during the sport season, weight losses are experienced initially and are followed by weight balance. While this is loosely called getting-in-shape, it can more accurately be described as getting in balance. These same players usually gain weight in the immediate post-sport season—when the caloric intake is maintained while the caloric expenditure through physical activity is decreased.

In a study involving 213 West Bengal Indians employed by one company, Mayer et al. observed obesity to be related to inactivity (Fig. 8–16).

Physical inactivity was also found by Bronstein et al, Bruch,[11,12] and Rony to be the underlying characteristic of obese individuals.

---

* Football players are singled out because they represent a control group in that a training table usually is provided (a high caloric intake is assured) and a high caloric expenditure guaranteed.

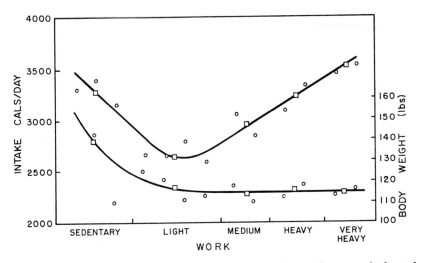

Fig. 8–16. Body weight and caloric intake expressed as a function of physical activity. For similar caloric intakes, persons who were physically inactive (sedentary workers) weighed more than persons who were physically active (those who perform very heavy work). (Adapted from Mayer et al.)

Fry and Peckos questioned the role of overeating in the etiology of obesity in children. In both studies physical inactivity was found to be more pronounced in the obese groups.

Johnson et al. found the caloric intake patterns between 28 obese and 28 nonobese greater Boston high school girls to be similar. Strikingly noticeable, however, was the decreased caloric expenditure pattern of the obese girls (Tables 8–9 and 8–10).

Greene also found inactivity to occur simultaneously with body weight gains in 67.5% of cases. Gain in body weight which was attributed to an increase in food intake occurred in only 3.2% of cases.

TABLE 8–9.   Average Daily Caloric Intake of Obese Girls and of Control Girls, by Class and Age (From Johnson et al.[37])

		Calories per day				
Group	Number	>2500	2500–2000	<2000	Mean Intake	Standard Deviation
Obese	28	3	6	19	1,965	453
Controls	28	15	10	3	2,706	633

TABLE 8–10.   Analysis of Representative Activities of Obese Girls and of Control Girls, Showing Mean Hours per Week Reported for Most Common Activities of Group with Standard Deviations (From Johnson et al.[37])

Group	Obese (hr)	Control (hr)
Sleep and lying still, awake	61±6	63±5
Sitting	84±8	75±8**
Standing	1±1	3±4*
Grooming	7±3	10±2**
"Baby sitting"	1±4	1±2
Playing piano and driving car	1.4±2	1.2±2
Housework	3.6±4	3.3±2
Active sports and other strenuous acts	4±4	11±5**

Asterisks denote the order of statistical significance of differences between obese and controls: *$p < 0.02$, **$p < 0.01$.

The futility of engaging in physical activity as a means of weight control is often seemingly substantiated by calculating the caloric equivalent of oxygen uptake or of work accomplished. Upon closer examination of these data, the discerning reader may discover the calculations to be based solely on the work phase. Since the calorific equivalent of recovery from work may equal or even exceed the caloric cost of work, the *net cost of work* must be considered (see also Chap. 11).

Net cost of work: Work $\dot{V}O_2$ + recovery $\dot{V}O_2$ − Rest $\dot{V}O_2$ for comparable periods.

Often post-work oxygen uptake values may not return to pre-work values until twenty-four to thirty-six hours later. Until the post-work and pre-work values are comparable, i.e., within the limits of intraindividual variability, recovery is deemed incomplete. Mathematical calculations of the net cost of work must reflect the *total* recovery period as well as work period.

Obesity discussions may take many forms; however, few discussions can be concluded without implicating the endocrine glands. Yet, in light of the present state of knowledge, endocrine involvement in the etiology of obesity is minimal. Admittedly, much additional knowledge must be obtained through research. Even the question of the timing of food ingestion must be resolved. For example, Cohn and Joseph have determined that spaced, full meals as contrasted with nibbling (i.e., frequent, small feedings) was a most effective causative factor to obesity in rats. Forced feeding (full meals) resulted in decreased thyroid function and decreased thyrotropic hormone formation and release by the pituitary gland. These authors have suggested a hindered enzymatic activity resulting from the frequency and quantity of ingested food.

Hyperphagia (overeating, gluttony), coupled with minimal levels of physical activity, results in positive energy balance and obesity. Lastly, the search for particular calories from particular foodstuffs, i.e., those calories which do not cater to obesity, has been as fruitful as the search for the Holy Grail. Calories are calories are calories (Fig. 8–17).

All calories produce the same results if taken in excess of expenditure.

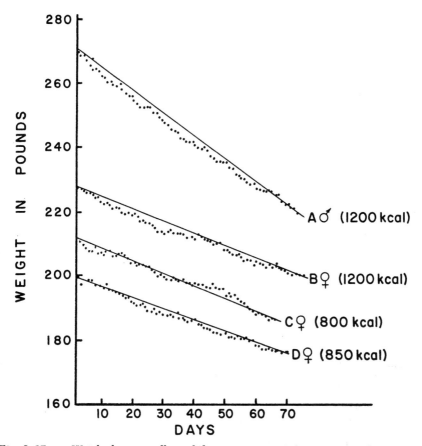

Fig. 8–17.   Weight loss regardless of dietary mixture. Subject *A*, normal, age 25; *B*, diabetic, age 42; *C*, patient with pituitary disorder, age 26; *D*, epileptic, age 60. Caloric intake listed within parentheses. Composition of diet had been changed at intervals: carbohydrate intake varied from 3 to 64% of total intake; protein intake 14 to 36% of total; fats 12 to 83%. As is evident, caloric reduction, not foodstuff source, provides basis for "calories are calories are calories" concept. (Adapted from Kinsell et al.)

Caloric expenditure in human performance is affected by many factors including: body mass, duration and intensity of effort, ambient and atmospheric conditions, resistance offered by ground or floor surface (or water), and degree of physiological-physical efficiency. Listed in Table 8–11 are the energy costs of a few activities. Note that energy expenditure is expressed in gross kcal/min which is more realistic, although less dramatic, than reporting energy expenditure in kcal/hr.

TABLE 8–11.   Energy Cost of Various Activities

Activity	Energy Expenditure (gross kcal/min)	Considerations
Sleeping	0.9— 1.2	Degree of restful sleep
Sitting	1.2— 1.5	Degree of relaxation
Floating	1.0— 2.0	Body density of subject, relative calmness of water
Reading	1.5— 2.0	Complexity of subject matter
Driving a car	2.5— 3.0	Speed, type of road, traffic conditions, type of transmission (standard vs automatic)
Walking	4.0— 7.0	Intensity of effort, type of terrain
Golfing	5.0— 6.0	Terrain, type of competition
Bicycling	5.0— 7.0	Speed, type of bicycle (multigeared vs single gear)
Dancing, lively waltz	5.0— 7.0	
Dancing, polka	8.0—10.0	
Shovelling	6.0— 8.0	Type of substance, soil conditions, or distance substance is to be moved
Tennis Handball Badminton	7.0—12.0	Skill level of performer as well as skill level of opponent
Chopping and splitting cord wood	9.0—11.0	
Swimming, competitive (crawl stroke)	13.0—15.0	

REFERENCES

1. Asmussen, E.: Aerobic recovery after anaerobiosis in rest and work. *Acta Physiol. Scand.*, *11*:197–210, 1946.

2. Astrand, P. O.: Human physical fitness with special reference to sex and age. *Physiol. Rev.*, *36*:307–335, 1956.

3. Behnke, A. R.: Quantitative assessment of body build. *J. Appl. Physiol.*, *16*:960–968, 1961.

4. Behnke, A. R., Feen, B. G., and Welham, W. C.: The specific gravity of healthy men. Body weight + volume as an index of obesity. *J.A.M.A.*, *118*:495–498, 1942.

5. Bock, A. V., Dill, D. B., and Edwards, H. T.: Lactic acid in the blood of resting man. *J. Clin. Invest.*, *11*:775–788, 1932.

6. Brobeck, J. R.: Energy exchange. *In* Ruch, T. C., and Fulton, J. F. (Eds.): *Medical Physiology and Biophysics*, 18th Ed. Philadelphia, W. B. Saunders Co., 1961.

7. Brobeck, J. R.: Intermediary metabolism. *In* Ruch, T. C., and Fulton, J. F. (Eds.): *Medical Physiology and Biophysics*, 18th Ed. Philadelphia, W. B. Saunders Co., 1961.

8. Bronstein, I. P., Wexler, S., Brown, A. W., and Halpern, J.: Obesity in childhood. *Am. J. Dis. Child.*, *63*:238–251, 1942.

9. Brozek, J., and Keys, A.: The evaluation of leanness-fatness in man: norms and interrelationships. *Br. J. Nutrition*, *5*:194–206, 1951.

10. Brozek, J., Brock, J. F., Fidanza, F., and Keys, A.: Skinfold caliper estimation of body fat and nutritional status. *Fed. Proc.*, *13*:19, 1954.

11. Bruch, H.: Obesity in childhood. III The food intake of obese children; physiologic and psychologic aspects. *Am. J. Dis. Child.*, *59*:739–781, 1940.

12. Bruch, H.: Obesity in childhood. IV Energy expenditure of obese children. *Am. J. Dis. Child.*, *60*:1082–1109, 1940.

13. Campbell, J.: Fat metabolism. *In* Best, C. H., and Taylor, N. B. (Eds.): *The Physiological Basis of Medical Practice*. 7th Ed. Baltimore, The Williams & Wilkins Co., 1961.

14. Castiglioni, A.: *A History of Medicine*. 2nd Ed. Edited by E. B. Krumbhaar, New York, Alfred Knopf Co., 1958.

15. Cathcart, E. P., and Markowitz, J.: The influence of various sugars on the respiratory quotient. A contribution to the significance of the R.Q. *J. Physiol.*, *63*:309–324, 1927.

16. Christensen, E. H.: Physiological valuation of work in the Nykroppa iron works. *In* Floyd, W. F., and Welford, A. T.: *Ergonomics Society Symposium on Fatigue*. London, H. K. Lewis, 1953.

17. Christensen, E. H., and Hogberg, P.: Steady-state, O_2 deficit, and O_2 debt at severe work. *Arbeitsphysiol, 14*:251–254, 1950.

18. Cohn, C., and Joseph, D.: Role of rate of ingestion of diet on regulation of intermediary metabolism ("meal eating" vs "nibbling"). *Metabolism*, *5*:492–499, 1960.

19. Consolazio, C. F., Johnson, R. E., and Pecora, L. J.: *Physiological Measurements of Metabolic Functions in Man*. New York, McGraw-Hill Book Co., 1963.

14

20. Cowan, C. R., and Solandt, O. M.:   The duration of the recovery period following strenuous muscular exercise measured to a base line of steady, mild exercise. *J. Physiol.*, 89:462–466, 1937.

21. Cowgill, G. R.:   A formula for estimating the specific gravity of the human body with a consideration of its possible uses. *Am. J. Clin. Nutrition*, 5:601–611, 1957.

22. Crescitelli, F., and Taylor, C.:   The lactate response to exercise and its relationship to physical fitness. *Am. J. Physiol.*, 141:630–640, 1944.

23. Dill, D. B.:   The economy of muscular exercise. *Physiol. Rev.*, 16:263–291, 1936.

24. Dill, D. B., and Fölling, A.:   Studies in muscular activity. II A nomographic description of expired air. *J. Physiol.*, 66:133–135, 1938.

25. Dill, D. B., Edwards, H. T., and Consolazio, W. V.:   Blood as a physiochemical system. XI Man at rest. *J. Biol. Chem.*, 118:635–648, 1937.

26. Edwards, H. T.:   Lactic acid in rest and work at high altitude. *Am. J. Physiol.*, 116:367–375, 1936.

27. Fowler, W. S., Blackburn, C. M., and Helmholz, H. F.:   Determination of basal rate of oxygen consumption by open and closed-circuit methods. *J. Clin. Endocrinol.*, 17:786–796, 1957.

28. Fry, P. C.:   A comparative study of "obese" children selected on the basis of fat pads. *J. Clin. Nutrition*, 1:453–468, 1953.

29. Greene, J. A.:   Clinical study of the etiology of obesity. *Ann. Inst. Med.*, 12:1797–1803, 1939.

30. Grollman, S., and Phillips, N. E.:   Possible relationship of ketone bodies to the alactacid oxygen debt. *Am. J. Physiol.*, 177:73–76, 1954.

31. *Handbook of Respiratory Data in Aviation*, Committee on Aviation Medicine, Washington, D.C., 1944.

32. Harmon, F. L.:   Reliability of metabolism measurements by the closed circuit method. *J. Appl. Physiol.*, 5:773–778, 1953.

33. Henry, F. M., and DeMoor, J.:   Lactic and alactic oxygen consumption in moderate exercise of graded intensity. *J. Appl. Physiol.*, 8:608–614, 1956.

34. Hill, A. V.:   *Muscular Movement in Man: The Factors Governing Speed and Recovery from Fatigue.* New York, McGraw-Hill Book Co., 1927.

35. Hill, A. V., and Lupton, H.:   Muscular exercise, lactic acid, and the supply and utilization of oxygen. *Quart. J. Med.*, 16:135–171, 1923.

36. Hunt, T. C.:   Determination of the basal metabolic rate, *Lancet*, 210 (1): 172–173, 1926.

37. Johnson, M. L., Burke, B. S., and Mayer, J.:   Relative importance of inactivity and overeating in the energy balance of obese high school girls. *Am. J. Clin. Nutrition*, 4:37–44, 1956.

38. Johnson, R. E.:   What should a physiologist teach about muscle exercise and fitness? *Exercise and Fitness*, Chicago, Athletic Institute, 1960.

39. Karpovich, P. V.:   *Physiology of Muscular Activity.* 6th Ed. Philadelphia, W. B. Saunders Co., 1965.

40. Keys, A., and Brozek, J.: Body fat in adult man. *Physiol. Rev.*, 33:245–325, 1953.

41. Kinsell, L. W., Gunning, B., Michaels, G. D., Richardson, J., Cox, S. E., and Lemon, C.: Calories do count. *Metabolism*, 3:195–204, 1964.

42. Kottke, F. J., Kubicek, W. G., Olson, M. E., Hastings, R. H., and Harstad, K. Q.: Studies on the parameters of cardiac output and cardiac work during vocational rehabilitation, Washington, Vocational Rehabilitation Administration Grant No. 349, November 1963.

43. Lewis, R. C., Iliff, A., and Duval, A. M.: The comparative accuracy of the closed circuit bedside method and the open circuit chamber procedure for the determination of basal metabolism. *J. Lab. & Clin. Med.*, 28:1238–1245, 1943.

44. Lim, T. P. K., and Luft, U. C.: Editorial: Body density, fat, and fat-free weight. *Am. J. Med.*, 30:825–832, 1961.

45. Lucas, C. C., and Ridout, J. H.: Composition and energy content of foods: general metabolism. *In* Best, C. H., and Taylor, N. B. (Eds.): *The Physiological Basis of Medical Practice.* 7th Ed. Baltimore, The Williams & Wilkins Co., 1961.

46. Lukin, L., and Ralston, H. J.: Oxygen deficit and repayment in exercise. *Arbeitsphysiol.*, 19:183–193, 1962.

47. Margaria, R.: Personal communication.

48. Margaria, R., Cerretelli, P., DiPrampero, P. E., Massari, C., and Torelli, G.: Kinetics and mechanism of oxygen debt contraction in man. *J. Appl. Physiol.*, 18:371–377, 1963.

49. Margaria, R., Edwards, H. T., and Dill, D. B.: The possible mechanisms of contracting and paying the oxygen debt and the role of lactic acid in muscular contraction. *Am. J. Physiol.*, 106:689–715, 1933.

50. Margaria, R., Galante, E., and Cerretelli, P.: An efficient CO_2 absorber for experiments on metabolism. *J. Appl. Physiol.*, 14:1066–1068, 1959.

51. Mayer, J.: Genetic, traumatic and environmental factors in the etiology of obesity. *Physiol. Rev.*, 33:472–508, 1953.

52. Mayer, J., Roy, P., and Mitra, K. P.: Relation between caloric intake, body weight, and physical work: studies in an industrial male population in West Bengal. *Am. J. Clin. Nutrition*, 4:169–175, 1956.

53. Passmore, R., and Durnin, J. V. G. A.: Human energy expenditure. *Physiol. Rev.*, 35:801–840, 1955.

54. Passmore, R., and Johnson, R. E.: Some metabolic changes following prolonged moderate exercise. *Metabolism*, 5:452–455, 1960.

55. Peckos, P. C.: Calorie intake in relation to physique in children. *Science*, 117:631–636, 1953.

56. Rathbun, E. N., and Pace, N.: Studies on body composition. I The determination of total body fat by means of the body specific gravity. *J. Biol. Chem.*, 158:667–676, 1945.

57. Ricci, B.: Oxygen uptake and blood lactate relationships in subjects of diametric somatotype. *Ergonomics* (Supplement), pp. 87–90, October, 1965.

58. Ricci, B.: Oxygen uptake in subjects of vastly different somatotype. *Arbeitsphysiol.*, 20:173–177, 1963.

59. Robinson, S., and Harmon, P.: The lactic acid mechanism and certain properties of the blood in relation to training. *Am. J. Physiol., 132*:757–769, 1941.

60. Rony, H. R.: *Obesity and Leanness*. Philadelphia, Lea and Febiger, 1940.

61. Salter, J. M.: Protein metabolism. *In* Best, C. H., and Taylor, N. B. (Eds.): *The Physiological Basis of Medical Practice*. 7th Ed. Baltimore, The Williams & Wilkins Co., 1961.

62. Schapera, I.: *The Khoisan Peoples of South Africa*. London, Routledge & Kegan Paul Ltd., 1960.

63. Short, R.: *A Synopsis of Physiology*. 5th Ed. Edited by C. C. N. Vass, Baltimore, The Williams & Wilkins Co., 1961.

64. Talbot, N. B., Sobel, E. H., McArthur, J. W., and Crawford, J. D.: *Functional Endocrinology*. Cambridge, Harvard University Press, 1954.

65. Taylor, N. B.: The metabolism in starvation, semistarvation and obesity. *In* Best, C. H., and Taylor, N. B. (Eds.): *The Physiological Basis of Medical Practice*. 7th Ed. Baltimore, The Williams & Wilkins Co., 1961.

66. Tepperman, J.: *Metabolic and Endocrine Physiology*. Chicago, Year Book Medical Publishers, 1962.

67. Tepperman, J., and Brobeck, J. R.: Symposium on energy balance. *Am. J. Clin. Nutrition, 8*:527–774, 1960.

68. Van Liew, H. D.: Transfer and storage of small volumes of gas for the Scholander analyzer. *J. Appl. Physiol., 16*:578–580, 1961.

69. Weiss, R. A., and Karpovich, P. V.: Energy cost of exercise for convalescents. *Arch. Phys. Med., 28*:447–454, 1947.

70. Wells, J. G., Balke, B., and Van Fossan, D. D.: Lactic acid accumulation as a factor in determining work capacity. Randolph AFB, Texas, *USAF School of Aviation Med.*, Report 56–121, 1956.

71. Wells, J. G., Balke, B., and Van Fossan, D. D.: Lactic acid accumulation during work. A suggested standardization of work classification. *J. Appl. Physiol., 10*:51–55, 1957.

72. Willard, H. N., and Wolf, G. A.: A source of error in the determination of basal metabolic rates by the closed circuit technic. *Ann. Int. Med., 34*:148–162, 1951.

73. Winton, F. R., and Bayliss, L. E.: *Human Physiology*. 5th Ed. Boston, Little, Brown and Co., 1962.

Chapter

9

HOMEOSTASIS OF BODY FLUIDS

In man, physiologic variability is much less pronounced than is anatomic variability.

Irrespective of wide external fluctuations (of ambient temperature and relative humidity or of great fluid, heat, and caloric imbalances) the acid-base balance of body fluids fluctuates within rather narrow limits. An important function of the body fluid is that of providing a suitable medium within which chemical reactions can occur.

In 1857, the celebrated French physiologist Claude Bernard (1813–1878) presented a discussion of an internal environment, the blood, which "constitutes an actual organic environment intermediary between the external environment in which the complete individual lives [and the internal tissues which] cannot safely be brought into direct contact with this external environment. [Thus in the blood, all the tissues] are provided for the accomplishment of their functions with constant conditions of temperature, moisture, availability of oxygen, as well as nitrogenous materials, carbohydrates, and salts, without which the organs cannot be nourished."[16]

Our present knowledge of the constancy (equilibrium or homeostasis*) of the body fluids represents the contributions of many distinguished scientists, notably Harvard Professors Walter Cannon (1871–1945)[3] and Lawrence Henderson (1878–1942),† Karl Hasselbach (b. 1874),[4]† Rudolph Höber (1873–1953), John Peters (1887–1955) and Donald Van Slyke (b. 1883), who introduced the "alkali reserve" concept.

---

* The term, homeostasis, was coined by Cannon.

† Henderson and Hasselbach are names associated with the buffer equation for blood pH. Henderson described the important role of the kidney in base economy.

Body fluid regulation cannot be discussed without mention of the liver and kidney. Thus even a capsule history of body fluid regulation such as this would be seriously deficient without the recognition of such an eminent scientist as Claude Bernard, not only for his "internal environment" concept but also for his description of liver function in digestion and in sugar metabolism.[15]

TABLE 9–1.   Approximate Distribution of Body Fluids (80Kg ♂)*

Site	Per Cent of Body Weight	Volume in Liters
Extracellular	25	20.0
Interstitial spaces of tissues and organs	15 ⎤	12.0 ⎤
Intraocular, synovial, cerebrospinal	6 ⎬	4.8 ⎬
Plasma†	4 ⎦	3.2 ⎦
Intracellular	40	32.0
	65%	52.0L

* Extracellular and intracellular fluids are also termed extravascular fluids, denoting all body fluids found outside the blood vessels.

† Plasma volume represents approximately 4% of body weight; red cell and white cell mass represents approximately 3% of body weight. (For 80 kg individual: 80 kg × 0.03 = 2.4 L red and white cell volume; 80 kg × 0.04 = 3.2 L plasma volume = 5.6 L whole blood.)

And last, for their discovery or elucidation of kidney structure and function, the following men were accorded permanent honor: Marcello Malpighi (1628–1694), Lorenzo Bellini (1643–1704), Jacob Henle (1809–1865), and Sir William Bowman (1816–1892)[4] (see Fig. 9–3).

Extracellular and intracellular fluids comprise approximately 65% of man's total body weight (Table 9–1).

Lipids contain very small amounts of water; therefore, for individuals possessing large amounts of depot fat the percentage of body fluid by weight will decrease. It is, therefore, more precise to express body fluids in terms of lean body mass (LBM) or fat-free tissue.

Detailed discussions of methods of determining body fluids may be found in Haist, in Smith, and in Koch.

Fluid Balance

During the course of a given period, fluid intake balances fluid loss. Temporary fluid imbalance* occurs during periods of prolonged, elevated metabolic activity. Or, fluid imbalance may be caused by unfavorable climatic conditions such as high ambient temperature and high relative humidity or by the wearing of clothing which retards the body heat loss mechanisms. In any event, the fluid loss serves the important purpose of temperature regulation.

Body fluid is gained directly via the ingestion of foodstuffs and liquids and indirectly through the process of digestion and metabolism. Fluid intake, especially following participation in an intense athletic contest performed under a hot sun, is likely to be pronounced. This represents a readily visible source of intake. The amount of fluid intake in food is not readily visible (Table 9–2).

Fluid gain through digestion in particular and metabolism in general is substantial. Water is one of the end-products of the ever occurring series of biochemical reactions termed metabolism. According to Short,[21] the small intestine may absorb as many as ten liters of water per day (Fig. 9–1).

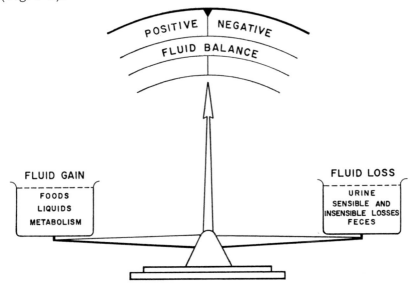

Fig. 9–1. Fluid balance. While fluid loss is influenced by a combination of physiological and physical factors, fluid gain is dependent primarily upon intake of food or liquid. Daily fluctuations in weight may be attributed primarily to these factors. Any temporary but severe imbalances, e.g., those caused by diarrhea, produce a profound effect on body weight.

---

* Imbalance may be described as being negative or positive; e.g., negative fluid balance indicates that fluid loss exceeds fluid gain.

TABLE 9–2. Water Content of Certain Foodstuffs (From data of Watt and Merrill[24])

Foodstuff	Approximate Water % (per 100 grams edible portion)
Beverages:	
alcoholic	
beer (3.6% alcohol by wgt.)	92
table wine (9.9% alcohol by wgt.)	86
nonalcoholic	
coffee	98
cola type	90
milk	87
special dietary drinks with artificial sweetener (less than 1 cal/oz)	100
Bread, white or cracked wheat	35
" toasted	25
" rolls	22–30
Broccoli, cabbage	89–93
Butter	15
Cheese (except cottage)	40
Chewing gum	3
Coleslaw	80
Fried chicken	54
Eggs (omelete, poached, scrambled)	72
Gelatin dessert	84
Fried haddock	66
Ice cream	63
Lima beans	90
Onions	87
Pies	35–60
Brownies	10
Potatoes	80

Despite the fluid imbalances, the internal environment of the cells (the pH of the blood and extravascular fluid) remains remarkably stable. The maintenance of pH constancy is accomplished through a series of biochemical reactions, through the role of the muscle system as a fluid reservoir, through respiratory activity, and as a result of the important roles played by the liver and kidneys.

Reservoirs of Body Fluids

Fluid gained from the usual source of foodstuffs is absorbed into the upper intestinal tract and dispersed via the blood stream to several locations. In descending order of fluid capacity, the liver, muscle tissues, and kidneys comprise the principal reservoirs of body fluids.

Distinctive as the largest gland in the body, the liver constitutes approximately 2% of body weight. It is richly supplied with blood vessels; an estimated 1.5 L/min blood flow courses through the gland (Fig. 9–2).

TABLE 9–3. Liver Function

Glucogenic:	Glycogen formed from glucose and lactic acid (Cori cycle)
Phospholipogenic:	Phospholipids formed from fatty acids (Krebs cycle)
Enzymatic:	Esterases—catalyze organic compounds formed from alcohol and carboxylic acid
	Phosphatases—liberate inorganic phosphate from the phosphoric esters.* (Of particular interest is the presence of the alkaline phosphatase in the blood stream, intestinal tract, kidney, muscle, and other tissues which become active at pH 8.6.)
Bile production:	Digestive function—important in fat emulsification, retards putrefaction (detoxifying agent), increases peristalsis; bile produced at rate of approximately 15ml/kg body wgt/day; max. rate of production between 2nd and 5th postprandial hours; especially pronounced after protein and fat ingestion
Anticoagulant:	Heparin formation, blood anticoagulant
Glycogenolytic:	Hydrolysis† of glycogen and conversion into glucose
Gluconeogenetic:	Formation of glucose and glycogen from protein and fats
Ketogenetic:	Production of acetone or ketone bodies
Deamination:	Removal by hydrolysis of amino group (NH_2) from amino compound
Storage:	Glycogen, fats, proteins, iron, vitamins A, B complex, D, blood
Excretory:	Cholesterol, urea, uric acid
Protective:	Bile retards putrefaction

---

* Esters: organic chemical compounds formed from alcohol and carboxylic acid.
† Hydrolysis: formation of simpler chemical compounds and water through chemical reaction requiring enzymatic action.

The important role of the liver in the conversion of lactic acid through the Cori cycle was discussed earlier. Additional functions of the liver which are of particular significance in the conduct of physical effort are presented in Table 9–3.

The volume of the liver is variable. Following fluid ingestion, the liver swells; during physical effort of high metabolic intensity, liver volume is decreased as a result of blood shunting. Rowell et al. noted a large decrease in liver and total splanchnic blood flow to occur during the performance of moderate to severe treadmill running exercise.

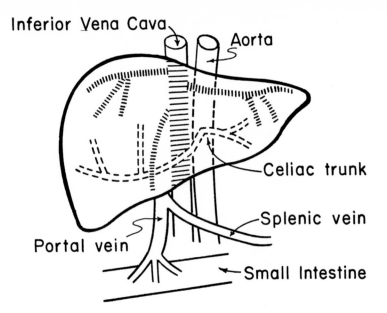

Fig. 9–2. Anterior aspect of the liver. Blood supply to the liver is from aorta, through common hepatic artery (broken line) shown at celiac trunk. A second blood supply is through portal vein from intestinal tract. Before blood from this latter source flows into general circulation via hepatic veins and inferior vena cava (depicted by cross hatch lines), the liver performs many important functions, thereby aiding in the maintenance of blood pH constancy (see Table 9–3). Liver is dually innervated from parasympathetic (vagus nerve) and sympathetic fibers (celiac plexus). (Adapted from Gray.)

Usually considered only for their peculiar ability to respond to various stimuli from which motion results, muscle tissues must also be considered for their important role in fluid storage. Muscle tissue is extensive and constitutes approximately 40% of body weight (80kg $\times$ .40 = 32.0kg muscle tissue). Due primarily to its large surface area, muscle tissue is capable of absorbing and temporarily storing as much as 30 liters of fluid.

The kidneys represent another great reservoir of body fluid. These paired organs are located on the posterior, upper abdominal cavity at the level of the lowermost rib. They are richly supplied with blood and lymph vessels. In proportion to organ weight, the kidneys receive the greatest blood flow. At rest, this flow amounts to between $\frac{1}{5}$ and $\frac{1}{4}$ of the cardiac output. Assuming a cardiac output of 5.2 L/min (and renal blood flow amounting to $\frac{1}{4}$ of cardiac output), the renal blood flow would be approximately 1300 ml/min whereas plasma flow would amount to approximately 600 ml/min. Fluid is filtered through both kidneys at the rate of approximately 125 ml/min. In the course of 24 hours, although 180 L fluid pass through the kidneys, only 1.5 L is excreted as urine and 178.5 L is reabsorbed into the system. In other words the kidneys reabsorb 124 ml of the 125 ml/min of fluid filtered and excrete but 1 ml/min as urine. During prolonged periods of physical activity, which are characterized by copious fluid losses through sensible and insensible sweating, the volume of urine is decreased considerably.

Control of flow rates within the afferent and efferent arterioles* is accomplished through innervation from the sympathetic (splanchnic) nerve pathway. Both afferent and efferent nerve fibers terminate in the smooth muscle of afferent and efferent arterioles. Efferent nerve fiber terminations are more numerous in the proximal tubules. Alteration of the lumen in afferent and efferent arterioles is one method of controlling and altering the filtration rate within the glomeruli.† Actually, lumen reduction not only results in a decreased fluid flow through the renal tubules, but also affects the osmotic pressure of the fluids within the glomeruli. As a consequence of this combined effect, the rate of filtration is reduced and is accompanied by a reduced rate of urine formation. Except in vigorous exercise, filtration rate is fairly constant. Urine production is regulated by the antidiuretic hormone ADH (pp. 211–212).

Arterial blood pressure, in addition to rate of blood flow, influences glomerular filtration. A drop in arterial blood pressure results in a decrease in filtration rate and a decrease in urine formation. Urine production ceases when arterial blood pressure falls to approximately 60 mm Hg.

Effects of Exercise

Kattus et al. noted a negligible antidiuretic effect resulting from treadmill walking exercise of light metabolic intensity. Aas and Blegen also noted similar reductions in renal plasma flow during short periods of exercise. White and Rolf reported a slight reduction in renal plasma flow and filtration rate resulting from light running exercise. Radigan and Robinson, Chapman et al.,[6] and Chapman, Henschel, and Forsgren observed decreased renal plasma flow during exercise. Moderate to severe running exercise produced profound effects: renal plasma flow

---

* Predominately, capillary networks are interspersed between arterioles and venules. Afferent and efferent arterioles within the kidneys represent a unique exception.

† Glomerular filtration rate (GFR) is determined by inulin clearance. A small known amount of the polysaccharide *inulin* is injected intravenously. Inulin is filtered completely within the glomeruli and is neither reabsorbed nor excreted by the renal tubules, hence the amount present in the urine serves as an accurate basis of clearance. Clearance rates, corrected to body surface area, range between 100-150 ml/min; 125 ml/min represents mean clearance rate of inulin, hence the filtration rate.

rates and filtration rates were reduced to at least one-half of resting values. Barclay et al. reported similar results produced by running the quarter-mile at full speed. On the basis of their data, White and Rolf indicated that during heavy exercise as much blood as one liter/min may be shunted from the kidney and diverted to more active tissues.

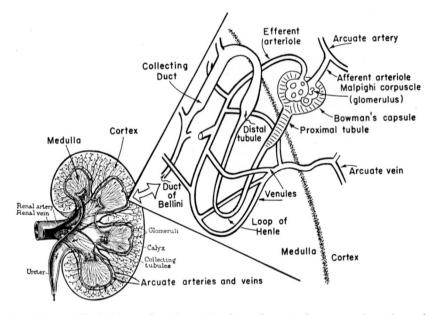

Fig. 9–3.   The kidney and nephron. Renal circulation is from aorta through renal artery, interlobar and arcuate arteries, afferent and efferent arterioles, venules, arcuate and interlobar veins to renal vein and inferior vena cava. Within the nephron, afferent and efferent arterioles, each capable of independent venomotor changes, maintain independent control of blood flow through corpuscle of Malpighi and Bowman's capsule. Lymph vessels are abundant within the cortex region only. To maintain constancy of blood pH, the kidneys reabsorb an extremely high percentage of the inorganic substances while allowing a very small amount of fluids to be excreted. (Adapted from Gray.)

Acid-Base Balance

Hydrogen ion concentration, or pH, is a measure of the alkalinity (basicity) or acidity of a solution which is expressed in terms of the negative logarithm of the hydrogen ion concentration. Acid-base balance also may be expressed as pOH, the negative logarithm of the hydroxide ion concentration.

$$pH = -\log [H^+]$$

$$\text{or } pH = \log \frac{1}{[H^+]}$$

In other words, pH is expressed as the negative power to which the common logarithm of a number must be raised in order to equal the hydrogen ion concentration:

$$[H^+] = 10^{-pH}$$

The relationship between $[H^+]$ and pH is presented in Table 9–4.

TABLE 9–4. Relationship of Hydrogen Ion Concentration to pH Values

$[H^+]$	pH	Solution	Strength
10^0 or 1	0.0		Strong acid
10^{-1}	1.0		
10^{-2}	2.0		↓
10^{-3}	3.0	Acid	Weak acid
10^{-4}	4.0		
10^{-5}	5.0		
10^{-6}	6.0		↓
10^{-7}	7.0	Neutral	Neutral
10^{-8}	8.0		
10^{-9}	9.0		
10^{-10}	10.0		↓
10^{-11}	11.0	Alkaline	Weak base
10^{-12}	12.0		
10^{-13}	13.0		↓
10^{-14}	14.0		Strong base

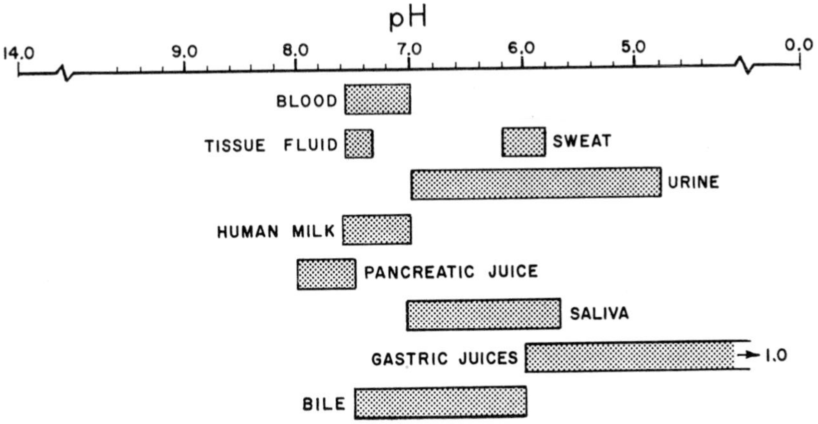

Fig. 9–4. Normal variability in pH of certain body fluids. Venous blood, containing greater amounts of CO_2, has a lower pH than that of arterial blood. Change in blood pH induced by respiration or metabolism is termed *alkalemia* if pH is increased above 7.45, and *acidemia* if below 7.35. Not depicted, but mentioned for purposes of comparison, is the pH of a strong acid (hydrochloric, HCl, pH 2.0) and of a fairly strong base (sodium hydroxide, NaOH, pH 10.0).

Hydrogen ion concentration, then, expresses the deviation from neutral of any solution. A pH of 7.0 is that of distilled water. The pH of body fluids, for example, is expressed in relation to neutral, or pH 7.0, or distilled water. A pH less than 7.0 indicates a greater hydrogen ion concentration than that of distilled water, and the substance is said to be acid (Fig. 9–4). Conversely, a pH greater than 7.0 indicates a decreased hydrogen ion concentration, and the substance is labeled as alkaline or base.

Cells cannot tolerate wide fluctuations in pH. Beyond rather narrow pH limits, which vary among body fluids, biochemical activity ceases and the cells become necrotic. Blood pH varies from 7.58 to 7.0. During prolonged demanding work periods, blood pH falls gradually and effects a greater oxygen utilization by the tissues (see Fig. 6–10, p. 129).

Principal among the many factors which alter blood pH levels are such end-products of metabolism as acid metabolites, lactic acid, and carbon dioxide. Even greatly elevated metabolic levels lower blood pH to a small degree, the relatively narrow fluctuations in pH being attributed to biochemical activity of the acid-base *buffer* system. A buffer solution is expressed as a ratio of a weak acid or base to its conjugate acid or base pair. (Conjugate acid or base pair describes two similar molecules which differ with respect to the presence or absence of hydrogen ion only.) For example:

$$\frac{H_2CO_3}{HCO_3^-} = \frac{\begin{array}{c}CO_2 \text{ carried principally in this bicarbonate form} \\ \text{(weak carbonic acid)}\end{array}}{\text{salt}}$$

Basically, the biochemical activity that is responsible for the regulation of blood pH takes place within the circulatory-pulmonary systems and within the kidneys as well.

The large amount of carbon dioxide which is carried in the venous blood is buffered by plasma:

$$CO_2 + H_2O = H_2CO_3 \text{ (carbonic acid, weak)}$$
$$(H_2CO_3 = HCO_3^- + H^+)$$

Ultimately this reaction produces an even weaker acid thereby resulting in insignificant changes in blood pH.

$$H^+ + HbO_2^- = HHb + O_2$$
$$\text{(acid weaker strength than } H_2CO_3)$$

Also present within the blood stream, within the erythrocyte in particular, is the enzyme *carbonic anhydrase* which catalyzes the conversion of carbon dioxide into carbonic acid (H_2CO_3) and thus is important to the buffer system.

Carbon dioxide generally provides for its own removal (see Fig. 6–12); however, during greatly elevated metabolic states, ventilation rate, which initially increases linearly with metabolic rate, reaches a plateau at a much lower level. The amount of carbon dioxide which is exhaled is substantial; however, carbon dioxide production exceeds its elimination rate and is reflected in a slight reduction in blood pH level. Nonetheless, the pulmonary mechanism is highly effective in helping to maintain rather stable blood pH levels. For a detailed discussion of acid-base balance, refer to Singer and Hastings; for a concise discussion, refer to Lambertsen.

In addition to the carbon dioxide, which is singled out for discussion, lactic acid and acid metabolites compound the problem of pH fluctuation. The presence of acid buffers and of base buffers presents widespread fluctuation of fluid and cell pH throughout the body.

Kidney involvement in pH regulation of blood and body fluids is extensive and is reflected in the quantity as well as composition of urine. Within the proximal tubules bicarbonate, phosphate, and protein (the more important buffer systems) as well as sodium, glucose, potassium, and the amino acids are reabsorbed. Within the distal tubule water, additional sodium and chloride are reabsorbed (Fig. 9–3). Such organic constituents as urea, the chief end-product of nitrogen metabolism, as well as uric acid are partly absorbed by the tubules. Absorption within the proximal and distal tubules is dependent upon osmotic pressure as well as hormonal influence exerted by the hypophysis.[23] (The hormonal secretion [ADH] of the hypophysis or pituitary gland produces an antidiuretic effect.)

Ammonium is produced from aminonitrogen and amide which are extracted from the renal arterial blood. Its excretion in urine, along with the anions of strong acids, serves to conserve such fixed cations as sodium and potassium. By this mechanism, ammonium plays an important role in acid-base balance. Essentially, ammonia buffers secreted hydrogen ions thus permitting a continuous exchange of hydrogen ions for either sodium or potassium ions. (Potassium is secreted by the hydrogen-sodium exchange.)

In maintaining acid-base balance, an important interrelationship exists between respiratory and renal mechanisms. Carbon dioxide is transported to the lungs via the blood stream and expelled into the atmosphere. Because of the time lag between production and removal, carbon dioxide is detectable in extracellular fluids. Carbon dioxide concentration in extracellular fluid would vary directly with metabolic level (and cause immediate fluctuations in fluid pH levels) were it not for an effective pulmonary ventilation elimination route for carbon dioxide.

Carbon dioxide, which enters the renal tubules via the extracellular fluids (or directly through cell metabolism), triggers hydrogen ion excretion. Through involvement of carbonic anhydrase, carbonic acid is formed and readily dissociates into carbonate ions and hydrogen ions. The hydrogen ion is secreted into the renal tubule. As a result of this hydrogen ion introduction, a sodium ion (or other cations such as potassium, magnesium, or calcium) is absorbed into the renal epithelium and carried in extracellular fluid.

Usually, the rate of hydrogen ion secretion into the renal tubules is balanced by the filtration of bicarbonate ions, and acid-base balance is maintained. If, however, the hydrogen ion secretion exceeds bicarbonate filtration, it is excreted into the urine and the fluid pH shifts in the alkaline direction. Conversely, should the filtration of bicarbonate ions exceed the secretion of hydrogen ions, the sodium bicarbonate would be lost via the urine and the fluid pH would shift in the acid direction.

Urine

Wide positive or negative fluctuations in fluid balance produce little effect on the pH of body fluids. Urine volume and composition reflect fluid balance, diet, and level of metabolic activity. As stated earlier (p. 207), urine is formed at the rate of approximately 1 ml/min. Yet, during this time interval, an additional 124 ml of fluid is reabsorbed. In this process most of the inorganic as well as the majority of the organic substances are reabsorbed and the acid-base balance preserved.

In Table 9–5 is a listing of the principal substances present in urine formed from a mixed diet and a rested metabolic state.

The quantity of urine excreted is controlled by several factors, principally the influence of the antidiuretic hormone (ADH). This hormonal

TABLE 9–5. Inorganic and Organic Substances in Urine Formed from a Mixed Diet in Rested Metabolic State (Based on 1.5 L Volume) (From data of Pitts[18] and Short[21])

Inorganic Substances (gm)		Organic Substances (gm)	
Water	1470.0	Urea	30.0
Sodium chloride (NaCl)	15.0	Creatinine	1.5
Sodium (Na$_2$O)	6.0	Uric acid	0.8
Potassium (K$_2$O)	3.0	Hippuric acid	0.7
Sulphuric acid (S$_2$O$_3$)	2.5	Potassium salt	0.01
Phosphoric acid (P$_2$O$_5$)	2.5		
Ammonia	0.7		
Magnesium (MgO)	0.3		
Calcium (CaO)	0.3		
Iron	0.005		

Urine pH values may range from 4.7 to 8.0; specific gravity varies between 1.012 and 1.025

secretion, controlled by blood osmotic concentration, regulates the reabsorption of the plasma. During periods of temporary negative fluid balance, as during prolonged physical exertion, ADH influence is manifested in increased water reabsorption and reflected in concentrated urine. Positive fluid balance and pressure increases within glomerular capillaries result in increased urine production; however, the urine is less concentrated.

Analysis of post-exercise urine samples reveals extensive kidney involvement which is reflected in decreased urine production as well as decreased pH and altered urine composition.[10] As a result of fluid losses through sensible and insensible means, urine specific gravity is increased. Increases in blood lactic acid levels result in a decreased urine pH to acidity levels; small amounts of lactic acid also may be detected in the urine. Excessive bicarbonate also contributes to the acidification of urine. Creatinine substances are elevated. Functional albuminuria is normally present following prolonged muscular effort. Albuminuria, indicated by the presence of protein (usually albumin) in urine, is indicative of renal dysfunction; however, its presence in urine following physical exertion is usual.

Urine provides information about the kidneys and urinary tract and, being an end-product of metabolism, the whole body. No conclusions can be drawn from urinalyses alone: the nature of the work load and of the physiologic response must be considered.[7]

REFERENCES

1. Aas, K., and Blegen, E.: The renal blood flow and the glomerular filtration rate in congestive heart failure and some other clinical conditions. *Scand. J. Clin. Lab. Invest.*, 1:22–32, 1949.

2. Barclay, J. A., Cooke, W. T., Kenney, R. A., and Nutt, M. E.: The effects of water diuresis and exercise on the volume and composition of the urine. *Am. J. Physiol.*, 148:327–337, 1947.

3. Cannon, W. B.: Organization for physiological homeostasis. *Physiol. Rev.*, 9:399–431, 1929.

4. Castiglioni, A.: *A History of Medicine.* 2nd Ed. Edited by E. B. Krumbhaar, New York, Alfred A. Knopf, 1958.

5. Chapman, C. B., Henschel, A., and Forsgren, A.: Renal plasma flow during moderate exercise of several hours' duration in normal male subjects. *Proc. Soc. Exper. Biol. and Med.*, 69:170–171, 1948.

6. Chapman, C. B., Henschel, A., Minckler, J., Forsgren, A., and Keys, A.: The effect of exercise on renal plasma flow in normal male subjects. *J. Clin. Invest.*, 27:639–644, 1948.

7. Clendening, L.: *The Human Body.* 4th Ed. New York, Alfred A. Knopf Co., 1959.

8. Gray, H.: *Anatomy of the Human Body.* 28th Ed. Edited by C. M. Goss, Philadelphia, Lea & Febiger, 1966.

9. Haist, R. E.: Blood volume: body water: water balance. *In* Best, C. H., and Taylor, N. B. (Eds.): *The Physiological Basis of Medical Practice.* 7th Ed. Baltimore, The Williams & Wilkins Co., 1961.

10. Hawk, P. B., Oser, B. L., and Summerson, W. H.: *Practical Physiological Chemistry.* 13th Ed. New York, McGraw-Hill, 1954.

11. Höber, R.: *Physical Chemistry of Cells and Tissues.* Philadelphia, Blakiston Co., 1945.

12. Kattus, A. A., Sinclair-Smith, B., Genest, J., and Newman, E. V.: The effect of exercise on the renal mechanism of electrolyte excretion in normal subjects. *Bull. Johns Hopkins Hosp., 84:*344–368, 1949.

13. Koch, A.: The kidney. *In* Ruch, T. C., and Patton, H. D. (Eds.): *Physiology and Biophysics,* 19th Ed. Philadelphia, W. B. Saunders Co., 1965.

14. Lambertsen, C. J.: Transport of oxygen and carbon dioxide by the blood. *In* Bard, P. (Ed.): *Medical Physiology.* 11th Ed. St. Louis, C. V. Mosby Co., 1961.

15. Nordenskiöld, E.: *The History of Biology.* New York, Tudor Publishing Co., 1936.

16. Olmsted, J. M. D., and Olmsted, E. H.: *Claude Bernard and the Experimental Method in Medicine.* New York, Henry Schuman, 1952.

17. Peters, J. P., and Van Slyke, D. D.: *Quantitative Clinical Chemistry.* 2nd Ed. Baltimore, The Williams & Wilkins Co., 1946.

18. Pitts, R. F.: *Physiology of the Kidney and Body Fluids.* Chicago, Year Book Medical Publishers, 1963.

19. Radigan, L. R., and Robinson, S.: Effects of environmental heat stress and exercise on renal blood flow and filtration rate. *Am. J. Physiol., 159:*585–586, 1949.

20. Rowell, L. B., Blackmon, J. R., and Bruce, R. A.: Indocyanine green clearance and estimated hepatic blood flow during mild to maximal exercise in upright man. *J. Clin. Invest., 43:*1677–1690, 1964.

21. Short, R.: *A Synopsis of Physiology.* 5th Ed., Edited by C. C. N. Vass, Baltimore, The Williams & Wilkins Co., 1961.

22. Singer, R. B., and Hastings, A. B.: An improved clinical method for the estimation of disturbances of the acid-base balance of human blood. *Medicine, 27:*223–242, 1948.

23. Smith, H. W.: *The Kidney. Structure and Function in Health and Disease.* New York, Oxford University Press, 1958.

24. Watt, B. K., and Merrill, A. L.: *Composition of Foods.* Agricultural Handbook No. 8, Agricultural Research Service, U. S. D. A., Washington D.C., 1963.

25. White, H. L., and Rolf, D.: Effects of exercise and of some other influences on the renal circulation in man. *Am. J. Physiol., 152:*505–516, 1948.

C h a p t e r

10

SELECTED TOPICS

Human physical performance is the result of complex interdependent physiological, psychological, and physical processes. Action is stimulated by inducements ranging from the preservation of life to the gratification of a whim.

Although much remains to be learned about the processes that govern man, there exists a rather extensive body of knowledge from which one can draw information. In this chapter, discussion is focused on selected topics relating to exercise, including some beliefs that are widely held but inconsistent with known facts.

Ergogenic Aids (So-Called)

By definition, an ergogenic aid is a work-producing aid; however, claims are often inconsistent with the data of carefully controlled research.

Ergogenic aids may take the following forms:

1. Nutritional: special foods, food supplements, and beverages
2. Pharmaceutical: preparations introduced orally or hypodermically, or applied topically
3. Inhalation of gases in pure or mixed form

Irrespective of the method of administration, an ergogenic aid is *supposed* to result in the achievement of greater physiological and physical goals than those previously attainable.

Nutritional Considerations

Foodstuffs, in their myriad forms, represent not only a source of nourishment to the consumer, but a source of revenue to the producer, distributor, and marketer. One of the characteristics of an affluent, free society is the extent of advertising which is conducted through mass communication media. Through the buying power of the credulous, fat profits are realized for the distributor, and often, many profits in fat are acquired by the consumer. Engel has singled out the role of ailments, especially in the older age group, as a contributing factor in the formation of food fads. Olson relates some food faddism to "acute or chronic aberrations."

High on the list of nutritional supplements are vitamins and tonics. Vitamins are organic substances which are present in natural foodstuffs and are essential to normal metabolism. A lack of these essential substances results in deficiency diseases. It is quite possible for vitamin deficiencies to occur; however, this condition must be clinically established. Tonics are remedies which promote vigor.

The ergogenic benefit from supplemental vitamin feeding has eluded the careful researcher. In a study conducted by Karpovich and Millman placebos were determined to be as beneficial as vitamin B_1 tablets. Working with a slightly younger group of males, from twelve to seventeen years of age, Montoye et al. noted that strength and endurance were unaffected by vitamin B_{12} administration.[59] Keys and Henschel noted that strength, endurance, dexterity, resistance to fatigue, and

TABLE 10–1.   Use of "Health" Foods and Reasons for Use
(From Jalso et al.[36])

	% of Subjects					
	"Faddist" group			"Non-faddist" group		
		Reasons for use			Reasons for use	
Nutritional Supplement or "Health" Food	Used	Medi-cal*	Non-medi-cal†	Used	Medi-cal*	Non-medi-cal†
Vitamins	73.6	24.5	49.1	58.4	47.9	10.4
Iron tonic	20.7	11.3	9.4	2.1	2.1	—
Wheat germ	56.6	1.9	54.7	6.2	—	6.2
Yogurt	37.8	1.9	35.9	2.1	—	2.1
Molasses	52.8	—	52.8	14.6	—	14.6
Honey	67.9	7.5	60.4	14.6	—	14.6
Brewer's yeast	45.3	3.8	41.5	—	—	—
Safflower oil capsules	30.2	1.9	28.3	2.1	—	2.1
Organically grown vegetables and fruits	50.9	7.5	43.4	2.1	—	2.1

* Refers to doctor's prescription.
† Includes friends suggestion, own decision, magazine, or newspaper.

TABLE 10-2.   Avoidance of Certain Foods and Reasons for Avoidance

| | "Faddist" group | | | | "Non-faddist" group | | | |
| | | Reasons for avoidance† | | | | Reasons for avoidance† | | |
Foods	Avoided	Health	Personal taste or religious restriction	Harmful	Avoided	Health	Personal taste or religious restriction	Harmful
Saturated fats	52.8	41.5	5.7	5.7	4.2	2.1	—	2.1
Foods treated with pesticide	37.7	35.9	1.9	20.8	—	—	—	—
Refined foods	39.6	37.7	5.7	17.0	—	—	—	—
Enriched foods	32.1	30.2	5.7	11.3	—	—	—	—
Fortified foods	30.2	28.3	5.7	17.0	—	—	—	—
Foods fertilized with chemicals	30.2	28.3	3.8	15.1	—	—	—	—

% of Subjects

* Some subjects checked more than one food; thus columns do not total 100%.
† In some cases, more than one reason was checked.

recovery from physical exertion were unaffected by the supplemental administration of five B-complex vitamins and vitamin C (ascorbic acid).

In this relation, the study of Jalso et al. is most interesting (see Tables 10–1 and 10–2).

The use of vitamins by 73.6% of the "faddists" and by 58.4% of the "nonfaddists" suggests the effectiveness of nonmedical advice and of advertising. Wheat germ is eaten almost totally for nonmedical reasons by the "faddist" and "nonfaddist" groups.

Wheat germ oil, a source of vitamin E (antisterility vitamin), was shown by Cureton[13] and by Cureton and Pohndorf[14] to be beneficial to the physical performance of middle-aged men, but Cureton and Pohndorf[15] were unable to detect beneficial effects on young men. Thomas was also unable to observe the beneficial influence of vitamin E on the performance levels of young males.[85] (Vitamin E also is contained in the oils of cotton seed, palm, and rice and in whole grain cereals.)

In their comprehensive review, Mayer and Bullen report, "It would appear that a clear demonstration of the beneficial effects of vitamin E has yet to be given."[53]

Members of the Committee on the Medical Aspect of Sports of the American Medical Association caution that vitamins must not be taken indiscriminately in the hope that "if the diet is vitamin deficient, vitamin supplements will combat the deficiency."

Tuttle has stated:

Nothing takes the place of vitamins in cases of vitamin deficiency, but there are no more useless products as a means of warding off fatigue, or increasing capacity to do work, in the absence of vitamin deficiency. . . . Supercharging the diet with vitamins is of no use, either for warding off fatigue, increasing capacity to do work, or improving health.[87]

The topic of nutrition for the athlete in particular as well as the topic of nutrition in general is an especially lively one. In the opening paragraph of their comprehensive review, Mayer and Bullen state:

We thus feel that we should state at the outset that the conclusion of this review will be that recent work has not brought new facts; the concept that any well-balanced diet is all that athletes actually require for peak performance has not been superseded.[53]

Excesses of particular foodstuffs, such as fats and protein, are unwarranted and are detrimental to physical performance of moderate duration. Nevertheless, fat (exemplified by milk, butter, and animal fat) constitutes more than one-third of the American diet including the so-called training table diet.

Excessive fat intake reduces peristaltic action, and thus affects gastric emptying and the digestive process. In the digestive process, ingested foodstuffs are converted into assimilable forms in rather specific locations. Gastric digestion is chiefly that of protein by the enzymes of the gastric juice. Upper intestinal tract digestion is that of carbohydrates, proteins, and fats. It is here that secondary digestion, the digestion process of great significance, takes place.

Protein catabolites present additional problems during periods of prolonged strenuous activity. These catabolites are eliminated only through urine elimination; urine can be excreted only by the kidneys. During such strenuous activity, effective kidney function is considerably reduced, thus urine formation practically ceases and protein catabolites are retained. Metabolic acidosis,* which normally accompanies such activity periods, is further aggravated by this additional fixed acid level.

Carbohydrates provide for the quickest and most abundant energy release. Furthermore, the catabolites (CO_2 and H_2O) are easily eliminated, primarily through the lungs, as carbon dioxide and water vapor, and through the sweat glands as perspiration. (Turn to discussion of "protein sparers," p. 172.)

Guild, who is a distance runner and a medical doctor, places great stress on carbohydrates, especially for pre-athletic contest meals. (Journalistic license has even allowed newsmen to report: "Harvard Doctor Advocates Spaghetti for Pre-Game Meal.") Spaghetti, a starch, is in fact an excellent carbohydrate source.

Despite the fact that America is a conglomerate of races and culture groups, the Puritan influence relative to the imbibing of alcoholic beverages has been profound and long lasting. Milk, fruit juices, water, coffee, and tea persist as the usual beverages taken with the meal of the athlete. Many European athletes imbibe beverages of low alcohol content, such as wine and beer.†

The fond regard of the South European for wine is based on its ritualistic use[47] as well as its bouquet and exquisite taste. Malt beverages serve as a substitute in those North European countries which are not blessed with the proper soil and climate to practice viticulture.

Because of the debilitating effect of alcohol on the nervous system, wines and beer cannot be recommended to the athlete as a pre-athletic contest beverage; however, provided these beverages can be tolerated i.e., they do not impair mental or physical function, they may be imbibed during any season. Alcohol tolerance, which varies considerably

---

* Metabolic acidosis: a reduced alkali reserve (bicarbonate) of the blood and body fluids. Fluid pH levels may become decreased.

† Approximately 10% alcohol content

among individuals, is related to enzyme system effectiveness. Alcohol, catabolized by enzymes, is oxidized to acetaldehyde and acetic acid, an energy source. The end-products of this carbohydrate metabolism are carbon dioxide and water. An awareness that alcohol is quickly absorbed into the blood stream from the stomach provides a basis for raising tolerance levels slightly. Its absorption may be delayed by foodstuffs within the stomach. Small quantities of low alcohol content wines and beers *taken with meals* may be tolerated by the majority.

The general glow of warmth which accompanies alcoholic beverage ingestion is deceiving. Due to the vasodilatory effect of alcohol on peripheral blood vessels, body heat is lost at a quickened rate. Yet, because of this vasodilatory effect, it is often prescribed by some medical doctors as a means of reducing cardiovascular stress.[47]

Beverages such as coffee or tea contain caffeine which presents problems increasing in direct relation to the degree of reactivity to the substance. Although the caffeine content per cup of each is similar, tea is often advocated while coffee is not. The amount of caffeine in coffee or tea is dependent upon its concentration. A cup of strong coffee or tea contains approximately 0.1 to 0.15 gm of caffeine.[86] Obviously, the justification for tea is unwarranted unless "weak" tea is served.

Milk and fruit juices, or water, constitute the usual beverages served with pre-contest meals. To some, however, one or both of these beverages i.e., milk or fruit juices may serve as a mild cathartic.

While Mayer and Bullen recognize the benefits of convenience as well as camaraderie offered by training tables for athletes, they emphasize "there is no *nutritional* justification for training tables."[54]

Athletes generally require no special consideration. The principles of good nutrition apply equally to all people. The differences between the physically active athlete and the less active individual should be reflected in the caloric intake from a balanced diet. For all normal, healthy people, a balanced diet would include, bread, cereal, eggs, fruit, meat or fish, low fat milk and milk products, vegetables, and beverages. If the foregoing variety is achieved, proteins, fats, carbohydrates, vitamins, and minerals will normally be supplied.

Pre-athletic contest dietary rules are few: an avoidance of excesses of fats and proteins, of foods contributing to flatulence, and of alcoholic beverages is justified.

The goal of all is contained in a paraphrase of the oft-quoted message of the Roman satirical poet,* a sound meal in a sound body is something to strive for.

---

* Juvenal: "Orandum est ut sit mens sana in corpore sano" (A sound mind in a sound body is a thing to be prayed for).[89]

Pharmaceuticals

Man's quest for lotions, potions, or notions which restore vitality is part of his historical record. The search continues.

Adoption of nonprescription preparations or foodstuffs which purport to enhance vitality is convincing testimony to the success of advertising.[36] Fortunately, a number of preparations can be purchased only if medically prescribed. Unfortunately, an illicit drug trade flourishes and a ready market is found among the gullible or naive persons.

To what extent is the prolongation of effort enhanced by drugs or foodstuffs? On the ensuing pages, some of the more frequently used drugs or foodstuffs will be discussed.

Alkalies

Collectively, alkalies are fairly strong, basic preparations which serve as fluid buffers. Sodium and potassium hydroxide serve as examples of such alkalies (see Fig. 9–4, p. 209).

Their use as an ergogenic aid is couched in the logic of buffering the acid end-products of muscle metabolism, notably lactic acid. Small but gradual decreases in blood pH, caused by lactic acid, occur at the expense of the alkaline reserve. To a degree, a decrease in blood pH is beneficial and results in a greater unloading of oxygen at tissue level, thereby effecting greater oxygen utilization (see Fig. 6–10, p. 129). Astrand[3] and Dill[17] found blood pH levels to fall *below* 7.00 after gruelling exercise.

One of the limiting factors to continued performance is that of high concentrations of blood lactic acid. Physical performance becomes rather unbearable when blood lactic acid levels attain the order of 200 mg%. (As a matter of interest, one of the highest concentrations of blood lactic acid, 300 mg%, was reported by Crescitelli and Taylor.)

The inability of sufficient amounts of lactic acid to become resynthesized (via either the Cori cycle or through oxidation) contributes to the decrease in blood pH levels. Thus, reasoned some researchers, raising the blood pH levels *before* exercise by alkali ingestion seemed logical.

In 1926, Ronzoni fed alkaline salts to his subjects and found the practice to be feasible. In 1931, Dennig, Talbot, Edwards, and Dill reported an increase in endurance and oxygen debt capability (in treadmill and stationary bicycle performance) following alkali feeding of sodium citrate, sodium bicarbonate, and potassium citrate. One year later, Dill, Edwards, and Talbot reported an increase in oxygen debt capability but not in muscular performance.

Karpovich repeated the alkali feeding experiment.[40] He used the mixture reported to be beneficial by Dennig et al. and found the feeding to be ineffective as an aid to performance of varsity swimmers. Johnson and Black also found blood alkalinizers (a buffer addition advocated by Dennig* as well as phosphated sugar advocated by Embden et al.†) to be ineffective as ergogenic aids for cross-country runners.

Wolf recommends the daily feeding of 10 to 15 gm of sodium bicarbonate as an aid to achieving an alkalotic form of diet which is necessary to "relieve the [functional] disturbances and . . . regain form" lost through overtraining. Data were not presented.

Alkali ingestion may contribute to flatulence and catharsis. Run-to-exhaustion studies or human performance studies always stir the topic of discomfort-tolerance levels. The data on alkalinizers are not conclusive. Additional, carefully controlled, multivariate research is needed before the value of alkali feeding can be resolved.

Amphetamine (Benzedrine; "Pep Pills")

Benzedrine is related in molecular structure and in physiologic action to ephedrine‡ as well as to other sympathomimetic amines. All act as stimulants to the autonomic nerve fibers. Because it acts as a stimulant to the central nervous system, this drug is used by students, especially during final examination periods, as a means of combatting fatigue or of reducing the requirement for sleep.

Some gullible athletes have been adversely influenced to use them in their quest for greater physical achievement.

Alles and Feigen noted that amphetamine sulfate contributed to greater production in subjects who performed on an ergograph. Smith and Beecher reported significant improvement in swimming and in selected track and field performances. More recently, Ikai and Steinhaus noted gains in strength of the forearm flexors which they attributed to amphetamine.

On the other side of the ledger are those whose results are diametric in nature to those just cited.

Foltz et al. injected amphetamine intravenously into subjects who subsequently performed on a stationary bicycle; amphetamine proved deficient as an ergogenic aid. More recently Karpovich reported amphetamine lacking as an ergogenic aid for swimmers, trackmen, and

---

* Dennig, H.: *German Weekly Med. J.*, 63:733, 1937.

† Embden, G. E., Grafe, E., and Schmitz, E.: *Hoppe Seyler's Zeitschrift Physiol. Chem.*, 113:67, 1921.

‡ An andrenergic (sympathomimetic) agent which produces results similar to those produced by epinephrine.

treadmill runners.[39] In a study by Rasch et al., 26 subjects who were administered the drug failed to display ergogenic benefit. In 1963, Golding and Barnard also reported a lack of benefit from amphetamine for treadmill performance.

Amphetamine is a drug.[46] Its indiscriminate or excessive use constitutes a dangerous practice. Not only is the danger of addiction present, but the possibility of circulatory collapse has also been reported. The drug has gained usage by a substantial number of athletes.[70] Of 133 completed questionnaires, 46 (35%) contained reference to use by athletes during competition.

Ryan sums up the stand taken by the ad hoc Committee on Amphetamines and Athletics:

> Since the use of any drug to improve athletic performance has already been made grounds for disqualification by the International Amateur Athletic Federation, the Amateur Athletic Union, and the United States Olympic Association as being contrary to the highest ideals of sportsmanship, and since the use of amphetamines even in moderately small doses is known in many instances to result in habituation and harmful effects, the Committee has recommended that the use of amphetamines for this purpose be condemned. Because these drugs can be obtained legally only on prescription, a serious obligation devolves on physicians to help prevent such usage by prescribing them only for well recognized medical indications.

Aspartates

As is often the case, fragmented bits of evidence were pieced together into a convincing whole and potassium and magnesium aspartates became popularized as possessing anti-fatigue qualities.

Aspartate is a food, aspartic acid salt, and not a drug; however, its indiscriminate use is not justified.

While studying its ergogenic effect, researchers have obtained diametric results. Shaw et al., in a 1962 study involving 163 subjects, presented evidence in support of aspartates for fatigue relief. Fallis et al., whose study involved male prisoners who were weight lifters, reported a lack of benefit from potassium and magnesium aspartates. Consolazio et al. also presented evidence which contradicted the fatigue relief reported by Shaw et al.

The stated opinion of the membership of the A. M. A. Council on Drugs is presented:

A preparation containing potassium and magnesium aspartates is claimed to be useful in the management of the fatigue syndrome. However, since there is no precise experimental model analogous to fatigue in man, laboratory evidence of its actions cannot be directly transposed to human situation. The clinical trials do not convincingly demonstrate efficacy.[11]

Caffeine

The amount of caffeine ingested in such beverages as coffee or tea is obviously dependent upon the strength of the beverage (see p. 220). Caffeine is a stimulant to the central nervous system. Reaction to it is broad and in extreme cases may be manifested as dyspepsia, irritability, or palpitation. To some, caffeine contributes to insomnia. To the end that any of the above conditions contribute to depressed mental states, work capacity may well be affected.

Fallis et al. administered caffeine intravenously to four subjects who subsequently performed on a stationary bicycle; endurance was increased and recovery from work was hastened.

Ganzlen et al. noted the combination of caffeine and pentylenetetrazol (another powerful central nervous system stimulant) to produce ergogenic benefit, which was reflected in maximum oxygen consumption as well as in work capacity gains. A special note of caution must be inserted here. Pentylenetetrazol must be administered only by competent *medical* personnel. Its use in shock treatment therapy, to produce generalized convulsion, is testimony of its capability.

Caffeine, in the amounts found in coffee or tea, is the basis of controversial discussion. For some, it produces deleterious effects; for others, the reward is psychological nourishment. Its use must be governed by the degree of reactivity to it.

Gelatin

Gelatin, a derived protein formed from tissue collagen,* contains glycine; glycine is chemically related to creatine. Creatine, in both phosphate and phosphokinase forms, serves an important role in muscle contraction (see p. 11–13).† Presumably due to this chemical relationship, research into the ergogenic effects of gelatin was undertaken. Prominent among the researchers was Karpovich.

In 1941, Karpovich and Pestrecov conducted an extensive study involving college swimmers and other athletes. In addition, a group of county jail inmates served as subjects. The researchers concluded that gelatin did not possess ergogenic qualities. Psychological uplift was apparent. All inmates improved in performance after the ingestion of either gelatin or cereal (farina).

---

* Fibrillar connective tissue, located within the deeper or connective tissue layer of the skin, is collagenic; produces gelatin.

† Creatine phosphate (a compound of creatine with phosphoric acid) not only provides an energy source for muscle contraction, but furnishes energy for the resynthesis of ATP. Creatine phosphokinase (an enzyme) is also extremely important to muscle contraction due to its role in ADP formation.

Knehr et al. administered 60 gm of gelatin daily to their subjects and concluded that gelatin failed to influence performance.

In a more recent study, Hilsendager and Karpovich fed glycine and niacin to more than 60 subjects. (Niacin, perhaps remembered as nicotinic acid, is part of the vitamin B_1 complex.) One-third of the group performed on a stationary bicycle, the remaining subjects performed on an arm ergometer. Neither of the substances, either in combination or separately, was found to qualify as an ergogenic aid.

Gelatin may well be remembered as the dessert of the depression years; however, it was not (and is not) ergogenic.

Hormones

The influence of biochemically produced hormones is generally well understood. Synthetic hormones are presently being intensively researched. The outlook for their use as ergogenic aids is promising; however, there are some notable exceptions. One is singled out for discussion: anabolic steroids.

The human testes secrete the androgen testosterone which has been labeled the masculinizing hormone. Testosterone is also isolated from the testes of bulls and is commercially available. Apparently, a number of athletes have been directed to its use by those who have undoubtedly engaged in conjectural activity. Bulls are big and strong; what testosterone accomplishes for the bull might also be accomplished in the athlete through testosterone ingestion. Perhaps the inference is faulty, but so is the logic of those who accept it.

Testosterone, by promoting nitrogen balance, produces growth-promoting effects on bone and muscle tissue as well as the sex organs.

While commercially available androgenic steroids possess the same properties as testosterone, the side effects are serious. Many factors must be considered and these can be intelligently considered only by competent endocrinologists. They cannot be acquired through the "wise counsel" of a friend who ingests anabolic steroids.

Endocrinologists Talbot et al. note that testosterone which is administered under conditions of negative calorie balance may *accelerate* the rate at which body fat stores are depleted. They also point out the limits to muscular hypertrophy which may be induced by male hormonal action. The action of the protein anabolic effect of the androgens on the skeleton is also limited. These authors also caution, "androgens tend to accelerate epiphyseal calcification and epiphyseal closure." Especially to prepubertal males, the ingestion of steroids may result in a decreased ultimate height.

All males must consider that rather than weight gain, weight loss may result. Kidney damage may ensue. The increase in virilization may be a state of mind. From the American Medical Association comes this sobering thought: "If a course of therapy causes a greater rate of skeletal maturation than linear growth, reduction in the otherwise attainable adult height may result from premature closure of the epiphyses."[64] The council members also warn of liver function impairment caused by androgenic-anabolic steroid ingestion.

As an ergogenic aid, it is found lacking. Fowler et al. reported a lack of significant difference between young weight trainers who received steroids and those who received placebos with respect to work capacity, strength, or motor performance.

Salt. Refer to discussion of salt balance in Chapter 7.

Sugar

This carbohydrate group of monosaccharides contains many forms including cane, fruit, and malt, as well as the saccharine substance which is deposited by the honeybee. All are highly soluble in water and are readily digested. Except for those given intravenously, sugars take about one-half hour to be absorbed. Thus, the logic of eating candy or of imbibing sweetened high calorie drinks immediately before physical effort of short duration is faulty. Prolonged effort, e.g., a marathon race, is enhanced by the ingestion of sweetened drinks during the running of the event.

Many additional drugs or foodstuffs might be included in a discussion of ergogenic aids. Some drugs, such as cocaine, are in fact ergogenic aids but are habit forming. The use of drugs by athletes raises ethical questions and is of growing concern to the members of the medical profession.[88] It must also become the concern of all administrators, coaches, trainers, managers, and athletes.

Oxygen Inhalation

Oxygen inhalation has gained widespread acceptance by the American professional football player. To a lesser degree, the practice has been adopted by some collegiate players. Despite the fact that rules allow fewer substitutions in such running games as soccer and lacrosse, the oxygen tank is missing from the pitch and the lacrosse field. Physiologically considered, is the practice defensible?

Irrespective of blood pH fluctuation,* oxygen saturation of arterial blood is above 95%. Also, during increased work states, the diffusion coefficient for oxygen can increase from 75 ml/min to 90 ml/min. Mostyn

---

* For human blood: pH 7.58 — 7.00 normal fluctuation.

et al. observed a greater pulmonary diffusion capacity in accomplished swimmers than in individuals who led sedentary lives. In the accumulative sense, oxygen cannot be stored within the body. The problem is not that of a significant decrease of oxygen saturation of arterial blood,* nor is it related to pulmonary diffusion capacity. The problem appears to rest with the cardiovascular system in that the blood is not being circulated rapidly enough to meet the demands of the tissues.

Long before the Japanese redirected the interest of the world's athletes and coaches to pure oxygen inhalation,† Hill and Flack, in 1909 and 1910, reported ergogenic benefit from oxygen administration.[32,33] Not only was physical performance improved, but recovery was hastened. In 1911, Feldman and Hill had observed a lowered lactic acid accumulation which they attributed to pre-event oxygen inhalation. In 1934, Karpovich reported pre-event oxygen inhalation to be a contributing factor to speed in the hundred yard swim.[38] (The swimmers were comfortably able to dispense with the natural practice of breathing for longer-than-usual intervals.) In 1952, Miller administered oxygen before, during, and following treadmill exercise. Inhalation of pure oxygen, when compared with air of atmospheric mixture, did not contribute to beneficial changes in heart rate, blood pressure, blood lactate, or endurance. Miller also reported the presence of a psychological lift for those subjects who breathed atmospheric air from a tank which had been labeled "oxygen." Bannister and Cunningham reported results which are in agreement with those of Miller.[5] Just recently, Bjorgum and Sharkey noted that pre-event oxygen breathing (of one-minute duration) did not aid recovery following five-minute treadmill running. Cunningham reported oxygen breathing (70 to 73% O_2) during maximal treadmill running to be beneficial to performance and to recovery.

The reader of the preceding articles must conclude that ergogenic benefit may be gained from pre-event oxygen inhalation provided the work is of short duration, i.e., less than three minutes. The subjects in the Feldman and Hill study ran up and down stairs for intervals ranging from 1 to 2:56 minutes. Pre-event oxygen inhalation varied between 3 and 7 minutes; post-event oxygen breathing was continued for 30 minutes. Performance, in the study by Karpovich, was also of short duration,[38] a 100-yard swim.

From the following two studies, the reader is led to observe the ergogenic benefit of oxygen administration *during* work. (Note the oxygen percentage.)

---

* Rowell et al. noted that arterial desaturation can take place during heavy work.

† The success of the Japanese swimmers in the 1936 Olympic games was supposedly related to pre-event oxygen inhalation.

Bannister and Cunningham compared the effects of varying oxygen concentrations during exercise. Best results were reported when the mixture contained 66% oxygen. (Other mixtures were 21, 33, and 100%.) Four years later, in 1958, Balke and Wells also reported most beneficial results from a 66% oxygen mixture during strenuous work.

Breathing pure oxygen immediately before an athletic event of more than three minutes' duration has not been shown to be beneficial to improved performance. Recovery is not quickened. The inhalation of a reduced oxygen mixture (66%) *during* work is beneficial and must be considered as an effective ergogenic aid.

The value of oxygen inhalation as it is presently, indiscriminately practiced at the gridiron sidelines can only be viewed as a psychological aid. The duration of pre- and post-play-sequence gas mixture breathing requires additional research. The practicality of the practice is of administrative concern; the question of the physiological benefit of the practice requires further research.

Fatigue

Fatigue is experienced by all. It affects performance. Fatigue may be characterized by a state of impaired efficiency, a reduced capacity for work, a feeling of weariness. It may be caused by a myriad of factors spanning a continuum from boredom, resulting from monotony or general disinterest, to an accumulation of metabolites. Fatigue may be general or it may be specific to appendage or organ.

When intramuscular tension contributes to vasoconstriction,[*] the active tissues become hypoxic and metabolites accumulate; fatigue is hastened. For example, intermittent, static exercise or work forms characterized by great exertion which decreases or arrests blood flow through the working appendage hastens fatigue. Generally, rhythmic physical effort is physiologically defensible—especially if the rest intervals are sufficiently lengthy to enable restorative biochemical processes to occur.

There is little to be gained from studying the kymographic record of an isolated frog muscle. Conditions are strikingly artificial, for the muscle is removed from its normal, optimal environment. Experiments with the frog gastrocnemius do, however, force the conclusion that the site of fatigue is within the myoneural junction and that the nerve is seemingly indefatigable.

---

[*] Two classic studies are cited. Anrep and Saalfeld observed an immediate cessation of blood flow induced by tetanus within the dog gastrocnemius muscle. A. V. Hill showed a pressure of 300 mm Hg resulting from isometric contraction of the frog gastrocnemius.

To an extent, fatigue may be viewed objectively. Dill established "arbitrary limits" to moderate, hard, and maximal work.[17] He cited the influence of physical and environmental conditions. Because moderate work is characterized by small amounts of energy transformation it is of indirect interest to the physiologist. Hard and maximal work *are* affected by physical and environmental conditions. Fatigue, observed as a reduced work efficiency, is enhanced by prolongation of effort under less than optimal external and internal (biochemical) environmental conditions. Objectively viewed, moderate work as characterized by Dill is physical effort which results in an increase of metabolism which is less than 3 times the basal rate. Hard work is defined in terms of metabolism which is elevated between 3 and 8 times the basal rate. The metabolism of maximal work is in excess of 8 times the basal (see Figs. 8–8 and 8–9). Especially in this last category, the rapid depletion of energy stores and the accumulation of metabolites is pronounced and can be quantified. Christensen recognizes that a physiological view of work must include an optimal physical environment which enhances productivity yet decreases fatigue. Fatigue need not be experienced provided rate and load of work are "rightly adapted to the working capacity of the body." Working capacity may be revealed in body temperature, oxygen consumption, pulse rate, and fluid loss. Noltie contends:

Whatever definition of fatigue be agreed upon, insufficiency of oxygen is likely to be accepted as one of the possible causes of its onset. The oxygen may be essential either for removal of some substances causing the actual fatigue or for continuance of some self-regenerating cycle.

Margaria and Gualtierotti maintain that fatigue evaluation cannot be objectified by measuring lactic acid or other tissue metabolites because these analyses consider few aspects of the many probable factors which cause fatigue.[50] Their current efforts have been directed to the nervous system. Margaria et al. noted the effect of different stresses on human spinal reflexes.[51] Hypoglycemia and hypoxia induced by moderate and heavy exercise resulted in significant changes in spinal reflexes, i.e., in total reflex time, in endplate delay, and in motor and sensory pathway conduction speed. Luco and Rosenblueth observed a decrease in acetylcholine levels following repeated stimulation of muscle.

Factors that influence fatigue are legion; psychological overtones are dominant. Motivation, incentive, effort—all affect human performance. The designer of industrial machinery, of typewriters, of sculls; the military drill instructor; the athletic coach *must* reflect their concern for the economy of motion as well as psychological factors in the alleviation of fatigue.

The distinguished German biochemist Gustav Embden (1874–1933) analogized fatigue and death, the vital difference being that fatigue is reversible.

Like death, fatigue is inevitable. An acceptance of this fact might serve as the underlying principle of physical conditioning for any vocational, athletic, or recreational pursuit. The pedagogic bag-of-tricks must be filled with psychology: incentives, rewards, motivation.

For the complex human, mental-set, discomfort-tolerance levels, and psychological wants all play a role in fatigue discussion. External factors (environmental, physical) as well as physiologic factors (steady pace at low metabolic activity or rhythmical pace punctuated by sufficiently lengthy rest intervals) must also be considered. Fatigue is inevitable, but well-planned conditioning programs serve to delay its arrival.

Relative degrees of fatigue are couched in such words as staleness, overtraining, chronic fatigue, or exhaustion. Of these descriptive words, only fatigue and exhaustion may be partly quantified. Although used interchangeably, the words possess vastly different meanings. Exhaustion, defined as an extreme form of fatigue, is reserved by the exercise physiologist for use in describing an inability to respond to stimuli. Blood sugar concentrations differ significantly between fatigue and exhaustion. With exhaustion, the blood sugar concentrations are considerably reduced.

Fatigue may never be defined in precise terms; it is a conglomerate of characteristics. R. C. Browne noted:

It is a fact that prolonged application to a task produces symptoms in the subject and signs in the performance . . . that performance is related to environment . . . that it shows a natural diurnal and nocturnal rhythm. But it is a fiction that there is a single entity called fatigue and that the search has only to be long enough to find a single test for it. The human being has many functions and each one fits a different test.

Smoking

The harmful effects of long-term cigarette smoking have been thoroughly documented in the report of the advisory committee to the Surgeon General.[81] More recently, Federal legislation has been enacted requiring all cigarette manufacturers to label each package with a warning of the possible dangers to the health of the smoker. Nevertheless, the sale of cigarettes, pipes, and tobacco is at an all-time high. Success in tobacco merchandising is assured by an outlay of $250,000,000 yearly for advertising which features both sexes, and all occupations, social classes, races, and culture groups.

One can only surmise how effective would be an equally vigorous advertising campaign featuring a soft, dirge accompaniment to hacking and coughing or to the moaning of patients suffering from lung cancer or emphysema.

Apart from the threat to health, the effect of smoking on ventilation poses a perennial question. While the "exception can never prove the rule," a picture of the successful smoker-athlete who is featured in an extensive advertising campaign is convincingly soothing to the credulous viewer. The following evidence of the deleterious nature of smoking is related to its short-term effect on pulmonary function. The studies cited are of recent publication, since 1960, and involve young adults.

Wilson et al. noted a significant decrease in timed capacity (FEV_t), total lung capacity, and maximal breathing capacity of heavy smokers. Participating in this study were 14 heavy smokers and 14 nonsmokers.

Simonsson reported similar results with normal subjects as well as subjects with a variety of pulmonary diseases. Following inhalation of smoke from one or two cigarettes, decreases in timed capacities were noted among subjects. These decreased capacities persisted for one hour following the cessation of smoking.

Rothfeld et al., studying effect of smoking two cigarettes on the pulmonary function of 19 normal subjects and 23 patients with pulmonary disorders, reported a significant increase in ventilation equivalent in the normal subjects. An increased VE_{O_2} was attributed to impaired oxygenation, a reduced efficiency of ventilation.

Nadel and Comroe noted a 31% average decrease in airway conductance to result from 15 puffs of cigarette smoke within a five-minute period. The onset of the decreased airway conductance was noted to occur in sixty seconds and to last an average of thirty-five minutes (range ten to eighty minutes). Of particular significance is the fact that the airway conductance decrease occurred under conditions of rest. During maximum ventilation, the decrease would become more pronounced.

Martt observed a significantly decreased mean pulmonary diffusing capacity in 40 cigarette smokers who used one pack or more per day. Thirty-nine persons comprised the nonsmoker group. The mean age of the group was 27.5 years.

Shapiro and Patterson reported the largest vital capacities in 25 nonsmoking athletes as compared with 31 nonathletic smokers and 11 nonsmoking nonathletic subjects. They noted smoking to be associated with decreased maximal breathing capacity.

The studies of McFarland are interesting. McFarland, alone and with others,[55,56] noted that deep inhalation of smoke from one cigarette resulted in blood carbon monoxide saturation of approximately 2%. The effect of smoke inhalation from three cigarettes resulted in an elevation of blood carbon monoxide saturation equivalent to that produced by an altitude of 2286 m (7500 ft). Of great consequence is the 4% reduction in arterial oxygen saturation at this altitude. (In other words, the three-cigarette-inhaler is living at an altitude of 2286 m.)

Short-term effects of smoking have been noted: smokers generally perform less well in ventilatory function tests than nonsmokers. There are, however, additional factors that need to be considered. Levels of accomplishment on the pulmonary function tests described above are all subject to the caprices of mankind. Further, the possessor of high discomfort-tolerance levels can "give away" advantages such as the smoker athlete might. Desire can override discomfort. The long-term effects of smoking are deleterious to health. The smoking habit must be discouraged through example and persuasion rather than admonition.

Physical Activity and the Female

In the realm of sports participation there remains the lingering suspicion that a woman who inclines to sport most obviously possess characteristics of intersexuality. Erdelyi, reporting on 729 Hungarian female athletes, noted the supposition to be highly exaggerated. The few cases she found were of females who were originally classed as intersexual types.

There is a dearth of scientifically documented information relative to the effect of the menstrual cycle on physical performance. Sloan noted that the physical performance of 61 student-teachers of Cape Town (Africa) Training College was not influenced by menstruation. All subjects were Caucasian and were between 17 and 20 years of age. The weekly program of physical education consisted of six and one-half hours of varied activity participation for 13 students and 40 minutes a week of gymnastics for another 35 students. The remaining 13 women did not participate in the physical activity program. All of the 61 students were subjected, on two occasions, to modified Harvard step-testing. Pierson and Lockhart reported motor performance to be unaffected during menstruation. Erdelyi noted that participation in active, competitive sports did not interfere with menarche in her subjects.

Speaking on the topic of a minimum age for competition training, Thomas[84] noted that the average age of the 1964 American Olympic swimming team members was $15\frac{1}{2}$ years. The girls had competed for a minimum of five years previously, before menarche.

The effect of the menstrual cycle on physical performance will continue to be clouded by psychic influence unless premenstrual syndrome and dysmenorrhea become objectively assessed. Participation in physical activity during the menstrual period has not been shown to be a deleterious practice; however, the rule of participation must be personalized. Especially during adolescence is this true. The prevalence of menstrual disorders in adolescence mirrors the asynchronous functioning of hormonal factors during this interval of marked anabolism. Mitolo, recognizing the effect of premenstrual syndrome and dysmenorrhea on physical performance, emphasizes the importance of psychological readiness for participation.

The effect of athletic performance or of physical activity on parturition has been reported by Erdelyi, who noted a considerably shorter duration of labor as well as 50% fewer cesarean sections in the athlete-mother. The well developed perineal musculature presented no difficulty in the delivery process. On a related matter, Gendel reported the results of a five-year study of 35 mothers whose common postpartum complaint was that of chronic low backache. The mothers were young (18 to 23 years of age), nonobese, and healthy; however, muscle tone, especially of the abdominal group, was poor. Gendel concluded that years of physical inactivity contributed to impaired body mechanics. All women responded to graded exercise programs. The "need for planning for prevention of serious disability" constitutes a valid concern for physical educators and physicians.

Physical Fitness

A perusal of professional journals forces upon the reader the conclusion that the level of "physical fitness" of mankind is low by comparison with his forebears. The number of tests of physical fitness, however, is abundant. Although separated into a number of categories the tests fall basically under two categories: capacity tests as exemplified by cardiopulmonary function, pulmonary function, work capacity, muscular strength and endurance, and motor performance tests as exemplified by stimulus-response, motofacient, agility, skill, ability, and balance tests.

In a cognitive sense, the term physical fitness, like health, eludes precise definition. Common to the definitions of both is the concept of an "optimal" quality or a "state of well-being." In health, the functioning of an organism is optimal; in physical fitness the performance or achievement is optimal. The impression is easily fostered that because the concepts and definitions are synonymous, the terms are also interchangeable. A person who experiences cardiac arrest possesses poor health and a low fitness level; however, as recovery progresses, evaluation of the heart and of physical fitness may reveal a disparity of functional accomplishment. The terms possess interchangeable meanings only at the threshold of death. The concept may be likened to a cone: death is represented by the apex where all the lines converge, but at any point removed from the apex the concepts are likely to become widely separated.

The definitions, not unlike many other definitions, are also general. The concept of weight is general, yet it can become specific. A measure of the attractive force of the earth for the body mass is reduced to a numerical value and represents *generally* the attractive forces for the *components* of body mass. If appendage or segment weights are required, they may be ascertained through trigonometric function. In the case of body weight, the general concept is acceptable.

In the case of physical fitness a general concept is not only meaningless, but it also violates the concept of the essential unity of man. Human performance exemplifies an integrated effort of the nervous, skeletal, muscular, circulatory, visceral, and biochemical systems. Intensity of physical effort is influenced by the situation. Any physical situation which threatens to extinguish the strong desire to live is challenged by herculean effort. Psychological drives or challenges vary considerably between individuals and the influence of these drives and challenges is often ignored.

The Harvard step-test is a case in point. Pulse rate in recovery from bench-stepping forms the basis of the Harvard step-test score. Pulse rate is often used in the evaluation of cardiac response to exercise. The validity of this *single measure* to appraise fitness is open to question. Pulse rate is known to be influenced by emotional states, and this influence is especially observable during light and moderate levels of work intensity. Pulse rate is known to vary with the degree of hydration. Brouha observed pulse rate to be influenced by ambient temperature and relative humidity (see Fig. 7–6). Lundgren has shown pulse rate to vary with postprandial interval as well as with prolonged erect posture. Kjellberg et al. observed pulse rate to vary with total circulating hemoglobin.

The Harvard step-test is singled out because of its fame. It was carefully designed for simplicity, a factor which contributes to its extensive use. The test is of five-minutes' duration; however, an individual may stop the bench-stepping at any time before the fifth minute. Formula allowances favor the person who completes the test; however, unless all persons complete the test, can the test retain its label as an evaluator of cardiopulmonary endurance? Might not the test be also a measure of discomfort tolerance? The fact remains that when incentive is structured into the test, the percentage of test completion is remarkably high.

The psychological factor has been introduced into this discussion because it represents the essential difference between the definitions of health and of physical fitness. To a small degree, psychological states may alter some vital processes, but psychological influences alter considerably the evaluation of physical fitness.

Without belaboring the point further, several concluding remarks are in order. The suitability of the adjective *physical* to describe the noun *fitness* is questioned. Rather than physical, psychophysiological adaptation is being assessed. Melding the sum of many physiological functions and psychological influences into a single score is desirable but at present unattainable.

Physiological and physical adaptations to increased metabolic demands imposed by exercise can be measured and assessed by:

1. The oxygen consumed and the carbon dioxide produced during the execution of and recovery from a given exercise task. From the ratio of carbon dioxide produced to the amount of oxygen consumed, *a respiratory exchange ratio* (R) can be quickly calculated. The respiratory exchange ratio is then used as a basis for the evaluation of the *caloric requirement* of the body position in its static or dynamic state. *Maximum oxygen uptake* considered in relationship to body weight yields additional important data. From this point, the exercise physiologist can determine the *gross efficiency* or the *net efficiency* of the organism to the task. *Oxygen debt* levels can also be calculated, or the *net cost per minute* of the activity may provide a basis for comparison.

2. The changes in blood chemistry. Changes in *hydrogen ion concentration* (pH) or the *oxygen carrying capacity of the blood,* or *blood lactate* or *pyruvate* levels might also be considered in the process of evaluating physical and physiological performance. Further considerations could include the relative levels of *serum triglycerides* and *blood sugar.*

3. The changes in pulmonary responses. Spirographic tracings of *vital capacity, timed vital capacity, maximal breathing capacity,* and breathing patterns all provide important data which can be translated into an evaluation of the state of health of the lungs.

4. The changes in cardiovascular responses. *Cardiac frequency, cardiac output, stroke volume of the heart* yield important information as does the adaptation of the cardiovascular system to sudden changes in body positions.

5. The changes in heat regulating mechanisms. The degree of *acclimatization,* the rate of *sweat production,* the chemical composition of sweat, the internal and external body temperatures yield still further vital information.

6. The changes in urine composition. *Specific gravity, osmolarity,* relative presence of *ketones, glucose, protein,* and *uric acid* must also be considered in a complete physiological assessment.

7. The changes in somatotype. Evaluation of physical and physiological performance must also be considered in light of the *per cent of body fat,* the *lean body mass,* or the *specific gravity* of the body.

8. The changes in neuromuscular responses. *Reaction time, movement time,* gradation of *tendon reflex,* and kinesthetic sense must be appraised.

9. The changes in strength of muscle groups. Relationship of strength to body weight, the *breaking strength* of muscle groups, the physical assessment of *muscle atrophy* or of *hypertrophy,* represent still further bases for appraisal.

The foregoing list is not exhaustive, but it is sufficiently long to focus attention on the folly and futility of arriving at a single score calculated from a single parameter which is presented to describe the level of physical and physiological fitness of the complex organism called man.[71]

In the light of our present knowledge, man's many physiological-psychological adaptations cannot be reduced to a single meaningful score. Measurement of specific function and of specific adaptation to stress can be accomplished provided adequate refinements (psychological safeguards) are structured into the experimental design.

The challenge is before us. The charge was issued four centuries ago by the great Renaissance scientist Galilei, "Measure what can be measured and make measureable what cannot be measured."[66]

Many questions relative to fitness can be raised. One in particular might be, "How much fitness is necessary?" After the discussion of such provocative replies as "For what?" has subsided, the question might be qualified. From this, a host of tangent questions might arise. The relationship of fitness to longevity is one such question.

Some data are available on the longevity of athletes; however, these data must be interpreted with great care. An athlete, after all, is merely one who engages in sport. An accepted view that athletes are representative of a more physiologically fit group is generally true; however, one must recognize the widely dissimilar physiological demands imposed by such sports as wrestling and riflery. In 1928, Dublin raised the question of longevity of college athletes and concluded that perhaps athletes were not predestined to live long lives. In 1956, Montoye et al. not only provided an excellent review of the topic, but presented extensive data from which they concluded that longevity favored equally nonathletes and athletes.[61] In a follow-up study, Montoye et al. substantiated their previous conclusions.[60]

One must not engage in the practice of logic, which forces an erroneous conclusion:

1. Athletes are generally in good physical and physiological condition.
2. Longevity has eluded the athlete.
3. Therefore, being in good physical and physiological condition is of no consequence to the attainment of longevity.

Many discussions can emanate from such logic; however, a number of additional considerations must be kept in mind. An athlete is not one who exemplifies the once-in-shape-always-in-shape slogan. *Athlete* is a title not a quality. Athletes come in assorted varieties: some seasonal, some year-long (during high school or college years), some life-long. *Nonathletes* also can attain high levels of physiological fitness.

The relationship of physiological fitness to longevity offers a fertile topic for research. This longitudinal study would require computerized data treatment, detailed test batteries, and the assessment of many parameters. Within such an experimental design, the titles athletes, nonathletes, and ex-athletes become subordinated to the concept of current levels of physiological adaptation. The interrelationship of somatotype, sex, occupational environment, and health habits can be structured into the experimental design. Hereditary factors, especially those characterized by congenital diseases, also must be statistically considered.

The public has been made aware of the health implications of obesity and of the dangers of long-term smoking, but the question of fitness has been relatively unexplored.

Physical and Physiological Conditioning Regimen

Exercise programs which are carefully formulated are beneficial to physiological and mental health. It is extremely important, however, to recognize that the ideal program is not a single program or even a single mechanical contrivance to be employed in exercise. The human body is much too complex to derive lasting benefit from programs of exercise which can be performed within seconds. Neither are great expenditures of time or money necessary or justifiable. Ideal programs are more likely to emanate from a scientifically prepared "exercise smorgasbord."[71] Exercise goals must be established, adequate time must be allocated, and some resemblance of regularity of participation practiced. Most important, the inauguration of any exercise program must begin with a visit to a medical doctor.

Summary

Changes in physiological responses to elevated levels of metabolic activity have been enumerated throughout the text. Some of these may be classed as short-term effects, others as long-term effects of performance. The limits imposed by the genetic code are variable but only in slight degree. Function makes structure; meeting the challenge of successive physical tasks is reflected in an increased efficiency of performance. The physiological responses are automatic and are governed in varying degree by psychological states.

The essential unity of man is recognized. Body is the servant of mind. Man is myologic and morphologic and physiologic and psychologic.

> Each is given a bag of tools,
> A shapeless mass,
> A book of rules;
> And each must make—
> Ere life is flown—
> A stumbling block
> Or a steppingstone.
>
> R. L. SHARPE

REFERENCES

1. Alles, G. A., and Feigen, G. A.: The influence of Benzedrine on work-decrement and patellar reflex. *Am. J. Physiol.*, *136*:392–400, 1942.

2. Anrep, G. V., and Saalfeld, E. V.: The blood flow through the skeletal muscle in relation to its contraction. *J. Physiol.*, *85*:375–399, 1935.

3. Astrand, P. O.: Personal communication.

4. Balke, B., and Wells, J. G.: Ceiling altitude tolerance following physical training and acclimatization. *J. Aviation Med.*, *29*:40–47, 1958.

5. Bannister, R. G., and Cunningham, D. C.: The effects on the respiration and performance during exercise of adding oxygen to the inspired air. *J. Physiol.*, *125*:118–137, 1954.

6. Bjorgum, R. K., and Sharkey, B. J.: Inhalation of oxygen as an aid to recovery after exertion. *Res. Quart.*, *37*:462–467, 1966.

7. Browne, R. C.: Fatigue, fact or fiction. *In* Floyd, W. F., and Welford, A. T. (Eds.): *Fatigue.* London, H. K. Lewis, 1953.

8. Brouha, L. A.: Protecting the worker in "hot environments." *Ind. Hygiene Found. Bull.*, *29*:207–216, 1955.

9. Christensen, E. H.: Physiological valuation of work in Nykroppa iron works. *In* Floyd, W. F., and Welford, A. T. (Eds.): *Fatigue.* London, H. K. Lewis, 1953.

10. Consolazio, C. F., Nelson, R. A., Matoush, L. O., and Isaac, G. J.: Effect of aspartic acid salts (Mg + K) on physical performance of men. *J. Appl. Physiol.*, *19*:257–261, 1964.

11. Council on Drugs: New drugs and developments in therapeutics, potassium and magnesium aspartates (spartase). *J.A.M.A.*, *183*:362, 1963.

12. Cunningham, D. A.: Effects of breathing high concentrations of oxygen on treadmill performance. *Res. Quart.*, *37*:491–494, 1966.

13. Cureton, T. K.: Effect of wheat germ oil and vitamin E on normal human subjects in physical training programs. *Am. J. Physiol.*, *179*:628, 1954.

14. Cureton, T. K., and Pohndorf, R.: Influence of wheat germ oil as a dietary supplement in a program of conditioning exercises with middle aged subjects. *Res. Quart.*, *26*:391–407, 1955.

15. Cureton, T. K., and Pohndorf, R.: Improvements in physical fitness associated with a course of U. S. Navy trainees with and without dietary supplements. *Res. Quart.*, *34*:440–453, 1963.

16. Dennig, H., Talbot, J. H., Edwards, H. T., and Dill, D. B.: Effect of acidosis and alkalosis upon capacity for work. *J. Clin. Invest.*, *9*:601–613, 1931.

17. Dill, D. B.: The economy of muscular exercise. *Physiol. Rev.*, *16*:263–291, 1936.

18. Dill, D. B., Edwards, H. T., and Talbot, J. H.: Alkalosis and the capacity for work. *J. Biol. Chem.*, *97*:58–59, 1932.

19. Dublin, L. I.: Longevity of college athletes. *Harpers Magazine*, *157*:229–238, 1928.

20. Edwards, H. T., Margaria, R., and Dill, D. B.: Metabolic rate, blood sugar and the utilization of carbohydrate. *Am. J. Physiol., 108*:203–209, 1934.

21. Engel, R. W.: Food faddism. *Nutr. Rev., 17*:353–355, 1959.

22. Erdelyi, G. J.: Gynecological survey of female athletes. *J. Sports Med., 2*:174–179, 1962.

23. Fallis, N., Wilson, W. R., Tetreault, L. L., and Lasagna, L.: Effect of potassium and magnesium aspartates on athletic performance. *J.A.M.A., 185*:129, 1963.

24. Feldman, I., and Hill, L.: The influence of oxygen inhalation on the lactic acid produced during hard work. *J. Physiol., 42*:439–443, 1911.

25. Foltz, E. E., Ivy, A. C., and Barborka, C. J.: Th influence of amphetamine (Benzedrine) sulfate, D-desoxyephedrine hydrochloride (Pervitine) and caffeine upon work output and recovery when rapidly exhausting work is done by trained subjects. *J. Lab. & Clin. Med., 28*:603–606, 1943.

26. Fowler, W. H., Jr., Gardner, G. H., and Egstrom, G. H.: Effect of an anabolic steroid on physical performance of young men. *J. Appl. Physiol., 20*:1038–1040, 1965.

27. Ganzlen, R. V., Balke, B., Nagle, F. J., and Phillips, E. E.: Effects of some tranquilizing analeptic and vasodilating drugs on physical work capacity and orthostatic tolerance. *Aerospace Med., 35*:630–633, 1964.

28. Gendel, E. S.: Pregnancy, fitness and sports. Paper presented at the Seventh National Conference on The Medical Aspects of Sports, Philadelphia, November 28, 1965.

29. Golding, L. A., and Barnard, J. R.: The effect of D-amphetamine sulfate on physical performance. *J. Sports Med. & Phys. Fitness, 3*:221-224, 1963.

30. Guild, W. R.: Pre-event nutrition, with some implications for endurance ath letes. *Exercise and Fitness*, Chicago, The Athletic Institute, 1960.

31. Hill, A. V.: The pressure developed in muscle during contraction. *J. Physiol., 107*:518–526, 1948.

32. Hill, L., and Flack, M.: The influence of oxygen on athletes. *J. Physiol., 38*:28–36, 1909.

33. Hill, L., and Flack, M.: The influence of oxygen inhalations on muscular work. *J. Physiol., 40*:347–372, 1910.

34. Hilsendager, D., and Karpovich, P. V.: Ergogenic effect of glycine and niacin separately and in combination. *Res. Quart., 35*:389–397, 1964.

35. Ikai, M., and Steinhaus, A. H.: Some factors modifying the expression of human strength *J.. Appl. Physiol., 16*:157–163, 1961.

36. Jalso, S. B., Burns, M. M., and Rivers, J. M.: Nutritional beliefs and practices. *J. Am. Diet. Assn., 47*:263–268, 1965.

37. Johnson, W. R., and Black, D. H.: Comparison of effects of certain blood alkalinizers and glucose upon competitive endurance performance. *J. Appl. Physiol., 5*:577–578, 1953.

38. Karpovich, P. V.: The effect of oxygen inhalation on swimming performance. *Res. Quart., 5*:24–30, 1934.

39. Karpovich, P. V.: Effect of amphetamine sulfate on athletic performance. *J.A.M.A., 170*:558–561, 1959.

40. Karpovich, P. V.: *Physiology of Muscular Activity.* 6th Ed. Philadelphia, W. B. Saunders Co., 1965.

41. Karpovich, P. V., and Millman, N.: Vitamin B₁ and enduiance. *New England J. Med., 226*:881–882, 1942.

42. Karpovich, P. V., and Pestrecov, K.: Effect of gelatin upon muscular work in man. *Am. J. Physiol., 134*:300–309, 1941.

43. Keys, A., and Henschel, A. F.: Vitamin supplementation of U. S. Army rations in relation to fatigue and the ability to do muscular work. *J. Nutr., 23*:259–269, 1942.

44. Kjellberg, S. R., Ruhde, U., and Sjöstrand, T.: The amount of hemoglobin (blood volume) in relation to the pulse rate and heart volume during work. *Acta Physiol. Scand., 19*:152–169, 1950.

45. Knehr, C. A., Dill, D. B., and Neufield, W.: Training and its effects on man at rest and at work. *Am. J. Physiol., 136*:148–156, 1942.

46. Leake, C. D.: *The Amphetamines: Their Action and Use.* Springfield, Charles C Thomas, 1958.

47. Leake, C. D.: Good-willed judgment on alcohol. *In* Lucia, S. P. (Ed.): *Alcohol and Civilization.* New York, McGraw-Hill Book Co., 1963.

48. Luco, J. V., and Rosenblueth, A.: Neuromuscular "transmission fatigue" produced without contraction during curarization. *Am. J. Physiol., 126*:58–65, 1939.

49. Lundgren, N. P. V.: The physiological effects of time schedule work on lumber-workers. *Acta Physiol. Scand., 13*:1–137, 1947.

50. Margaria, R., and Gualtierotti, T.: Functional fundamental characteristics of the nervous system in athletes and the effects of performance. *Health and Fitness in the Modern World,* Chicago, The Athletic Institute, 1961.

51. Margaria, R., Gualtierotti, T., and Spinelli, D.: Effect of stress on lower neuron activity. *Exp. Med. and Surg., 96*:166, 1958.

52. Martt, J. M.: Pulmonary diffusing capacity in cigarette smokers. *Ann. Int. Med., 56*:39–45, 1962.

53. Mayer, J., and Bullen, B.: Nutrition and athletic performance. *Physiol. Rev., 40*:369–397, 1960.

54. Mayer, J., and Bullen, B.: Nutrition and athletic performance. *Exercise and Fitness,* Chicago, The Athletic Institute, 1960.

55. McFarland, R. A.: Experimental evidence of the relationship between ageing and oxygen want: in search of a theory of ageing. *Ergonomics, 6*:339–366, 1963.

56. McFarland, R. A., Roughton, F. J. W., Halperin, M. H., and Niven, J. I.: The effects of carbon monoxide and altitude on visual thresholds. *J. Aviation Med., 15*:381–394, 1944.

57. Miller, A. T.: Influence of oxygen administration on cardiovascular function during exercise and recovery. *J. Appl. Physiol., 5*:165–168, 1952.

58. Mitolo, M.: La donna a la dottrina delle "costituzioni" di fronte all'esercizio dello sport. *Sport e Salute,* Roma, Edizioni Istituto "Gregorio Mendel," 1961.

59. Montoye, H. J., Spata, P. J., Pinckney, V., and Barron, L.: Effects of vitamin B_{12} supplement on physical fitness and growth of young boys. *J. Appl. Physiol.,* 7:589–592, 1955.

60. Montoye, H. J., Van Huss, W. D., and Nevai, J. W.: Longevity and morbidity of college athletes: a seven-year follow-up study. *J. Sports Med. & Phys. Fitness,* 2:133–140, 1962.

61. Montoye, H. J., Van Huss, W. D., Olson, H. W., Hudec, A., and Mahoney, E.: Study of longevity and morbidity of college athletes. *J.A.M.A., 162*:1132–1134, 1956.

62. Mostyn, E. M., Helle, S., Gee, J. B. L., Bentivoglio, L. G., and Bates, D. V.: Pulmonary diffusing capacity of athletes. *J. Appl. Physiol., 18*:687–695, 1963.

63. Nadel, J. A., and Comroe, J. H.: Acute effects of inhalation of cigarette smoke on airway conductance. *J. Appl. Physiol., 16*:713–716, 1961.

64. *New Drugs.* Council on Drugs, A. M. A., Chicago, 1965.

65. Noltie, H. R.: A factor in postponing the onset of fatigue. *In* Floyd, W. F., and Welford, A. T., (Eds.): *Fatigue.* London, H. K. Lewis, 1953.

66. Nordenskiöld, E.: *The History of Biology.* 2nd Ed. New York, Tudor Publishing Co., 1936.

67. Olson, R. E.: Food faddism . . . why? *Nutr. Rev., 16*:97–99, 1958.

68. Pierson, W. R., and Lockhart, A.: Effect of menstruation on simple reaction and movement time. *Brit. Med. J.* 1:796–797, 1963.

69. Rasch, P. J., Pierson, W. R., and Brubaker, M. L.: The effect of amphetamine sulfate and meprobamate on reaction time and movement time. *Arbeitsphysiol., 18*:280–284, 1960.

70. *Report of the Committee to Study The Use of Drugs in Athletes.* American College of Sports Medicine, April, 1958.

71. Ricci, B.: *Physical and Physiological Conditioning for Men.* Dubuque, Wm. C. Brown Co., 1965.

72. Ronzoni, E.: The effect of exercise on breathing in experimental alkalosis by ingested sodium bicarbonate. *J. Biol. Chem., 67*:25–27, 1926.

73. Rothfeld, E. L., Biber, D., and Berstein, A.: The acute effect of cigarette smoking on pulmonary function studies. *Dis. Chest, 40*:284–290, 1961.

74. Rowell, L., Taylor, H. L., Wang, Y., and Carlson, W. S.: Saturation of arterial blood with oxygen during maximal exercise. *J. Appl. Physiol., 19*:284–286, 1964.

75. Ryan, A. J.: Use of amphetamines in athletics. *J.A.M.A., 170*:562, 1959.

76. Shapiro, W., and Patterson, J. L.: Effects of smoking and athletic conditioning on ventilatory mechanics, including observations on the reliability of the forced expirogram. *Am. Rev. Resp. Dis., 85*:191–199, 1962.

77. Shaw, D. L., Chesney, M. A., Tullis, I. F., and Agersburg, H. P. K.: Management of fatigue: a physiologic approach. *Am. J. Med. Sci., 243*:758–769, 1962.

78. Simonsson, B.: Effect of cigarette smoking on the forced expiratory flow rate. *Am. Rev. Resp. Dis., 85*:534–539, 1962.

79. Sloan, A. W.: Effect of training on physical fitness of women students. *J. Appl. Physiol., 16*:167–169, 1961.

80. Smith, G. M., and Beecher, H. K.: Amphetamine sulfate and athletic performance. *J.A.M.A., 170*:542–557, 1959.

81. *Smoking and Health.* Report of the Advisory Committee to the Surgeon General of the Public Health Service, U.S. Department of Health, Education and Welfare.

82. Steinhaus, A. H.: Chronic effects of exercise. *Physiol. Rev., 13*:103–147, 1933.

83. Talbot, N. B., Sobel, E. H., McArthur, J. W., and Crawford, J. D.: *Functional Endocrinology.* Cambridge, Harvard University Press, 1954.

84. Thomas, C.: Women's participation in vigorous athletic activity. Talk delivered to postgraduate course in sports medicine, sponsored by the University of Colorado Medical School and the American Academy of Orthopedic Surgeons, August, 1966.

85. Thomas, P.: The effects of vitamin E on some aspects of athletic efficiency. Dissertation, U. Southern Calif., 1957.

86. Turner, D.: *Handbook of Diet Therapy.* Chicago, The University of Chicago Press, 1965.

87. Tuttle, W. W.: The development of fatigue. Paper presented at National Athletic Trainers Convention, Kansas City, Missouri, 1950.

88. Ullmark, R.: The dangers of doping. *J. Sports Med. & Phys. Fitness, 3*:248–249, 1963.

89. Wilson, H.: *Juvenal Satires.* New York, University Publishing Co., 1903.

90. Wilson, R. H., Meador, R. S., Jay, B. E., and Higgins, E.: The pulmonary pathologic physiology of persons who smoke cigarettes. *New England J. Med., 262*:956–961, 1960.

91. Wolf, W.: A contribution to the question of overtraining. *Health and Fitness in the Modern World,* Chicago, The Athletic Institute, 1961.

Chapter

11

CALCULATION METHODS

The symbols used throughout this chapter, in fact throughout the book, are those established by Pappenheimer et al. The reader is urged to make frequent reference to formulae, laws, definitions, conversion tables, and nomograms which are contained within the appendix.

Mathematical calculations of the energy cost of various physical activities, of efficiency, of oxygen debt, of cardiac output, of respiratory exchange ratio, to name a few, are an inseparable part of an exercise physiology text. Unless the student masters the calculations, mathematical values become less meaningful, are memorized, and are easily forgotten. The present chapter is designed to acquaint the reader with some of the techniques of calculations.

The employment of a calculator would hasten the task of mathematical calculation; however, these machines are not always available. A slide rule can be purchased at small cost and is, therefore, within reach of all students. Within minutes the technique of multiplication and division is accomplished; within hours of conscientious effort, mastery is achieved.

Slide Rule Operation

At the risk of offending some readers, the following examples of the simplicity of slide rule operation are presented.

For multiplication and division mastery, the language of the slide rule includes:

The cursor: a clear plastic, moveable indicator containing a central line called the *hairline.*

"C" scale: located on the *slide,* is identical to the "D" scale, and is used in conjunction with it for multiplication and division.

243

"D" scale: located on the *body* of the rule.

Index: the *mark* which is associated with the primary number *"1."* There is a left and right index on both the "C" and "D" scales.

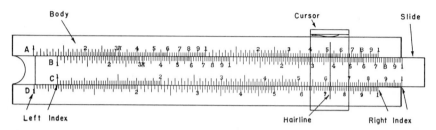

Body   Cursor   Slide

Left Index   Hairline   Right Index

Fig. 11–1.   The slide rule, an invention of French artillery officer Amédée Mann-heim in 1859, is based on the idea of Englishman Edmund Gunter who in 1622 marked equal logarithmic scales on strips and was thus able to multiply and divide by sliding one strip along the other.

Two additional considerations are important. First, the numbers along either the "C" or "D" scales may express differing values which the user places on them, e.g., the figure 2 may also represent 20, 200, 2,000, 20,000 or any other multiple or 0.2, 0.02 and so on. Second, decimal point positions are first determined by making rough calculations. This technique affords the user the opportunity not only to establish the decimal place, but also to approximate the significant numbers.

Example. To multiply 5.5 by 3 (rough calculation, $5 \times 3 = 15$ *followed* by decimal point):

1. Set *hairline* of *cursor* on 5.5 on "D" scale.
2. Set *index* of "C" scale on *hairline.*
3. Move *cursor* to left until hairline is over 3 of "C" scale.
4. Read answer on "D" scale (answer: 16.5)
   Return the slide to closed position.

Example. To divide 16.5 by 3 (rough calculation, $16 \div 3 = 5$ *followed* by decimal point):

1. Move *hairline* of *cursor* to 16.5 of "D" scale.
2. Move slide until 3 of "C" scale appears above 16.5.
3. Read answer at *index* of "C" on the "D" scale (answer: 5.5)

Notice from the above example that multiplication and division are reversed processes.

With one exception (see Table 11–4) all calculations that appear in this text were accomplished through the use of a large slide rule; there-fore, answers are subject to parallax errors in reading which may amount to less than 1%.

TABLE 11-1.	Examples of Slide Rule Operation	
	Rough Calculation	Slide Rule Answer
39.2 × 21.0*	Round off to nearest whole numbers, e.g., 40 × 20 = 800. Answer will be *approximately* 800 *followed* by decimal place.	823.
0.92 × 0.93	Answer will remain a fraction since *neither* value is a whole number 0.9 × 0.9 = 0.81	0.856
8.27 × 0.50	Answer will be a whole number but will be approximately one-half the value of the multiplier. 8 × 0.5 = 4.0	4.13
4325 ÷ 8400†	4 is one-half (or 0.5) the value of 8. Answer will be a fraction 0.5xxx	0.514
0.24 ÷ 0.21	The numerator 24 is larger than the denominator 21. Answer will be a whole number—approximate value of *1*—followed by a decimal point. 24 ÷ 21 = 1.xxx	1.142

* If 39.2 were placed in the D scale and the slide moved to the left (so that *right* index mark of C scale was above 39.2) the value 21.0 would be off the scale. The beginner is urged to reverse the procedure, i.e., move the slide to the *right*, place *left* index mark of C scale over 39.2, then move cursor to right until hairline is over 21.0 on C scale. Read answer on D scale. (With more advanced rules, it is unnecessary to move the slide, as in the case above; instead the folded scales CF and DF can be used.)

† Move cursor until hairline is over 4325 on D scale, then move slide to left until 8400 is under hairline. Read answer on D scale under right index mark of C scale.

Metric System

Strong pleas are presented for the use of the metric system as opposed to the English system in the calculation of scientific data. The metric system is a logical system, is easy to learn, and simple to use. The metric system is internationally used and reported. Lastly, even the English plan to abandon their system of weights and measures.[4]

Oxygen Uptake, Closed Circuit System

Closed circuit indirect calorimetry involves the employment of a known, initial amount of gas which is contained in a source (bell or container) and is an integral part of a complete or closed circuit. The source may be filled with reagent grade oxygen, or with a gas mixture containing varying amounts of carbon dioxide, nitrogen, and oxygen, or other gases. Or, atmospheric air may be drawn into the source.

Nose clips prevent the escape of gas from the bell or the introduction of ambient air into the bell. A mouthpiece and valve arrangement ensure that the gas is inspired from the source by the subject and is expired into the source.

Simply stated, the volume of gas that is present in the source after a given time period (V_f) is subtracted from the initial volume V_i and represents the amount consumed (Vo_2) by the subject.

$$Vo_2 = V_i - V_f$$

A number of careful steps and precautions must be taken. Principal among these is the use of a firmly attached nose clip which will ensure the integrity of the closed system. Also important is the use of respiratory valves which offer little resistance to the flow of air, thus reducing the possibility of respiratory hypoxia.

The closed circuit may be regarded as a demand system; i.e., the subject voluntarily inspires an amount of gas. No pressure, save atmospheric, is placed around the source gas.

Because all gas volumes must be corrected to Standard Temperature and Pressure of a Dry gas (STPD), the source gas temperature must be recorded and utilized in calculations.

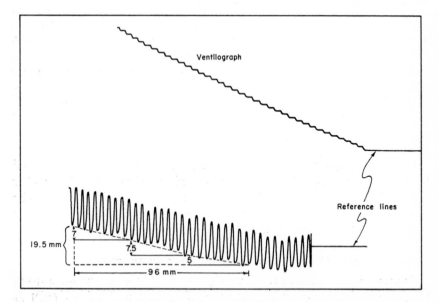

Fig. 11–2.   Oxygen uptake of a sitting, rested male subject calculated from an actual tracing. Tracing is read from right to left. Each of the intervals is of one minute duration, i.e., each base line is 32 mm in length. Numbers under the slope of lower tracing represent "h." Total volume displacement for 3 min (96 mm) is 19.5 mm. Upper tracing is produced by a second pen—a ventilograph (see Fig. 11–4). Spirometer, of 13.5 L capacity, was filled with 100% O_2.

19

Finally, because expired air contains an appreciable percentage of carbon dioxide gas, a carbon dioxide absorber (e.g., a liquid: KOH, potassium hydroxide; or crystals: $CaCo_3$, calcium carbonate) is placed between the subject and the source on the return line. In this manner, carbon dioxide is absorbed and the source does not become contaminated with increased amounts of carbon dioxide gas (see Fig. 8–3).

Apparatuses designed for use in spirometry or in indirect calorimetry are described as spirometers, respirometers, or gasometers (Fig. 8–2). These systems vary in size from approximately 9 to 200 liters and may be of the recording or nonrecording types. (The larger type, i.e., 120 liter capacity, is also called a Tissot spirometer or gasometer.)

If the spirometer is of the recording type (a revolving drum and usually an ink tracing), the calculations are easily accomplished. If specially designed lined paper is used on the revolving drum, the calculations are further simplified. Irrespective of the refinements in recording, the underlying formula used in the determination of gas volume is:

$$\text{Volume} = (\pi r^2)^{*}(h)$$
$\pi = 3.14159$, $r =$ radius of spirometer bell,
$h =$ linear indication of gas displacement

Recording Spirometer, Tracing on Plain Paper

The paper attached to the revolving drug which turns at a designated speed (usually 32 mm/min) receives the excursions of the bell through a pen and ink recording (Fig. 11–2). Thus, for a given time period, as measured by the distance in millimeters the drum has moved, volumetric changes are easily calculated. An important first step is to secure a base or reference line on the unlined paper. This is accomplished by operating the drum while the outlet valve from the bell is kept in the closed position.

---

* On all commercially produced spirometers, πr^2 is designated as a numerical factor which is stamped on the apparatus and is called a bell factor. For example, volume of spirometer bell in liters $= (\pi r^2)(h)$. $\pi = 3.14159$, radius of spirometer bell $= 11.462$ cm, height of bell $= 32.8$ cm.

$$
\begin{aligned}
V &= (3.14159 \times 11.462^2) \, (32.8\text{cm}) \\
&= (3.14159 \times 131.377) \, (32.8) \\
&= (412.73 \text{ cc/cm}) \, (32.8\text{cm}) \\
&= 13537\text{cc} = 13.5\text{L} = \text{rated capacity of respirometer.}
\end{aligned}
$$

Obviously, for a given spirometer the bell factor (πr^2) does not change; however, the excursion of the spirometer bell corresponds to a volume displacement of 412.7 cc/cm or 41.27 cc/mm or 0.4127 L/cm. (*Note:* 1 L = 1000 cc or 1000 ml.) For all subsequent calculations, the "h" will refer to linear displacement of spirometer bell and from this, the gas volume within the bell will be calculated by the formula:

$$
\begin{aligned}
V &= (\pi r^2) \, (h) \\
&= (\text{factor}) \, (h)
\end{aligned}
$$

If one minute intervals are to be plotted graphically, oxygen consumption for each interval must be calculated. If average $\dot{V}O_2$ is desired, an "h" of 6.5 mm $\dfrac{(5 + 7.5 + 7)}{3}$ may be used in the formula. Or, the baseline may be extended 96 mm (32×3) from arrow and an "h" of 19.5 mm used in the formula. For the latter method, final corrected volume must be divided by 3.

$$
\begin{aligned}
\dot{V}O_2 &= (\pi r^2) \ (h) \times STPD_{correction} \\
&= (factor) \ (h) \times STPD_{correction} \\
&= 41.27 \ cc/mm \times 19.5 \ mm \times STPD_{correction} \\
&= 805.0 \ cc \times STPD_{correction} \\
&= 805.0 \ cc \times 0.870 \\
&= 702 \ cc \ (for \ 3 \ min) \\
&= 702 \ cc \div 3 \\
\dot{V}O_2 &= 234 \ cc/min \ corrected \ to \ STPD
\end{aligned}
$$

Recording Spirometer, Tracing on Special Design Lined Paper

It is important to read the instructions relating to the interpretation of the tracing on the lined paper. These instructions usually appear along the bottom edge of the paper. This enables the manufacturer to utilize one paper for several spirometer models (Fig. 11–3).

Drum speed is 32 mm/min; each interval between vertical lines represents 1 minute. Gas temperature is 24°C, barometric pressure 749 mm Hg, and $STPD_{correction} = 0.870$.

Calculation procedure is nearly identical to previous calculation (plain paper), except that horizontal and vertical lines simplify process. Instructions along base of paper read: "For 9 liter respirometer, use above figures; for 13.5 liter respirometer, double above figures." A 13.5 liter respirometer was used in this instance.

Calculation for indicated interval:

$$
\begin{aligned}
MV &= V_t - V_1 \\
&= V_t - V_1 \quad 3555 \ cc \\
& -\ \underline{3400 \ cc} \\
& \ \ \underline{155 \ cc} \\
& \times 2 \quad (13.5 \ liter \ \therefore \ double \ the \ value) \\
&= \ \underline{310 \ cc} \ (uncorrected)
\end{aligned}
$$

$$
\begin{aligned}
MV &= 310 \ cc \times 0.870 \ (STPD_{correction}) \\
&= 269.70 \ cc/min = (\Lambda O_2) \ corrected \ to \ STPD \ (Note: \ in \ this \ instance \ MV
\end{aligned}
$$
indicates volume of O_2 consumed/ min $\therefore$ may be designated by $\dot{V}O_2$)

By disregarding all lines in Figure 11–3, calculation method for plain paper may be used.

$$
\begin{aligned}
\text{MV} &= (\text{factor})\ (\text{h}) \\
&= (41.27\ \text{cc/mm})\ (7.5\ \text{mm}) \\
&= 309.5\ \text{cc (uncorrected)} \\
&= 309.5\ \text{cc} \times 0.870\ (\text{STPD}_{\text{correction}}) \\
\text{MV or } \dot{V}_{O_2} &= 269.3\ \text{cc/min corrected to STPD}
\end{aligned}
$$

Note: 0.4 cc discrepancy between methods represents a percentage error of 0.14% (and was caused by the visual acuity of the author).

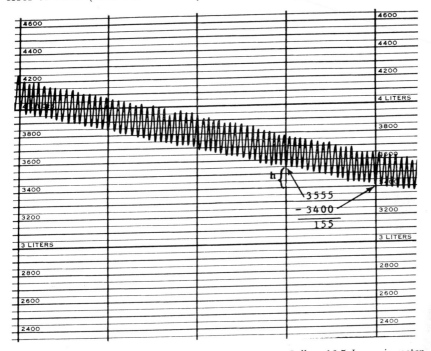

Fig. 11–3. Calculation of oxygen uptake by using a Collins 13.5 L respirometer and special design chart paper.

Nonrecording Type, 120 L Spirometer

The source gas in this large spirometer is also contained in a metal bell which is sealed by water at its base. A counter-balanced pulley arrangement causes the bell to respond to volumetric changes which occur with each inspiration and expiration. A stationary meter-stick located adjacent to the moveable chain mechanism which responds to respiration changes thus affords the opportunity to convert linear excursion to volumetric values.

TABLE 11–2

Meter Stick

Initial Height (cm)	Final Height (cm)	Difference (cm)	Factor πr^{2}*	Volume Uncorrected (L)	STPD Correction	Volume Corrected (L)	Time (min)	Minute Volume† (L)
Sitting rest 78.2	77.0	1.2	1.334	1.601	0.880‡	1.408	5	.282

* $133.4 = \pi r^{2}$ (factor stamped on spirometer). *Note:* 133.4 cc/mm = 1.334 L/cm
† In this example MV = $\dot{V}o_2$ L/min.

Gas temperature = 25.0°C, Barometric Pressure = 755.5 mm Hg, water vapor tension = 23.8 mm Hg (from Table 2, Appendix).

‡ $$STPD_{correction} = \frac{P_B \ (mm \ Hg) - PH_2O \ (mm \ Hg)}{760 \ (mm \ Hg)} \times \frac{273}{273 + t°c}$$

$$= \frac{755.5 - 23.8}{760} \times \frac{273}{298}$$

$$= \frac{731.7}{760} \times \frac{273}{298}$$

$$= 0.96 \times 0.92$$

$$= 0.880$$

Interpretation. The above example involved a resting subject for a five-minute period; therefore, the minute volume (MV) $= \dfrac{Volume}{Time} =$ $\dfrac{1.408L}{5} = .282$ L/min = 282 cc/min. The oxygen consumed per minute may also be expressed: $\dot{V}o_2 = 282$ cc/min.

Subdivisions of Lung Volume

A number of useful calculations can be made from tracings such as those shown in Figure 11–4.

The basic formula continues to be $V = \pi \, r^2h$. There is one important substitution in correction factors: BTPS is used in place of STPD. The temperature of lung air is equal to that of the body, 37°C; lung air is saturated with water vapor. When collected in a spirometer, the volume of air is decreased due, basically, to decreases in temperature and moisture content. As the air passes through the CO_2 absorber, the moisture content is considerably reduced; the calcium carbonate is a desiccant as well as a CO_2 absorber. The temperature of the collected air decreases by approximately 10°C. This necessitates a correction factor which expresses conditions within the lungs. Such a factor is

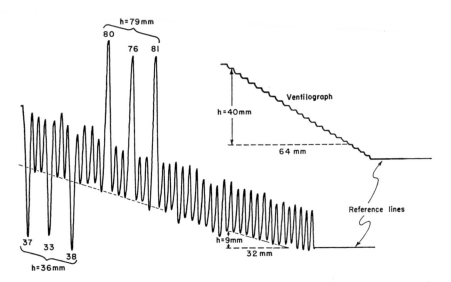

Fig. 11–4.   Actual spirogram of a standing, rested male subject. Two-stage vital capacity tracing is depicted at left: $\overline{IC}$ = 79 mm, $\overline{ERV}$ = 36 mm. The descriptive term *two-stage* vital capacity indicates that the IC phase is separated from the ERV phase. This procedure is less fatiguing and reflects vital capacity more accurately. Upper tracing is that of ventilograph. For sake of accuracy, V_T must be calculated from this tracing: "h" 40 mm (for 2 min period). V = bell factor $\times$ h $\times$ 11.09 $\times$ BTPS correction. $V_T = \dfrac{MV}{f}$.

termed BTPS: collected volumes are corrected to Body Temperature, ambient barometric Pressure, Saturated water vapor (see Table 1, Appendix).

Based on Figure 11–4, the following calculations can be made:

V_T Tidal Volume: volume of gas inhaled or exhaled per breath

IRV Inspiratory Reserve Volume: maximum volume inhaled from end-tidal inhaled level.

ERV Expiratory Reserve Volume: maximum volume exhaled from resting exhaled level.

VC Vital Capacity: one stage—maximum volume exhaled following maximum volume inhaled; two stage—maximum volume inhaled, interspersed with intervals of normal breathing (V_T), combined with maximum volume exhaled (Fig. 11–4).

IC Inspiratory Capacity: maximum volume inhaled from resting exhaled level.

MV Minute Volume: total volume of gas inhaled and exhaled per minute.

$\dot{V}_{O_2}$ Oxygen Uptake: oxygen consumed per unit time. Base lines must be established for each calculation and must be constructed parallel to the reference line. The measurement of the vertical displacement, "h," is preceded by the drawing of a line *perpendicular* to the base line at any desired point on the tracing.

Two mathematical calculations will be shown here in detail; all other calculations can be completed in similar manner.

Vital Capacity

Spirometer factor 41.27 cc/mm, drum speed 32 mm/min, gas temperature $= 25°C$, $P_B = 750$ mm Hg.

$VC = (\pi r^2)(h)$

$VC_{uncorr} = $ (bell factor) (h)

     $= 41.27$ cc/mm $\times$ 115 mm (IC = 79 mm, ERV = 36 mm, see Fig. 6–3 also)

     $= 4746.05$ cc

$VC_{corr} = VC_{uncorr} \times$ correction factor*

     $= 4746.05 \times 1.075$

     $= 5102$ cc corrected to BTPS

Comroe et al. introduced the following formulas for the calculation of predicted vital capacity of adults and young adults:

♂ $VC_{cc} = (27.63 - [0.112 \times \text{age}])$ (Hgt cm)

♀ $VC_{cc} = (21.78 - [0.101 \times \text{age}])$ (Hgt cm)

Oxygen Uptake

$\dot{V}_{O_2} = $ (bell factor) (h) $\times$ STPD$_{correction}$

     $= 41.27$ cc/mm $\times$ 9 mm $\times$ STPD$_{correction}$

     $= 371.5$ cc $\times$ 0.874

     $= 324.5$ cc/min

Ventilation Equivalent for Oxygen

Ventilation equivalent for oxygen, VE_{O_2} is defined as the amount of ventilation required per 100 cc/min oxygen consumption. During rested states an elevated VE_{O_2} indicates hyperventilatory practice which may be caused by anxiety states. From Figure 11–4, ventilation was calculated to be 9840.2 cc, $\dot{V}_{O_2} = 324.5$ cc/min.

---

* From Table 1, Appendix; for gas t 25°C, factor to convert to 37°C saturated = 1.075 or by formula:

$$BTPS_{correction} = \frac{273°K + 37°C}{273°K + t°C} \times \frac{P_B \text{ (mm Hg)} - P_{H_2O} \text{ (mm Hg)}}{P_B \text{ (mm Hg)} - 47 \text{ (mm Hg)}}$$

$$= \frac{273 + 37}{273 + 25} \times \frac{750 - 23.8}{750 - 47.0}$$

$$= \frac{310}{298} \times \frac{726.2}{703}$$

$$= 1.04 \times 1.032$$

$$= 1.075$$

$$VEo_2 = \frac{\text{Ventilation (L/min)}}{\dot{V}o_2 \text{ (cc/min)}} \times 100$$

$$= \frac{9.840}{324.5} \times 100$$

$$= 3.03 \quad \text{L/100 cc}$$

Normal values for rest range between 2.2 L and 2.8 L/100 cc. When calculated from open circuit data, VE_{O_2} may be used as a rough indicator of ventilation efficiency. A more precise indicator of efficiency would be based on alveolar ventilation.

The reciprocal of VE_{O_2} indicates the rate of oxygen removal. Normal values range from 38 to 48 cc/L. Values will be reduced by hyperventilation.

$$\text{Rate of } O_2 \text{ removal} = \frac{\dot{V}o_2 \text{ (cc/min)}}{\text{Ventilation (L/min)}}$$

$$= \frac{324.5}{9.840}$$

$$= 32 \text{ cc/L}$$

Minute Volume and Tidal Volume

Calculation of V_T (and of MV) from the tracing in Figure 11–4 is subject to many errors due primarily to a fluctuation in V_T and to the difficulty in establishing lines depicting average linear displacement. Precise determination of V_T can be obtained through the use of a second pen which records inhalations (only) as upward excursions. Through a clutch mechanism, exhalations are recorded as lateral tracings. To accommodate great volumes, a gear reduction mechanism is installed within the pulley system of the second pen (see Fig. 11–4).* The second pen is called a ventilograph: gear reduction ratio is 1/11.09th.

Spirometer factor 41.27 cc/mm, drum speed 32 mm/min, ventilograph factor 11.09, gas temperature $= 25°C$, $P_B = 750$ mm Hg.

$$V = \pi r^2 h$$
$$= \text{(bell factor) (h) (ventilograph factor)}$$
$$V_{uncorr} = (41.27 \text{ cc/mm} \times 40 \text{ mm} \times 11.09)$$
$$= 18,307.32 \text{ cc}$$
$$MV_{uncorr} = \frac{18,307.32}{2} = 9,153.66 \text{ cc}$$

Note: base line measured 64 mm (or 2 mins) $\therefore MV = \frac{Vol}{2}$.

$$MV = MV_{uncorr} \times \text{conversion factor}$$
$$= 9,153.66 \times 1.075$$
$$= 9,840.20 \text{ cc corrected to BTPS}$$

---

* The equipment being described is that of the Warren E. Collins Co., Boston, Massachusetts.

Minute volume represents the total volume of gas inhaled and exhaled per minute, the product of depth and frequency of respiration:

$$MV = V_T \times f$$

by rearrangement

$$V_{Tm1} = \frac{MVcc}{f\ min} \quad (Note: f = 18 \text{ for } 2 \text{ min} \therefore 9/min)$$

$$V_T = \frac{9,840.20\ cc}{9}$$

$$= 1093.3 \text{ cc corrected to BTPS}$$

It is also possible to calculate V_T from the tracing proper. The accuracy of such calculations is reduced due to the difficulty of establishing reference lines representing the average excursion of the pen. Since $MV = V_T \times$ calculation of MV from the tracing proper is also likely to be inaccurate. Because accuracy as well as ease of measurement, is greatly increased by the ventilograph, its use for MV, V_T and MBC* calculations is urged.

Maximal breathing capacity measurement presents some problems. In addition to problems relating to learning effect and motivation, deep yet rapid breathing must be accomplished by the subject. The time intervals are challengingly long. Carbon dioxide contamination of source gas presents an additional problem (Fig. 8–3). (*Note*: rapid breathing is accomplished at the rate of approximately 120/min. Assuming V_T to be 1.50 L, MBC converted to 30 sec rate would be: 1.50 L × 60 = 90.0 L.)

The problem just cited can be avoided by substituting another pulmonary function test, the timed vital capacity (FEV_t). Miller and Blyth showed that MBC can be reliably and conveniently established from FEV_t ($R = > 0.91$).[18] Aside from its diagnostic or screening values, e.g., respiratory obstruction, asthmatic, tubercular, or emphysematous conditions, comparisons of vital capacity measurements can justifiably be made since a common time limit is imposed. Time limits of 0.5 sec, 0.75 sec, or 1.0 sec are frequently used.

A fast-tracing, one-second timed capacity is depicted in Figure 11–5.

Irrespective of the placement of the paper, accurate calculations can be made, provided the reference line is available and long enough.

---

* MBC = maximal breathing capacity—the maximal amount of air which is exchanged per unit time, usually 15 or 30 sec. Motley advocates the shorter interval, whereas Comroe[7] and Gaensler[11] advocate the longer one.

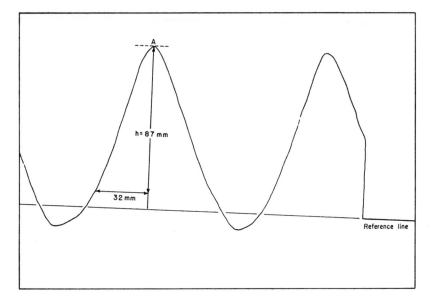

Fig. 11–5.   Fast tracing (actual): one-second timed vital capacity $FEV_{1.0}''$. Kymograph speed was set at 1920 mm/min. Linear distance is now represented by the relationship 32 mm = 1 sec ($\dfrac{1920 \text{ mm/min}}{60 \text{ sec}}$ = 32 mm/sec). The importance of obtaining a reference line on all tracings is readily apparent—the paper was deliberately placed in this manner. Note that reference line is extended and a line *perpendicular* to the reference line is dropped from the beginning of the downward stroke of the pen at A. The 32 mm line, which is *parallel* to the reference line, bisects the tracing and establishes an end-point from which the value of "h" for the expiratory volume can be measured.

Forced Expiratory Volume $FEV_{1.0''}$

Kymograph speed 32 mm/sec, gas t = 25° C, P_B = 750 mm Hg conversion factor, volume to 37°C saturated, 1.075.

$FEV_{1.0''}$ = (bell factor) (h) ($BTPS_{correction}$)
= (41.27) (87) (1.075)
= 3860 cc corrected to BTPS

Timed vital capacities also may be expressed as a percentage of the total vital capacity

$$\%VC_{tot} = \frac{FEV_{1.0''}}{VC \text{ actual}}$$
$$= \frac{3860 \text{ cc}}{5102 \text{ cc}} \times 100$$
$$= 75.5\%$$

According to Gaensler, a normal individual is expected to exhale at least 75% of his vital capacity in 1 second, 85% during the first 2 seconds, and 95% during the first 3 seconds.[10] The tracing in Figure 11–5 is that of an individual who was well conditioned to endurance events (running), but was not "conditioned" to the apparatus. The basic message here is that for utmost reliability, measurement must be preceded by an initial learning period.

Often, more meaningful comparisons of performance can be made by expressing the performance as it relates to some other attribute. For example, oxygen uptake values reflect a number of occurrences; however, oxygen uptake also reflects body mass. Generally, the larger the frame (the mass), the higher will be the oxygen uptake. Thus, to rule out the effect of mass, the uptake is expressed as a function of body weight (lean body mass or fat free weight). (See p. 265.)

It may be advantageous to express pulmonary performance in the same manner. Frequently, the pulmonary performance is expressed in relation to body surface area. The BSAm² (for the subject whose tracing appears in Figure 11–4) is taken from Table 5, Appendix (74 kg, 178 cm: BSA = 1.92m²). Minute volume corrected to BTPS was 9840.20 cc.

$$\text{MV/BSAm}^2 = \frac{9{,}840.20 \text{ cc}}{1.92 \text{m}^2}$$
$$= 5125.10 \text{ cc/min/BSAm}^2 \text{ at BTPS}$$

Additional measurements of pulmonary function can be accomplished with a two-speed recording spirometer. Detailed discussion of measurement techniques may be found in the text by Comroe et al.

Oxygen Uptake, Open Circuit System

Open circuit indirect calorimetry involves the intake of atmospheric air and the collection of expired respiratory gases in plastic, rubber, or metallic containers. With a nose clip firmly affixed, the subject breathes ambient air through a two-way respiratory valve and mouthpiece. The valve system allows the air to pass in one given direction where it is collected (see Fig. 8–4).

Analysis of collected respiratory gases for oxygen and carbon dioxide contents may be accomplished with expensive, sophisticated equipment costing several thousand dollars or, achieving the same degree of accuracy, with apparatus costing less than 200 dollars.*

---

* Scholander apparatus is singled out because it is amazingly accurate (if reagents are carefully prepared) and is easy to operate.

Volumetric determinations of expired gases must be accomplished as well as gas temperatures noted. Both determinations can be accomplished in one easy operation with a dry-gas meter, calibrated in liters, and a centigrade thermometer affixed to the meter inlet (see Fig. 8–5).

Several calculation methods will be presented. The student should master one but be familiar with all. (Data taken from Table 11–3.)

	MV = 7.120 L		
	Per cent	Liters	
O_2	17.9	1.27	1.49 L O_2 inspired (N_2 liters × 0.265 = O_2 inspired)
CO_2	3.0	0.21	0.22 $\dot{V}O_2$ L/min (220 ml/min) corrected to STPD
N_2	79.1	5.64	0.95 R (respiratory exchange ratio)
	100.0	7.12	

1. The oxygen and carbon dioxide percentages were determined through analysis. Nitrogen %, not analyzed, is the differential of the oxygen and carbon dioxide percentage from 100% (100 − 20.9 = 79.1). By analysis, nitrogen gas content in inspired air is 79.03%. In the above example, N_2% is 79.10. This discrepancy is explained by the fact that the blood usually removes a slightly greater amount of O_2 than it adds in the form of CO_2. This slight reduction in alveolar gas volume results in an increase in N_2 concentration. This is known as the *RQ effect* (Respiratory Quotient effect).

2. The actual amount of O_2, CO_2, and N_2, second column, is obtained by multiplication of percentages of each gas by the minute volume divided by 100 (7.12 × 17.9; 7.12 × 3.0; 7.12 × 79.1).

3. The amount of oxygen inspired, third column, is the product of the multiplication of N_2 liters × 0.265[*] (5.64 × 0.265 = 1.49L).

4. Oxygen consumed, $\dot{V}O_2$ L/min, is obtained by subtraction of the figure representing the actual liters of oxygen (present in the exhaled air within the Douglas bag), second column, from the liters of oxygen inspired, previous step (1.49 L − 1.27 L = 0.22 $\dot{V}O_2$ L/min).

5. By division of CO_2 liters, second column, by $\dot{V}O_2$ L/min the respiratory exchange ratio is obtained (0.21 ÷ 0.22 = 0.95 R).

A second method involves the formula:

$$Vo_2 = \frac{MV}{100} \times (\%N_2 \text{ exhaled air} \times 0.265 - \%O_2 \text{ exhaled air})$$

---

[*] 0.265, a constant, represents the ratio of O_2/N_2 of atmosphere; 20.93/79.04 = 0.265

TABLE 11-3

Bag No.	Elapsed time	Vol uncorr (L)	Gas temp (°C)	STPD corr	Vol corr	Time	MV (L)	Gas Analysis O₂%	Gas Analysis CO₂%	N₂	T, (°C)	HR (min)
1	0–5	40.48	25.0	0.380	35.60	5	7.120	17.9	3.0		37.2	69

Sitting rest

Data from Table 11–3

$$\dot{V}o_2 \text{ (ml/min)} = \frac{MV \text{ (ml)}}{100} \times (\%N_2 \text{ exhaled air} \times 0.265 - \%O_2 \text{ exhaled air})$$

$$= \frac{7120}{100} \times (79.1 \times 0.265 - 17.9)$$

$$= 71.20 \times (20.96 - 17.9)$$

$$= 71.20 \times 3.06$$

$$\dot{V}o_2 = 218 \text{ ml/min corrected to STPD}$$

A third method of calculating oxygen uptake involves the nomogram of Dill and Fölling (Fig. 11–6).

Using the same minute volume, oxygen, and carbon dioxide percentages presented in Table 11–3, the oxygen uptake is calculated by using the following formula:

$$\dot{V}o_2 \text{ ml/min} = \frac{\text{True } O_2\%^*}{100} \times MV$$

Calculations:

1. $O_2\%$ right column 17.9%; $CO_2\%$ (left column) 3.0%
2. By placing a straight-edge from right column, $O_2\%$, to the left column, $CO_2\%$ one can find the True $O_2\%$: 3.05%

$$\dot{V}o_2 \text{ ml/min} = \frac{\text{True } O_2\%}{100} \times MV \text{ ml}$$

$$= \frac{3.05}{100} \times 7120$$

$$= .0305 \times 7120$$

$$\dot{V}o_2 = 217.2 \text{ ml/min corrected to STPD}$$

Respiratory exchange ratio R is obtained by direct reading: 0.95

In the cited example, the percentage error among the three methods amounts to 0.014%.

Note also that all values are corrected to STPD. If the suggested format as in Table 11–3 is followed, no further calculations are necessary because the minute volume value will have been corrected to STPD. If the format is not followed, i.e., if the MV is not corrected to STPD, the formulae which appear on p. 286 must be used.

---

* Dill and Fölling labeled the product ($\%N_2$ exhaled air $\times$ 0.265 $-$ $\%O_2$ exhaled air) the True Oxygen Per Cent.

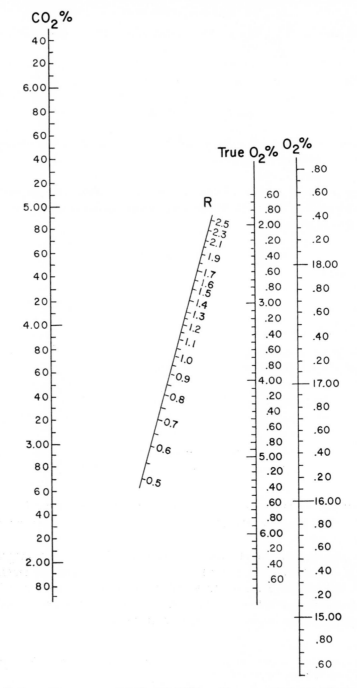

Fig. 11–6.   Nomogram of Dill and Fölling (R = respiratory exchange ratio).

Work

Considered in the physical sense, work is the product of force acting against mass through distance; W = Fs.

Several preliminary statements are in order. Performed work may be either positive or negative. Performance on a flight of stairs offers an example of both forms. Climbing steps exemplifies positive work, for the ascent is accomplished in opposition to the gravitational force and the body mass must be lifted step by step. Descending a flight of stairs offers an example of negative work. There is a step-by-step assist from the gravitational force as the body mass is being lowered. Energy is required for the performance of both work forms and the energy requirement is a function notably of velocity of muscle shortening, vertical displacement, and height of stair risers. The considerations are many; however, the energy cost of negative work ranges between one-third to one-tenth the energy cost of positive work. At an arm ergometer, flexing the forearm in order to overcome the resistance offered by the load exemplifies positive work. Extending the arm, with an assist from the load, represents the negative aspect of the performance.

In the physical sense, work is not accomplished in walking on a level surface (0%). Energy is expended and can be measured, but in this example, the vertical distance being traversed is zero; therefore, the product of body mass times vertical distance is zero.

Work of treadmill performance can be calculated provided treadmill grade is established. Grade, or incline, is expressed in percentage and reflects the units of rise or vertical displacement per hundred horizontal units. For example, +4% grade is interpreted as a 4-meter vertical displacement for every 100 meters of belt movement.

All calculations of treadmill performance which are provided in this text are based on a belt length of 5.55 meters/revolution (see Table 11–4).

Speed* and grade: 10 km/h + 6%
Total revolutions for an 8 min performance: 252
Weight of subject: 92.6 kg

$$W_{kgm} = (F)_{kg} \times (S_m)$$
$$= (Wgt_{kg})(\text{Total revolutions} \times \text{belt length in meters} \times \text{grade } \%)$$
$$= (92.6)(252 \times 5.55 \times .06)$$
$$= (92.6_{kg})(84.9_m)$$
$$W = 7861 \text{ kgm (note: for 8 min period)}$$

Expressed as work/min $= \dfrac{W_{Tot}}{\text{mins}}$

$$= \dfrac{7861 \text{ kgm}}{8}$$

$$W = 982.6 \text{ kgm/min}$$

---

* Speed of performance is reported and serves the purpose of giving more complete meaning to the intensity of effort.

18

TABLE 11-4

Subject SS ♂
Date: 5/5/65
P_B 752 mm Hg

Bag No.	Elapsed time	Vol uncorr (L)	Gas temp (°C)	STPD corr	Vol corr (L)	Time (min)	MV (L)	O₂%	Expired air CO₂%	N₂%	$\dot{V}O_2$ (L/min)	R
Rest												
1	0–5	60.0	25.5	0.875	52.50	5	10.50	17.40	3.50	79.10	0.374	0.983
Work 10 km/h + 6% Total rev 252												
2	0–1	57.6	25.5	0.875	50.40	1	50.40	16.50	4.20	79.30	2.275	0.930
3	1–2	90.4	25.5	0.875	79.10	1	79.10	16.40	4.70	79.80	3.755	0.990
4	2–4	193.6	25.5	0.875	169.20	2	84.50	16.30	5.00	79.70	4.073	1.037
5	4–6	208.5	26.0	0.875	182.50	2	91.25	16.30	4.90	78.80	4.181	1.069
6	6–8	200.1	26.0	0.875	175.00	2	87.50	16.30	4.60	79.10	4.079	0.987
												R 1.002
Recovery												
1	0–1	82.6	26.0	0.875	72.40	1	72.40	16.80	4.50	78.70	2.936	1.110
2	1–2	60.4	26.0	0.875	52.80	1	52.80	17.80	3.90	78.30	1.557	1.322
3	2–4	61.8	26.0	0.875	54.00	2	27.00	18.00	3.60	78.40	0.750	1.297
4	4–6	51.2	26.0	0.875	44.80	2	22.40	17.90	3.30	78.80	0.668	1.107
5	6–8	45.2	25.5	0.875	39.50	2	19.85	17.50	3.20	79.30	0.698	0.911
6	8–10	36.0	25.5	0.875	31.50	2	15.80	17.90	3.10	79.00	0.480	1.021
1	10–12	34.1	25.5	0.875	29.80	2	14.90	17.60	2.90	79.50	0.517	0.836
2	12–14	34.7	25.5	0.875	30.30	2	15.15	18.10	2.80	79.10	0.434	0.979
3	14–16	29.7	25.5	0.875	26.00	2	13.00	17.90	2.90	79.20	0.401	0.939
4	16–18	29.0	25.5	0.875	25.30	2	12.60	17.70	3.00	79.30	0.418	0.905
5	18–20	24.4	25.5	0.875	21.20	2	10.60	17.90	2.80	79.30	0.330	0.899
												$\overline{R}$ 1.029

These are actual data taken on a male subject, SS, 22 years of age, hgt 189 cm, wgt 92.6 kg. This represents the 36th and final performance on the motor driven treadmill at 10 km/h + 6% grade. Work periods were of 10 mins duration except for this final day. The slide rule was used in the calculation of STPD and Vol$_{corr}$. All other results were obtained by computer analysis: University of Massachusetts Research Computing Center, Control Data 3600.

20

Gross Cost of Exercise. Amount of energy required in the *conduct of* and *recovery from* running. In the following example, energy is expressed in terms of oxygen uptake.
From Table 11–4:

Time Interval	$\dot{V}O_2$ (L/min)	VO_2 (tot)	
		Work Oxygen	
0–1	2.275	2.275	
1–2	3.755	3.755	
2–4	4.073	8.146	*Note:* 2-min intervals
4–6	4.181	8.362	$\therefore$ VO_2 values have
6–8	4.079	8.158	been doubled.

Work O_2 = 30.696L

		Recovery Oxygen	
0–1	2.936	2.936	
1–2	1.557	1.557	
2–4	0.750	1.500	
4–6	0.668	1.336	
6–8	0.698	1.396	
8–10	0.480	0.960	*Note:* 2-min intervals
10–12	0.517	1.034	$\therefore$ VO_2 values have
12–14	0.434	0.868	been doubled.
14–16	0.401	0.802	
16–18	0.418	0.836	
18–20	0.330	0.660	

Recovery O_2 = 13.685L

Gross Cost of Work.[*] Total O_2 utilized during work and recovery.

$$= \text{Work } O_2 + \text{Recov } O_2$$
$$= 30.696 \text{ L} + 13.685 \text{ L}$$
$$= 44.381 \text{ L}$$

Net Cost of Work. Amount of oxygen required in the *conduct of* and *recovery from* activity minus the resting oxygen uptake for a comparable interval of time. (*Note:* the word *oxygen* has been substituted for the word *energy.*)

Net cost of work = gross cost of exercise − (oxygen uptake for rest × comparable time period for work and recovery)

Note: work period 8 min, recovery period 20 min
$$= 44.38 \text{ L} - (.374 \text{ L/min} \times 28 \text{ min})$$
$$= 44.38 \text{ L} - 10.47 \text{ L}$$
$$= 33.91 \text{ L}$$

---

[*] Work, exercise, and physical performance are synonymous terms

$$\text{Gross Efficiency} = \frac{\text{energy output}}{\text{energy input}} \times 100$$

$$= \frac{\text{work performed}}{\text{gross cost of work}} \times 100$$

$$= \frac{7861 \text{ kgm}}{30.696 \text{ L O}_2 + 13.685 \text{ L O}_2 \times 2153^*} \times 100$$

$$= \frac{7861 \text{ kgm}}{44.381 \text{ L O}_2 \times 2153} \times 100$$

$$= \frac{7861 \text{ kgm}}{95,500 \text{ kgm}} \times 100$$

$$= 8.25\%$$

$$\text{Net Efficiency} = \frac{\text{energy output}}{\text{net energy input}} \times 100$$

$$= \frac{\text{work performed}}{\text{net cost of work}} \times 100$$

$$= \frac{7861 \text{ kgm}}{33.91 \text{ L O}_2 \times 2153} \times 100$$

$$= \frac{7861 \text{ kgm}}{73,000 \text{ kgm}} \times 100$$

$$= 10.77\%$$

The net cost of exercise provides a clue to the effectiveness of physical activity in negative energy balance discussions (see pp. 191–196). Net cost of exercise may be separated into two phases:

Net cost of work phase = gross work O_2 — rest O_2 for comparable time period.
= 30.696 L — (.374 L/min × 8 min.)
= 30.696 L — 2.992
= 27.70 L

Net kcal = 27.70 L × 5.0
= 138.5 kcal

Net cost of recovery phase = gross recovery O_2 — rest O_2 for comparable time period.
= 13.685 L — (.374 L/min × 20 min.)
= 13.685 L — 7.480 L
= 6.205 L

Net kcal = 6.20 L × 5.0
= 31.0 kcal

Net Work O_2 = 27.70 L = 138.5 kcal 81.7% of total
Net Recovery O_2 = 6.20 L = 31.0 kcal 18.3% of total
169.5 kcal

Oxygen Debt

Oxygen debt is represented by the elevated oxygen uptake during the recovery period which reflects the deficiency incurred during work; the net cost of recovery from work.

---

*1 L O_2 = 2153 kgm equivalent. Note also from Table 11–4 that the average work R is 1.002.

O_2 debt = recovery O_2 − (O_2 uptake for rest × duration of recovery in mins)

= 13.685 L O_2 − (0.374 L/min × 20 min)

= 13.685 L − 7.480 L

= 6.205 L

Negative Energy Balance

Read discussion in Chapter 8 and see Figure 8–15. 3500 represents calorific value of 0.454 kg of human fat after allowances for body water and connective tissue have been made.

$$3500 \text{ kcal} = 0.454 \text{ kg equivalent}$$

At this rate, 169.5 kcal, three weeks of daily effort would be required for the loss of 0.454 kg (1 lb) of body fat.

$$\left(\frac{3500 \text{ kcal}}{169.5 \text{ kcal/day}} = 21 \text{ days} \right)$$

Other nonathletic subjects would be less efficient and would expend more calories for the same effort. Even in well-trained subjects, the metabolic rate might remain elevated for eighteen to twenty-four hours. This would reflect an even greater than usual caloric expenditure.

Oxygen Uptake Expressed per Kilogram of Body Weight

Comparisons of oxygen uptake of two individuals will greatly reflect differences in body mass. The greater the mass, the greater the oxygen consumption.

Expressing oxygen consumption per kilogram of body weight allows for justifiable comparisons to be made. Note the comparisons of one male and one female subject of comparable age. Both were enrolled in their final semester at college. The female subject was an accomplished track athlete who specialized in 880-yard dashes as well as in cross-country events. The male was a professional athlete (baseball); both performed on the motor driven treadmill at 10 km/h + 6% grade.

	Age	Height (cm)	Weight (kg)	$\dot{V}_{O_2}$ ml/min during 4 to 6 min of work	$\dot{V}_{O_2}$ ml/kg/min
JC ♀	22	164	53.5	2500	46.7*
SS ♂	22	189	92.6	4181	45.1

$$* \ \dot{V}_{O_2} \text{ ml/kg/min} = \frac{\dot{V}_{O_2} \text{ ml/min}}{\text{Wgt kg}}$$

$$= \frac{2500 \text{ ml/min}}{53.5 \text{ kg}}$$

$$= 46.7$$

Work Performed on Bicycle Ergometer

Work performed on the bicycle ergometer may be designated in kilogram-meters (kgm) or in kilopond-meters (kpm).

Friction (resistance) afforded by a brake belt along a flywheel rim is utilized in the construction and operation of one type of bicycle ergometer.*

The resistance (load on weight pan) is reflected in a spring scale reading. A pedal revolution counter constitutes another essential appurtenance.

Basic formula $W = F\,s$

W = work in kgm, F = resistance (kilogram scale units), s = distance travelled by flywheel rim (circumference $\times$ pedal revolutions)

Example: circumference of flywheel rim 1.5 m, ratio of pedal to flywheel rim revolutions 1:3, load on weight pan reflected as 2.5 kg on scale

$$
\begin{aligned}
W(kgm/min) &= (F_{resistance})\ (\text{flywheel circumference }_m \times \text{pedal rev }_{min}) \\
&= (2.5\ kg)\ (4.5\ m/rev \times 150\ rev) \\
&= (2.5\ kg)\ (675\ m) \\
&= 1687.5\ kgm/min
\end{aligned}
$$

Work accomplished in the course of riding another type of bicycle ergometer† is read in kpm units. Knowledge of the pedal to flywheel rim revolution ratio is essential as is the load in kg on the weight panel.

Example: ratio of pedal revolutions to distance traveled by flywheel rim = 1:6, apparatus is loaded with 1 kg, pedal rev/min 50

$$
\begin{aligned}
W(kpm/min) &= (F_{kg})\ (s_{m/min}) \\
&= (1\ kg)\ (\text{pedal rev/min} \times \text{ratio}) \\
&= (1\ kg)\ (50 \times 6) \\
&= (1)\ (300) \\
&= 300\ kpm/min
\end{aligned}
$$

In still another type of bicycle ergometer, resistance is provided by an electric brake mechanism. Within a rather wide range, the number of pedal revolutions is not an important consideration. Linearity of output, in watts, is assured by circuit design and principle of operation. Any increases in pedal revolutions are in effect increases in current (I) permitted through the brake; therefore, resistance (R) is decreased. Likewise, decrease in pedal revolutions results in a decreased current flow and an increased resistance.

---

* Refer to Karpovich for construction details for friction type bicycle ergometer.
† See von Döblen for description of ergometer.

$$W(\text{kgm/min}) = (\text{F or Power}_{\text{watts}}) (\text{conversion factor}^* {}_{\text{factory calculated}})$$
$$= (150 \text{ watts}) (6.1189)$$
$$= 917.8 \text{ kgm/min}$$

Cardiac Output (Fick Principle Modified)

As was indicated in Chapter 5, precise determination of cardiac output requires sophisticated techniques and apparatuses.

TABLE 11–5*

$\dot{V}_{O_2}$ (ml/min)	Art — Ven O_2 Diff (ml/ml)
250	0.045
325	0.048
400	0.050
500	0.055
600	0.060
800	0.065
1000	0.075
1200	0.083
1400	0.090
1600	0.098
1800	0.103
2000	0.109
2200	0.115
2400	0.120
2600	0.125
2800	0.130
3000	0.135
3200	0.139
3400	0.143
3600	0.146
3800	0.150

* Based on the data of Rushmer; refer to Fig. 5–12 also.

For purposes of approximation only, cardiac output can be calculated from known oxygen uptakes and from the arteriovenous oxygen differences which appear in Table 11–5.

From page 265, $\dot{V}$ for the fifth minute of work for the female subject was 2500 ml/min (heart rate HR was 130/min)

---

* watts to kilograms

$$\dot{Q}(\text{ml/min}) = \frac{\dot{V}o_2 \text{ ml/min}}{\text{A-V } O_2 \text{ diff (ml/ml)}}$$

$$= \frac{2500}{.120}$$

$$\dot{Q} = 20{,}833 \text{ ml/min or } 20.8 \text{ L/min}$$

$$SV(\text{ml}) = \frac{\dot{Q}(\text{ml/min})}{HR}$$

$$= \frac{20833}{130}$$

$$SV = 160 \text{ ml}$$

Note: The use of Table 11–5 is intended ONLY for the purpose of providing the reader with data from which the calculation of cardiac output and stroke volume can be accomplished in order that the learning process be strengthened.

Oxygen Pulse

Oxygen pulse expresses the extent of tissue oxygen delivery per heart beat. Such an index assumes greater importance when it is considered in the light of additional cardiopulmonary data.

The following calculation is based on the steady-state performance of a female subject (p. 265). $\dot{V}o_2 = 2500$ ml/min, pulse frequency 130/min.

$$\text{Oxygen pulse} = \frac{\dot{V}o_2 \text{ ml/min}}{\text{pulse frequency}}$$

$$= \frac{2500}{130}$$

$$= 19 \text{ ml}$$

Rest values range from 4 to 6 ml; during exercise of severe intensity, the index may increase to 30 ml ($\dot{V}o_2$ 6000 ml/min; pulse frequency 200/min).

Cardiac Index

Cardiac index expressed in relation to physical characteristics is accomplished by calculating the cardiac index. Physical characteristics such as height and weight are converted into a single figure—that of body surface area; see Table 5, Appendix. Cardiac index during the fourth to sixth minute interval was calculated to be:

$$\text{Cardiac index} = \frac{\dot{Q} \text{ L/min}}{\text{BSA m}^2}$$

$$= \frac{20.83}{1.57}$$

$$= 13.25 \text{ L/min/m}^2$$

Rest values extend from 3.0 to 5:5 L/min/m². During severe work, cardiac indices may range from 17.0 to 9.0 L/min/m².

Postural Mean Blood Pressure Index: The Hyman Index

A demonstrable relationship between general physical fitness and postural hypotension was reported by Hyman. Athletes, normal non-athletes, and patients with various cardiac disabilities served as subjects. The postural mean blood pressure index PMBPI is calculated from the mean blood pressure indices of four basic positions:

OSMBP — Original (initial) standing mean blood pressure (taken after 1 minute standing)

RMBP — Recumbent mean blood pressure (taken after 3 minutes of recumbent lying)

QSMBP — Quick standing mean blood pressure (Blood pressure taken immediately)

RSMBP — Restoration standing mean blood pressure (Taken after 1 minute standing—i.e., from quick standing)

Mean blood pressure is obtained by dividing the pulse pressure by 3* and adding the result to the diastolic blood pressure.

In essence, the PMBPI is obtained by calculating the mean blood pressure differences in the recumbent and quick standing positions.

Accomplished treadmill performers as well as nonathletic types possess indices similar to the one calculated below (SBP = systolic blood pressure, DBP = diastolic blood pressure):

| Representative Data | Blood Pressures in mm Hg | | | |
| | Recumbent | | Quick Standing | |
	SBP	DBP	SBP	DBP
Treadmill performers	125	90	118	88
Sedentary	110	80	120	85

---

* During any cardiac cycle, mean arterial blood pressure values were found to approximate diastolic pressure rather than systolic values. Through a strain gauge needle inserted into arterial lumen, pressure curves were obtained and were plotted against clinical blood pressure data. The clinically obtained pulse pressure, when added to the diastolic pressure, was found to exceed the formula values. The factor 3 (representing the range of discrepancy from 2.8685 to 3.0854) is a correction factor. By mathematically adjusting the diastolic pressure, actual and calculated mean blood pressures were found to compare to within ± 5%.

$$\text{Basic formula} = MBP = \frac{SBP - DBP}{3} + DBP$$

Treadmill runners:

$$RMBPI = \frac{125 - 90}{3} + 90$$

$$= \frac{35}{3} + 90$$

$$= 11.6 + 90$$

$$= 101.6$$

$$QSMBPI = \frac{118 - 88}{3} + 88$$

$$= \frac{30}{3} + 88$$

$$= 10 + 88$$

$$= 98$$

$$PMBPI = \frac{QSMBPI - RMBPI}{RMBPI} \times 100$$

$$= \frac{101.6 - 98}{101.6} \times 100$$

$$= \frac{3.6}{101.6} \times 100$$

$$= 3.5\%^{\circ}$$

Values reported by cardiologist Hyman are presented below:

Subjects	PMBPI range
Athletes N = 340	+5.75% to −3.0%
Patients with various cardiopulmonary disorders	−18.62% to −42.65%
Nonathletic normal	+10.025% to −18.75%

Somatotypology

Many physiological parameters become more meaningful when they are interpreted in the light of the physical or anatomical characteristics of the subject. Without such an important reference point, data may be erroneously interpreted. A case in point involves the interpretation of oxygen consumption values (see p. 265). When expressed as ml/kg body weight, the oxygen uptake values become more meaningful and comparative.

Body mass consists of a lean and a fat component.[15] Because body fat is metabolically inert, relatively speaking, the total amount must be determined and parceled out mathematically before meaningful interpre-

---

° Comparisons are made to RMBPI. If QSMBPI is *less* than RMBPI, PMBPI values will be *minus;* if QSMBPI is *greater* than RMBPI, then PMBPI values will be *positive.* Calculations of PMBPI of sedentary subject in above table will have positive value.

tations can be made. For example, Miller and Blyth noted lean body mass to offer the highest predictive value in forecasting basal oxygen consumption than either body surface area or body weight.[17,18]

A number of somatotyping techniques may be utilized. Body surface area nomograms may be used to express somatotype in elementary form. See Table 5 in the appendix. For example, oxygen consumption may be expressed as $\dot{V}_{O_2}$/BSAm². Likewise, VE_{O_2} or VC also may be expressed in relation to BSAm².

Subjects may be described through such growth records or nomograms as those of Hall or Meredith or Wetzel.

The Sheldon technique is valid when anterior, lateral, and posterior photographs of a nude body provide the basis for observation and measurement. From the negatives portraying the three body positions, Sheldon utilized an index (height $\div \sqrt[3]{weight}$) and seventeen body diameters which he then subjected to lengthy mathematical treatment. The numerical value, 7 expresses the highest component of endomorphy, mesomorphy, or ectomorphy; the lowest component is assigned the value of 1. Three distinct body types emerge: 7-1-1, endomorphy; 1-7-1, mesomorphy; 1-1-7, ectomorphy. The Sheldon technique allows for the numerical portrayal of the varieties of human physique. The technique is laborious and lends itself to computer analysis.

The technique of Tanner et al. is interesting and represents a practical incorporation of the photogrammetric technique into the Sheldon method.

The Sheldon procedure has been badly distorted* by those who attempt to differentiate, by visual means only, the components of somatotype. Only in the hands of an extremely few, well-trained students of Sheldon is the visual technique valid.

Accurate determination of lean body weight may be accomplished through the use of the Behnke method.[3]

The inadequacy of height-weight scales was vividly portrayed by Welham and Behnke who noted a high body specific gravity of "overweight," professional football players. The lean body mass and low fat content reflected in a high body specific gravity is incompatible with the "overweight" classification. Tanner et al. found wrestlers to range from endomorphic mesomorphs to ectomorphic mesomorphs. Weight lifters were predominately endo-mesomorphic; mile runners were predominately meso-ectomorphic. The contributions of Brozek and associates[5,6] have added much to the understanding of body components.

---

* The author of this text has been somatotyped, by visual means, by a fair number of people and the results have varied considerably. A well-trained student of Sheldon concluded that 2 − 5½ − 3 was most descriptive. (The author is in full agreement with the mesomorphy component.)

The technique of Behnke[3] is advocated because precise assessment of body build can be quickly accomplished with minimal equipment. Arthropometer, stadiometer, and scale constitute the essential apparatus.

The method which is described below represents a simplification of an involved mathematical process. Through the use of constants derived from reference man and reference woman, eight body diameters plus body height are mathematically transformed into lean body weight (LBW). Percentage of body fat is calculated by employing the archimedian concept.

Diameters	Constants ♂	♀
Subject in Seated Position		
Biacromial (most lateral projections of the biacromial processes are measured)	21.6	20.4
Elbow (both elbows measured; forearm fully flexed, distance between condyles of humerus measured)	7.4	6.9
Wrist (both wrists measured; measurement incorporates styloid processes of radius and ulna)	5.9	5.6
Knee (both knees measured; knee flexed to 90°; measurement is at the tibiale; medial condyle is palpable; lateral condyle measurement is immediately superior to the head of fibula)	9.8	10.3
Subject in Standing Position		
Chest (measurement taken during normal breathing at level of 5th to 6th rib space; nipple line on males)	15.9	14.8
Bi-iliac (distance between iliac crests)	15.6	16.7
Bitrochanteric (Distance between most lateral projections of trochanters)	17.4	18.6
Ankles (both ankles measured; feet spread approximately 15 cm apart, measurement taken from behind; distance between malleoli of tibia and fibula)	7.4	7.4

The use of a calculator is recommended because all figures should be corrected to the second place beyond decimal.

The following measurements were taken on a 43-year-old male; height, 17.5 dm; weight, 77.18 kg:

Diameter	Measurement (cm)		Constants		Resultant
Biacromial	39.4	÷	21.6	=	1.82
Elbows R & L	14.3	÷	7.4	=	1.93
Wrists R & L	11.0	÷	5.9	=	1.69
Knees R & L	19.2	÷	9.8	=	1.95
Chest	30.0	÷	15.9	=	1.89
Bi-iliac	30.5	÷	15.6	=	1.95
Bitrochanteric	35.0	÷	17.4	=	2.01
Ankles R & L	14.3	÷	7.4	=	1.93

$$\Sigma = 15.17$$
$$\bar{X} \quad 1.90$$
$$\bar{X}^2 \quad 3.61$$

$$\begin{aligned} \text{LBW} &= \bar{X}^2 \times \text{hgt} \\ &= 3.61 \times 17.5 \\ &= 63.17 \end{aligned}$$

$$\begin{aligned} \text{Per cent of body fat} &= \frac{\text{Actual body wgt} - \text{Lean body wgt}}{\text{Actual body wgt}} \times 100 \\ &= \frac{\text{ABW} - \text{LBW}}{\text{ABW}} \times 100 \\ &= \frac{77.18 - 63.17}{77.18} \times 100 \\ &= 18.15\% \end{aligned}$$

Reference values: males 19% fat, females 25% fat

Behnke[2] has also proposed a simplified calculation procedure to obtain LBW:

$$\text{LBW} = \left(\frac{\text{Sum of 8 diameters}}{101}\right)^2 \times \text{hgt}$$

From the data provided (43-year-old male subject) the sum of diameters 193.7 cm

$$\begin{aligned} \text{LBW} &= \left(\frac{193.7}{101}\right)^2 \times 17.5 \\ &= 64.40 \end{aligned}$$

Note: 101 represents a constant for both male and female Caucasians. Behnke noted bi-iliac as well as chest diameters to be smaller in the Negro. As a somatotype technique for *both* sexes of Caucasian and Negro races, Behnke proposed the following formula:

$$\text{LBW} = \left(\frac{\text{Sum of 4 diameters}}{54.8}\right)^2 \times \text{hgt}$$

4 diameters (in cm) include: biacromial, bitrochanteric, both wrists, and both knees

54.8 = constant

Composition and Resolution of Forces

Trigonometric functions (sines and cosines) are used in the calculation of force resolution. Rectangular components are utilized in the diagrams on page 275. The relationship of the two sides of a right triangle to the hypotenuse is determined from one specified angle (see below). Note that the diagram has been placed on its side.

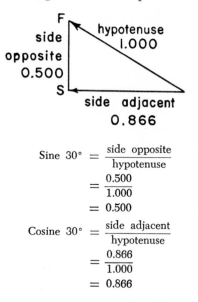

$$\text{Sine } 30° = \frac{\text{side opposite}}{\text{hypotenuse}}$$

$$= \frac{0.500}{1.000}$$

$$= 0.500$$

$$\text{Cosine } 30° = \frac{\text{side adjacent}}{\text{hypotenuse}}$$

$$= \frac{0.866}{1.000}$$

$$= 0.866$$

For the following discussion, bear in mind that force vector R depicts the rotatory force about the humero-ulnar joint; S represents the stabilizing component. In other words, vector R represents the rotational or useful component, vector S the "wasted component" or stabilizing or compression component.

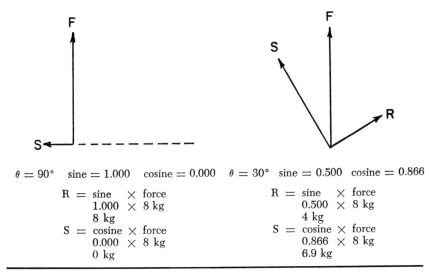

A
The arm-forearm relationship is established at 90°, theta angle 90°

B
The arm-forearm relationship is established at 150°, theta angle 30°

$\theta = 90°$ sine $= 1.000$ cosine $= 0.000$

R = sine × force
1.000 × 8 kg
8 kg
S = cosine × force
0.000 × 8 kg
0 kg

$\theta = 30°$ sine $= 0.500$ cosine $= 0.866$

R = sine × force
0.500 × 8 kg
4 kg
S = cosine × force
0.866 × 8 kg
6.9 kg

Note that forearm is flexed at 90°; B depicts a change of muscle insertion.

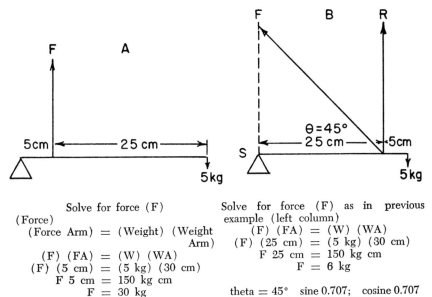

Solve for force (F)
(Force)
(Force Arm) = (Weight) (Weight Arm)
(F) (FA) = (W) (WA)
(F) (5 cm) = (5 kg) (30 cm)
F 5 cm = 150 kg cm
F = 30 kg

Solve for force (F) as in previous example (left column)
(F) (FA) = (W) (WA)
(F) (25 cm) = (5 kg) (30 cm)
F 25 cm = 150 kg cm
F = 6 kg

theta = 45° sine 0.707; cosine 0.707
R and S = (0.707) (F)
= (0.707) (6 kg)
= 4.24 kg

The rotary R as well as stabilizing component S is 70.7% of the original force.

REFERENCES

1. Behnke, A. R.: Personal communication. Feb., 1967.

2. Behnke, A. R.: Personal communication. Feb., 1967.

3. Behnke. A. R.: Quantitative assessment of body build. *J. Appl. Physiol.. 16*:960–968, 1961.

4. British Shift to Metric System to be Gradual 10-year Process. *New York Times,* Tuesday, May 25, 1965.

5. Brozek, J., and Keys, A.: The evaluation of leanness–fatness in man: norms and interrelationships. *Brit. J. Nutrition, 5*:194–206, 1951.

6. Brozek, J., Brock, J. F., Fidanza, F., and Keys, A.: Skinfold caliper estimation of body fat and nutritional status. *Fed. Proc., 13*:19, 1954.

7. Comroe, J. H.: *Methods in Medical Research.* Chicago, Year Book Medical Publishers, Inc., 1950.

8. Comroe, J. H., Forster, R. E., Dubois, A. B., Briscoe, W. A., and Carlsen, E.: *The Lung. Clinical Physiology and Pulmonary Function Tests.* 2nd Ed., Chicago, Year Book Medical Publishers, Inc., 1962.

9. Dill, D. B., and Fölling, A.: Studies in muscular activity. II. A nomographic description of expired air. *J. Physiol., 66*:133–135, 1928.

10. Gaensler, E. A.: Analysis of ventilatory defect by timed capacity measurements. *Am. Rev. Tuberc., 64*:256–278, 1951.

11. Gaensler, E. A.: Medical progress: clinical pulmonary physiology. *New England J. Med., 252*:177–184, 221–228, 264–271, 1955.

12. Hall, D. M.: *Keeping Fit: An Evaluation of the Fitness of Illinois' Young People.* Urbana, Cooperative Extension Service, University of Illinois, 1966.

13. Hyman, A. S.: The postural mean blood pressure index. A simple method of estimating general physical fitness, *Bull. Daitz Res. Fund, 62*:1–3, 1962.

14. Karpovich, P. V.: A frictional bicycle ergometer, *Res. Quart., 21*:210–215, 1950.

15. Keys, A., and Brozek, J.: Body fat in adult man. *Physiol. Rev., 33*:245–325, 1953.

16. Meredith, H. V.: A physical growth record for use in elementary and high schools, *Am. J. Pub. Health, 39*:878–885, 1949.

17. Miller, A. T. and Blyth, C. S.: Influence of body type and body fat content on the metabolic cost of work. *J. Appl. Physiol., 8*:139–141, 1955.

18. Miller, A. T., and Blyth, C. S.: Estimation of lean body mass and body fat from basal oxygen consumption and creatinine excretion. *J. Appl. Physiol., 5*:73–78, 1952.

19. Miller, W. F., Johnson, R. L., and Wu, N.: Relationships between maximal breathing capacity and timed expiratory capacities. *J. Appl., Physiol., 14*:510–516, 1959.

20. Motley, H. L.: Use of pulmonary function tests for disability appraisal: including evaluation standards in chronic pulmonary disease. *Dis. Chest, 24*:378–389, 1953.

21. Pappenheimer, J. R., Comroe, J. H., Cournand, A., Ferguson, J. K. W., Filley, G. F., Fowler, W. S., Gray, J. S., Helmholtz, H. F., Otis, A. B., Rahn, H., and Riley, R. L.: Standardization of definitions and symbols in respiratory physiology. *Fed. Proc., 9*:602–605, 1950.

22. Rushmer, R. F.: Control of cardiac output. *In* Ruch, T. C., and Fulton, J. F. (Eds.): *Medical Physiology and Biophysics.* 18th Ed. Philadelphia, W. B. Saunders Co., 1961.

23. Sheldon, W. H., Stevens, S. S., and Tucker, W. B.: *The Varieties of Human Physique.* 2nd Ed., New York, Harper & Brothers, 1940.

24. Tanner, J. M., Israelsohn, W. J., and Whitehouse, R. H.: Physique and body composition as factors affecting success in different athletic events. *Med. Sport., 14*:397–411, 1960.

25. von Döblen, W.: A simple bicycle ergometer. *J. Appl. Physiol., 7*:222–224, 1954.

26. Welham, W. C., and Behnke, A. R.: The specific gravity of healthy men. Body weight ÷ volume and other physical characteristics of exceptional athletes and of naval personnel. *J.A.M.A., 118*:498–501, 1942.

27. Wetzel, N. C.: Physical fitness in terms of physique, development, and basal metabolism. *J. A. M. A., 116*:1187–1195, 1941.

28. Williams, M., and Lissner, H. R.: *Biomechanics of Human Motion.* Philadelphia, W. B. Saunders Co., 1962.

APPENDIX

DEFINITIONS, FORMULAS, AND LAWS

Acceleration: Rate of change of velocity.

$$a = \frac{v_f - v_i}{t}$$

v_f, v_i = final and initial velocities respectively,

t = time

Accelerated Motion

$v_f = v_i + at$ also $v_f = v_i + gt$

$s = v_i t + \frac{1}{2}at^2$ also $s = v_i t + \frac{1}{2}gt^2$

$v_f = \sqrt{v_i^2 + 2as}$ also $v_f = \sqrt{v_i^2 + 2gs}$

$\dot{s}/sec = v_i + \frac{1}{2}a(2t - 1 \ sec)$ also $\dot{s}/sec = v_i + \frac{1}{2}g(2t - 1 \ sec)$

$\dot{s}/sec$ = displacement during final second,

v_f, v_i = final and initial velocities respectively,

a = acceleration, g = acceleration of gravity,

t = elapsed time, s = displacement

Avogadro's Law: Equal volumes of different gases under the same temperature and pressure contain the same number of molecules. One gram-atomic weight of any element contains 6.023×10^{23} atoms.

Beer's Law: The intensity of color or of light transmitted through a liquid is inversely proportional to the depth of the liquid.

BTPS: *B*ody *t*emperature and ambient barometric *p*ressure *s*aturated with water vapor.

$$BTPS_{correction} = \frac{273°K + 37°C}{273°K + t°C} \times \frac{P_B \ (mm \ Hg) - P_{H_2O} \ (mm \ Hg)}{P_B \ (mm \ Hg) - 47 \ (mm \ Hg)}$$

273 = freezing point of water on Kelvin scale ($0°C$), $37°C$ = (a constant) body temperature, $t°C$ = temperature of collected gas sample, P_B = ambient barometric pressure, P_{H_2O} = water vapor tension, i.e., pressure exerted by water vapor in collected gas sample. See Table 1, Appendix. 47 mm Hg = (a constant), water vapor tension at $37°C$.

Cardiac Output: Volume of blood ejected per unit of time (usually per minute).

$$MV = SV \times HR \qquad SV = \frac{MV}{HR}$$

$$\text{or} \quad Q = SV \times HR \qquad SV = \frac{Q}{HR}$$

$$\text{or} \quad \dot{Q}\text{ml/min} = SV\text{ml} \times HR \qquad SV\text{ml} = \frac{\dot{Q}\text{ml/min}}{SV}$$

$$\text{or} \quad \dot{Q}\text{ml/min} = \frac{\dot{V}o_2\text{ml/min}}{AVD\text{ml/ml}}$$

$$\text{or} \quad \dot{Q}\text{ml/min} = \frac{\dot{V}o_2\text{ml/min}}{AVD \text{ vol } \%} \times 100$$

MV = minute volume, SV = stroke volume, HR = heart rate, Q = blood flow, $\dot{Q}$ = blood flow per unit time, Vo_2 = oxygen uptake per unit time, AVD = arterial-venous oxygen difference (see Table 11–5).

Center of Gravity: Point at which the weight of a mass is concentrated. In the human body, the center of gravity may be calculated for one or all three planes (anteroposterior, lateral, or transverse) and for any body segment.

Conduction Velocity: Velocity of a transmitted electrical potential along a conductor.

$$V = \frac{s}{T1 - T2}$$

V = velocity, s = distance, T1, T2 = time interval between initial and final reference points

Density: The ratio of mass to volume of an object.

$$D_m = \frac{m}{v} \quad \text{also} \quad D_w = \frac{w}{v}$$

D_m = mass density, m = mass, v = volume
D_w = weight density, w = weight

Efficiency: A ratio of output to input.

$$\text{Gross eff.} = \frac{\text{energy output} \times 100}{\text{energy input}}$$

$$\text{Net eff.} = \frac{\text{energy output} \times 100}{\text{net energy input}^*}$$

---

* net energy input = gross energy input minus energy required to maintain metabolic processes for comparable time period.

Energy: The capacity for overcoming tension.

Potential energy $=$ mgh also PE $=$ wh

Kinetic energy $=$ $\frac{1}{2}mv^2$ also KE $= \dfrac{wv^2}{2g}$

m $=$ mass, g $=$ acceleration of gravity, h $=$ vertical distance, w $=$ weight, v $=$ velocity

Energy cost of physical activity

Gross Cost: Amount of oxygen* required in the *conduct* of and *recovery* from activity.

Net Cost: Amount of oxygen required in the *conduct* of and *recovery* from activity minus resting oxygen uptake for a *comparable* interval of time.

Gases

Boyle's Law: $\qquad pV = p'V'$

If temperature is constant, the volume of a mass of gas is inversely proportional to the pressure exerted upon it. p and V $=$ original pressure and volume; p'V' $=$ new pressure and volume. Temperature must remain constant (see p. 111).

Charles' Law: $\qquad \dfrac{V}{T_k} = \dfrac{V'}{T_k'}$

If pressure is constant, the volume of a mass of gas is directly proportional to absolute temperature (on Kelvin scale)

V and T_k $=$ original volume and Kelvin temperature.
V' and T_k' $=$ new volume and Kelvin temperature.

Combined Laws of Boyle and Charles:

$$\dfrac{pV}{T_k} = \dfrac{p'V'}{T_k'}$$

Dalton's Law: The total pressure of a mixture of gases is equal to the sum of the partial pressures of the component gases.

$P_{tot} = P_1 + P_2 + P_3 \ldots P_{final}$
$P_{tot} =$ total pressure; P_1, P_2 etc. $=$ pressure of component gases (see pp. 117–118).

---

* or kilocaloric or kilogram-meter equivalent

Henry's Law: The weight of a given gas dissolved in liquid varies directly with the partial pressure of the gas.

$$W \propto P_{gas}$$

W = weight, $\propto$ = varies as, P_{gas} = partial pressure of any gas

Combined Laws of Dalton and Henry: Component gases in a mixture of gases will dissolve in liquid in direct proportion to the partial pressures of the component gases.

or

component gases of a gas mixture will dissolve in liquid in direct proportion to their partial pressures.

Hooke's Law: Within the limits of elasticity of a body or tissue, stress (of stretch or compression) is proportional to strain or change in length.

$$\sigma = E\epsilon$$

σ = stress, E = modulus of elasticity, ϵ = strain

Kilopond Meter (kpm): Force acting on a mass of one kilogram at normal acceleration (of gravity) per unit of time. Usually expressed as kpm/min.

Law of Laplace: Tension exerted by liquid or gas is dependent upon its pressure and upon the radius of the vessel in which it is contained.

$$T = P\,r \qquad\qquad P \propto \frac{T}{r}$$

T = tension, P = pressure, r = radius, $\propto$ = varies as

Lever: A body segment moving about an axis.

1st class = EA, Ax, RA
2nd class = EA, RA, Ax
3rd class = Ax, EA, RA
EA = effort arm, Ax = axis, RA = resistance arm

Mechanical Advantage:

$$IMA = \frac{l_e}{l_r}$$

IMA = ideal mechanical advantage,
l_e = length of lever arm, l_r = length of resistance arm

Newton's Laws of Motion:

1st Law, Inertia: A body continues in its state of rest or uniform motion unless compelled by unbalanced forces to change its state.

2nd Law, Acceleration: A body is accelerated in the direction of and in direct proportion to the force exerted on it and in inverse proportion to its mass.

$$a \quad \frac{F}{m} \qquad F = ma$$

a = acceleration, $\propto$ = varies as, F = force, m = mass.

3rd Law, Interaction: For every action there is an equal and opposite reaction.

Ohm's Law:

The intensity of an electric current passing through a conductor is directly proportional to the electromotive force and inversely proportional to the resistance afforded by the conductor.

I = E/R
I = current in amperes, E = emf in volts, R = resistance in ohms.
then R = E/I
and E = IR

Oxygen Utilization Coefficient: Percentage of total amount of oxygen utilized by the tissues.

$$O_2 \text{ util. coeff.} = \frac{V_{O_2} \text{ tissue}}{\text{Art } O_2 \text{ content}} \times 100$$

or

$$O_2 \text{ util. coeff.} = \frac{\text{Art } O_2 \text{ vols \% } - \text{ Ven } O_2 \text{ vols \%}}{\text{Art } O_2 \text{ vols \%}} \times 100$$

V_{O_2} tissue = tissue oxygen uptake, Art O_2 vols % and Ven O_2 vols % = oxygen saturation in vols% in arterial and venous blood respectively.

Pascal's 1st Law:

Pressure applied on confined fluid is transmitted equally in all directions

$$p = \frac{F}{A}$$

p = pressure, F = force, A = area

Pascal's 3rd Law:

Pressure exerted by a fluid increases in direct proportion to the fluid depth

$p = hD_w$
$h =$ depth, $D_w =$ weight density

Poiseuille's Law:

The flow rate of viscous fluids is directly proportional to the pressure gradient, fluid viscosity, and tubing diameter. Hagen's recognition of the inverse relationship between the cohesive force of blood[*] and the blood vessel walls resulted in the following formula:

$$F = P_1 - P_2 \times \frac{(\pi r^4)}{(8L)} \times \frac{(1)}{(v)}$$

P_1, $P_2 =$ pressures at blood vessel ends, $\pi = 3.14159$, r^4, $L, =$ specifics of blood vessel dimensions, $8 =$ Hagen's integration — calculus derivation, $l/v =$ viscosity of fluid in poise units.

then $R = \dfrac{P}{F} = \dfrac{(8L)}{(\pi r^4)} = \dfrac{(v)}{(1)}$

Where $R =$ resistance to flow; $P =$ pressure, $F =$ force; $L =$ length; $r =$ radius.

Power: The rate of performing work.

$P = \dfrac{W}{t}$
$W =$ work, $t =$ time

Relative Humidity: Ratio of the water vapor saturation of a given volume of air to its maximum possible saturation. Reported as a percentage.

Resistance: The opposition to an electrical flow.

$R = \rho \dfrac{L}{A}$

$\rho =$ resistivity,[†] $L =$ length, $A =$ cross-sectional area of wire

Respiratory Exchange Ratio: Ratio of carbon dioxide produced to oxygen consumed

$$R = \frac{\text{Vol } CO_2}{\text{Vol } O_2}$$

---

[*] Blood is a non-Newtonian fluid, i.e., its flow is laminar, meaning that its axial flow is faster than its peripheral flow.

[†] Resistivity is a measure of the resistance of a wire 1 cm long and a cross-sectional area of 1 cm².

also $\quad R = \dfrac{\%CO_2 \text{ exhaled air } -0.03}{\%N_2 \text{ exhaled air } \times 0.265 - \%O_2 \text{ exhaled air}}$

$$R = \frac{CO_2 - 0.03}{V_{O_2}}$$

$0.03 = \%CO_2$ in atmospheric air, $0.265 =$ ratio of $\% O_2$ (20.93) and N_2 (79.04) in atmospheric air.

Resolution of Force of Gravity: The gravitational force separated into component forces acting in a specific direction.

$$\frac{W}{Wp} = \frac{L}{h}$$

$W =$ weight of object, $Wp =$ gravitational force, L, h, $=$ length and height of plane respectively.

Specific Gravity: Ratio of the density of a substance to a standard (usually water).

Solid or liquid

$$Sp.\ gr. = \frac{D_{sub}}{D_{water}}$$

D_{sub} and $D_{water} =$ density of substance (solid or liquid) and of water.

Solid

$$Sp.\ gr. = \frac{\text{wgt. in air}}{\text{buoyancy in water}}$$

STPD: Gas volumes reduced to standard conditions—barometric pressure 760 mm Hg, temperature 0°C, dry. The combined laws of Boyle and Charles.

$$STPD_{correction} = \frac{P_B \text{ (mm Hg)} - P_{H_2O} \text{ (mm Hg)}}{760 \text{ (mm Hg)}} \times \frac{273°K}{273°K + t°C}$$

$P_B =$ ambient barometric pressure, $P_{H_2O} =$ water vapor tension, i.e., pressure exerted by water vapor in collected gas sample. See Table 2, Appendix. $760 =$ (a constant) barometric pressure at sea level, $273 =$ freezing point of water on Kelvin scale $(0°C)$, $t°C =$ temperature of collected gas sample.

Temperature: A measure of absorbed or adsorbed heat.

Conversions:

Centigrade to Fahrenheit
$T_f = T_c \times 9 \div 5 + 32 = (T_f = 9/5\ T_c + 32)$
or
$T_f = (T_c \times 1.8) + 32$
Fahrenheit to Centigrade
$T_c = T_f - 32 \times 5 \div 9 = (T_c = 5/9\ [T_f - 32])$
Centigrade to Kelvin
$T_k = T_c + 273$
T_f, T_c, $T_k =$ Fahrenheit, centigrade, and Kelvin temperatures respectively

Velocity: Rate of displacement.

$$Vav = \frac{s}{t}$$

Vav = average velocity, s = displacement (distance), t = elapsed time.

Volume: Space occupied by matter (in a cylinder)

$$V = \pi r^2 h$$

$\pi = 3.14159$, r = radius, h = height

For closed circuit indirect calorimetry:

$Vo_2 = MV \times STPD_{correction}$

or

$\dot{V}o_2$ ml/min (or L/min) = MV ml (or L) $\times$ STPD$_{correction}$

Vo_2 = oxygen consumption, $\dot{V}o_2$ = oxygen consumption/unit/time, MV = minute volume, STPD = standard conditions (760 mm Hg, 0°C, dry gas)

For open circuit indirect calorimetry:

$$Vo_2 = \frac{MV}{100} \ (\%N_2 \text{ exhaled air} \times 0.265 - \%O_2 \text{ exhaled air})^*$$

$$\dot{V}o_2 = \frac{MV(ml \text{ or } L)}{100} \times \text{True } O_2\% \times STPD_{correction}$$

or

$\dot{V}o_2$ ml/min or L/min =

$$\frac{MV \text{ ml or L } (\% \text{ N}_2 \text{ exhaled air} \times 0.265 - \% \text{ O}_2 \text{ exhaled air } (STPD_{corr})}{100}$$

Vo_2 = oxygen consumption, $\dot{V}o_2$ = oxygen consumption/unit/time,
MV = minute volume, % N_2 exhaled air (100 − % O_2 + % CO_2 [by analysis]),
0.265 ratio of O_2/N_2 atmospheric air 20.93/79.04,
% O_2 exhaled air by analysis, STPD = standard condition
(760 mm Hg, 0°C, dry gas).

Work: Product of force acting against mass through distance.

$$W = F \ s$$
$$F = \text{force, } s = \text{distance mass is moved}$$

CONVERSION FACTORS

The metric system is a convenient, logical system. The meter is the linear unit of the metric system, the unit of volume is the liter, and the unit of weight is the gram. Prefixes of *Greek* derivation indicate *multiples* whereas prefixes of *Latin* derivation indicate *fractions* of the meter, liter, or gram.

---

* Note: (% N_2 exhaled air $\times$ 0.265 − % O_2 exhaled air) is the same as the True Oxygen % in the nomogram of Dill and Fölling (see Fig. 11–6); therefore, if nomogram is used formula becomes:

Multiples	Sym-bol	Expo-nent	Fractions	Sym-bol	Expo-nent
deka (10)	dk		deci (1/10 m, 0.1)	d	
hecto (100)	h	10^2	centi (1/100 m, 0.01)	c	10^{-2}
kilo (1,000)	k	10^3	milli (1/1,000 m, 0.001)	m	10^{-3}
myria (10,000)	my	10^4			
mega (1,000,000)	M	10^6	micro (1/1,000,000 m, 0.000001)	μ	10^{-6}

Prefixes are applied to symbols or words describing such units as length, mass, volume, heat, and electricity. For example the prefix kilo, symbol k, applied to the symbol for meter, m, describes a multiple of a unit of length: 1 km = 1000 m (1 kilometer equals 1000 meters). The prefix milli, symbol m, applied to the symbol for meter would describe a fraction of length: 1 mm = 0.001 m (1 millimeter equals 1/1000 of a meter).

Either the CGS or the MKS systems* may be used to further amplify the metric system. Force, for example, may be described in both systems. The dyne is a unit of force in the CGS system, which is required to accelerate one gram mass at one centimeter per second per second. The newton, also a unit of force, but in the MKS system, is the force required to accelerate one kilogram mass at the rate of one meter per second per second.

Area: outside surface measured in square units
    1 square centimeter = 0.155 square inch
    1 square meter = 1.1960 square yards = 10.764 square feet
    1 square inch = 6.452 square centimeters
    1 square foot = 0.0929 square meter
    1 square yard = 0.8361 square meter

Heat: thermal energy absorbed or adsorbed by a body
    Energy; Calorie: the amount of heat required to raise the temperature of 1 kilogram of water 1 degree centigrade (at 15°C); large calorie or kilocalorie (kcal), also known as the kilogram calorie (kg cal)
    1 kcal = 426.85 kilogram-meters = 3087.4 foot-pounds = 1000 gram-calories
    Note: large Calorie is capitalized
    Caloric yield of foodstuffs
    1 gram of carbohydrate = 4.1 Calories; 1 gram of protein = 4.3 Calories; 1 gram of fat = 9.3 Calories
    Temperature: a measure of the ability of a body to absorb or adsorb heat
    Fahrenheit to centigrade: $-32 \times 5 \div 9$
    centigrade to Fahrenheit: $\times 9 \div 5 + 32$

Linear Measure: a system of measurement of length
    1 meter = 10 decimeters = 100 centimeters = 1000 millimeters = 1.0936 yards = 3.28084 feet = 39.37 inches
    1 kilometer = 1000 meters = 0.6214 mile
    1 centimeter = 0.3937 inch
    1 inch = 2.54 centimeters
    1 foot = 30.4801 centimeters = 0.3048 meter
    1 mile = 1.6093 kilometers = 1609.35 meters = 1760 yards = 5280 feet

* The CGS system is a metric system of measurement in which centimeters, grams, and seconds are used as basic units. In the MKS system, the meter, kilogram, and second constitute the basic units.

Oxygen, Oxidation: the combustion of oxygen resulting in liberation of energy and heat

    1 liter of oxygen consumed (RQ = 1) = 5.047 Calories* = 2153 kilogram-meters = 15,575 foot-pounds. (**If used in 1 minute = 0.47 horsepower.**)

    1 liter of oxygen consumed in a closed circuit system: Post prandial state (RQ = 0.82) = 4.825 Calories. Mixed diet (RQ = 0.85) = 4.862 Calories.

Power: the rate of performing work

    1 kilowatt = 1000 watts = 0.239 Calorie per second = 15.34 Calories per minute = 1.341 horsepower

    1 metric force de cheval (horsepower) = 75 kilogram-meters per second = 0.98632 horsepower

    1 horsepower = 4564 kilogram-meters per minute = 76.07 kilogram-meters per second = 0.178 Calories per second = 10.964 Calories per minute = 2.1 liters of oxygen per minute = 746 watts = 0.746 kilowatts = 550 foot-pounds per second = 33,000 foot-pounds per minute

    1 Calorie per minute = 0.9351 horsepower

    1 watt = 1 joule per second = 10^7 ergs (Dyne, CGS unit of work, is the force required to accelerate 1 gram mass at the rate of 1 centimeter per second per second. The erg is a unit of work. 1 erg = work accomplished when a force of 1 dyne accelerates 1 centimeter in the direction of force.)

Pressure: the force applied to a unit area

    1 atmosphere = 760 millimeters of mercury = 29.92 inches of mercury = 10.33 meters of water = 33.89 feet of water = 14.7 pounds per square inch = 2116.3 pounds per square foot

Velocity: rate of displacement

    1 meter/sec. = 3.28083 feet/sec. = 2.2369 miles/hr.

    1 centimeter/sec. = 0.02237 miles/hr.

    1 mile/hr = 0.447 meters/sec. = 26.82 meters/min. = 1.6093 kilometers/hr. = 88 feet/min. = 1.4667 feet/sec.

    1 foot/sec. = 0.2048 meters/sec. = 18.29 meters/min. = 1.0973 kilometers/hr. = 0.6818 miles/hr.

Volume: space occupied by matter

    1 liter = 1000 cubic centimeters or 1000.028 milliliters = 1.057 quarts (1 quart = 0.946 cubic centimeters)

    1 cubic centimeter = 0.061 cubic inch

    1 cubic inch = 16.3872 cubic centimeters

    1 cubic foot = 28.317 liters = 0.02832 cubic meters

Weight: a measure of the attractive force of the earth for a distinct mass (or body)

    1 kilogram = 2.2 lbs = 35.27 ounces = 1000 grams

    1 pound = 0.4536 kilogram = 453.6 grams = 16 ounces

    1 ounce = 28.3495 grams

    1 gram = 0.035274 ounces

---

* 5.000 = approximate value

Work: The product of a force acting on matter through a distance (W = Fs); usually expressed per minute

1 kilogram-meter = 0.002343 Calorie = 2.343 gram-calories = 9.81 × 10^7 ergs = 7.233 foot-pounds

1 foot-pound = 0.13825 kilogram-meter = 0.000324 Calorie = 0.324 gram calorie

100 kilopond-meters = 723 foot-pounds = 16.35 watts

TABLE 1.   Factors to Convert Gas Volume to 37°C Saturated

Exhaled Gas	P_B mm Hg*		
$t°C$	750	760	770
20	1.102	1.102	1.101
20.5	1.100	1.099	1.099
21	1.097	1.096	1.096
21.5	1.094	1.093	1.093
22	1.091	1.091	1.090
22.5	1.089	1.089	1.088
23	1.086	1.085	1.085
23.5	1.083	1.082	1.082
24	1.080	1.079	1.079
24.5	1.077	1.077	1.076
25	1.074	1.074	1.073
25.5	1.071	1.071	1.070
26	1.069	1.069	1.068
26.5	1.066	1.065	1.065
27	1.063	1.062	1.062
27.5	1.061	1.060	1.060

* Note the small deviations produced by barometric pressures listed. If barometric pressure is between 750 and 770 mm Hg, values for 760 mm Hg may be used.

TABLE 2.   Vapor Pressure of Water (Values are for water in contact with its own vapor)

Temperature °C	0	1	2	3	4	5	6	7	8	9
					P$_{H_2O}$ mm Hg					
0	4.6	4.9	5.3	5.7	6.1	6.5	7.0	7.5	8.0	8.6
10	9.2	9.8	10.5	11.2	12.0	12.8	13.6	14.5	15.5	16.5
20	17.5	18.7	19.8	21.1	22.4	23.8	25.2	26.7	28.3	30.0
30	31.8	33.7	35.7	37.7	39.9	42.2	44.6	47.1	49.7	52.4
40	55.3	58.3	61.5	64.8	68.3	71.9	75.7	79.6	83.7	88.0
50	92.5	97.2	102	107	113	118	124	130	136	143
60	149	156	164	171	179	188	196	205	214	224
70	234	244	255	266	277	289	301	314	327	341
80	365	370	385	401	417	434	451	469	487	506
90	526	546	567	589	611	634	658	682	707	733
100	760									

Water vapor pressures obtained from *Handbook of Chemistry and Physics*, 45th Ed. Cleveland, Chemical Rubber Publishing Company, 1964–65.

TABLE 3. STPD$_{corr}$: Factors for Reducing Volume of Moist Gas to Volume Occupied by Dry Gas at 0°C 760 mm Hg

OBSERVED BAROMETRIC READING, UNCORRECTED FOR TEMPERATURE	15°	16°	17°	18°	19°	20°	21°	22°	23°	24°	25°	26°	27°	28°	29°	30°	31°	32°
700	0.855	851	847	842	838	834	829	825	821	816	812	807	802	797	793	788	783	778
702	857	853	849	845	840	836	832	827	823	818	814	809	805	800	795	790	785	780
704	860	856	852	847	843	839	834	830	825	821	816	812	807	802	797	792	787	783
706	862	858	854	850	845	841	837	832	828	823	819	814	810	804	800	795	790	785
708	865	861	856	852	848	843	839	834	830	825	821	816	812	807	802	797	792	787
710	867	863	859	855	850	846	842	837	833	828	824	819	814	809	804	799	795	790
712	870	866	861	857	853	848	844	839	836	830	826	821	817	812	807	802	797	792
714	872	868	864	859	855	851	846	842	837	833	828	824	819	814	809	804	799	794
716	875	871	866	862	858	853	849	844	840	835	831	826	822	816	812	807	802	797
718	877	873	869	864	860	856	851	847	842	838	833	828	824	819	814	809	804	799
720	880	876	871	867	863	858	854	849	845	840	836	831	826	821	816	812	807	802
722	882	878	874	869	865	861	856	852	847	843	838	833	829	824	819	814	809	804
724	885	880	876	872	867	863	858	854	849	845	840	835	831	826	821	816	811	806
726	887	883	879	874	870	866	861	856	852	847	843	838	833	829	824	818	813	808
728	890	886	881	877	872	868	863	859	854	850	845	840	836	831	826	821	816	811
730	892	888	884	879	875	871	866	861	857	852	847	843	838	833	828	823	818	813
732	895	890	886	882	877	873	868	864	859	854	850	845	840	836	831	825	820	815
734	897	893	889	884	880	875	871	866	862	857	852	847	843	838	833	828	823	818
736	900	895	891	887	882	878	873	869	864	859	855	850	845	840	835	830	825	820
738	902	898	894	889	885	880	876	871	866	862	857	852	848	843	838	833	828	822
740	905	900	896	892	887	883	878	874	869	864	860	855	850	845	840	835	830	825
742	907	903	898	894	890	885	881	876	871	867	862	857	852	847	842	837	832	827
744	910	906	901	897	892	888	883	878	874	869	864	859	855	850	845	840	834	829
746	912	908	903	899	895	890	886	881	876	872	867	862	857	852	847	842	837	832
748	915	910	906	901	897	892	888	883	879	874	869	864	860	854	850	845	839	834
750	917	913	908	904	900	895	890	886	881	876	872	867	862	857	852	847	842	837
752	920	915	911	906	902	897	893	888	883	879	874	869	864	859	854	849	844	839
754	922	918	913	909	904	900	895	891	886	881	876	872	867	862	857	852	846	841
756	925	920	916	911	907	902	898	893	888	883	879	874	869	864	859	854	849	844
758	927	923	918	914	909	905	900	896	891	886	881	876	872	866	861	856	851	846
760	930	925	921	916	912	907	902	898	893	888	883	879	874	869	864	859	854	848
762	932	928	923	919	914	910	905	900	896	891	886	881	876	871	866	861	856	851
764	936	930	926	921	916	912	907	903	898	893	888	884	879	874	869	864	858	853
766	937	933	928	924	919	915	910	905	900	896	891	886	881	876	871	866	861	855
768	940	935	931	926	922	917	912	908	903	898	893	888	883	878	873	868	863	858
770	942	938	933	928	924	919	915	910	905	901	896	891	886	881	876	871	865	860
772	945	940	936	931	926	922	917	912	908	903	898	893	888	883	878	873	868	862
774	947	943	938	933	929	924	920	915	910	905	901	896	891	886	880	875	870	865
776	950	945	941	936	931	927	922	917	912	908	903	898	893	888	883	878	872	867
778	952	948	943	938	934	929	924	920	915	910	905	900	895	890	885	880	875	869
780	955	950	945	941	936	932	927	922	917	912	908	903	898	892	887	882	877	872

Peters, J. P., and Van Slyke, D. D.: Quantitative Clinical Chemistry. Vol. II. (Methods) Baltimore: The Williams and Wilkins Co., 1932.

TABLE 4. Symbols for Respiratory Physiology

	Symbol	Definition, Dimensions and Conditions Must be Specified in Each Publication
I. General variables	V	Gas volume in general. Pressure, temperature and percentage saturation with water vapor must be stated.
	$\dot{V}$	Gas volume per unit time
	P	Gas pressure in general
	F	Fractional concentration in dry gas phase
	$\dot{Q}$	Volume flow of blood
	C	Concentration in blood phase
	f	Respiratory frequency—breaths per unit time
	R	Respiratory exchange ratio in general (volume CO_2/volume O_2)
	D	Diffusing capacity in general (volume per unit time per unit pressure difference)
II. Symbol for the gas phase (SMALL CAPS)	I	Inspired gas
	E	Expired gas
	A	Alveolar gas
	T	Tidal gas
	D	Dead space gas
	B	Barometric
III. Symbol for the blood phase	b	Blood in general
	a	Arterial (exact location to be specified in each publication)
	v	Venous (exact location to be specified in each publication)
	c	Capillary (exact location to be specified in each publication)
IV. Special symbols and abbreviations	$\bar{X}$	Dash above any symbol indicates a mean value
	$\dot{X}$	Dot above any symbol indicates a time derivative
	s	Subscript to denote the steady state
	STPD	Standard temperature, pressure, dry (0°C., 760 mm. Hg)
SMALL CAPS	BTPS	Body temperature, pressure, saturated with water
	ATPD	Ambient temperature, pressure, dry
	ATPS	Ambient temperature, pressure, saturated with water

Pappenheimer, J. R., Comroe, J. H., Cournand, A., Ferguson, J. K. W., Filley, G. F., Fowler, W. S., Gray, J. S., Helmholtz, H. F., Otis, A. B., Rahn, H., and Riley, R. L.: Standardization of definitions and symbols in respiratory physiology. *Fed. Proc.*, 9:602-605, 1950.

TABLE 5. Body Surface Area in Meters Squared (BSA m^2)

Height in centimeters	Weight in Kilograms																
	25	30	35	40	45	50	55	60	65	70	75	80	85	90	95	100	105
200							1.84	1.91	1.97	2.03	2.09	2.15	2.21	2.26	2.31	2.36	2.41
195						1.73	1.80	1.87	1.93	1.99	2.05	2.11	2.17	2.22	2.27	2.32	2.37
190				1.56	1.63	1.70	1.77	1.84	1.90	1.96	2.02	2.08	2.13	2.18	2.23	2.28	2.33
185				1.53	1.60	1.67	1.74	1.80	1.86	1.92	1.98	2.04	2.09	2.14	2.19	2.24	2.29
180				1.49	1.57	1.64	1.71	1.77	1.83	1.89	1.95	2.00	2.05	2.10	2.15	2.20	2.25
175	1.19	1.28	1.36	1.46	1.53	1.60	1.67	1.73	1.79	1.85	1.91	1.96	2.01	2.06	2.11	2.16	2.21
170	1.17	1.26	1.34	1.43	1.50	1.57	1.63	1.69	1.75	1.81	1.86	1.91	1.96	2.01	2.06	2.11	
165	1.14	1.23	1.31	1.40	1.47	1.54	1.60	1.66	1.72	1.78	1.83	1.88	1.93	1.98	2.03	2.07	
160	1.12	1.21	1.29	1.37	1.44	1.50	1.56	1.62	1.68	1.73	1.78	1.83	1.88	1.93	1.98		
155	1.09	1.18	1.26	1.33	1.40	1.46	1.52	1.58	1.64	1.69	1.74	1.79	1.84	1.89			
150	1.06	1.15	1.23	1.30	1.36	1.42	1.48	1.54	1.60	1.65	1.70	1.75	1.80				
145	1.03	1.12	1.20	1.27	1.33	1.39	1.45	1.51	1.56	1.61	1.66	1.71					
140	1.00	1.09	1.17	1.24	1.30	1.36	1.42	1.47	1.52	1.57							
135	0.97	1.06	1.14	1.20	1.26	1.32	1.38	1.43	1.48								
130	0.95	1.04	1.11	1.17	1.23	1.29	1.35	1.40									
125	0.93	1.01	1.08	1.14	1.20	1.26	1.31	1.36									
120	0.91	0.98	1.04	1.10	1.16	1.22	1.27										

DuBois, E. F.: *Basal Metabolism in Health and Disease.* 3rd Ed. Philadelphia, Lea & Febiger, 1936.

INDEX

ACCELERATION, 279
Acid-base balance, 208–212. See also *pH*.
Acidosis, metabolic, 136, 219
Action potential, 20, 21
Adaptation, sensory, 37
Albuminuria, 213
Alkalosis, metabolic, 136
Alpha and gamma efferents, 34, 35
Articulations, classification of, 55
Autonomic nervous system, 31
Avogadro's law, 174, 279

BEER's law, 279
Behnke technique, 270–273
Body surface area, table, 293
Bomb calorimeter, 160
Blood, glucose levels of, 169
  lactic acid in, 82, 184–187
  non-Newtonian fluid, 284
  oxygen carrying capacity of, 131
  per cent of body weight, 168
  pH of, 129, 136, 149, 221, 226
  volume in circulatory system, 202
Blood flow, Borelli effect, 84–85
  law of Laplace, 85
  Pascal's law, 83, 85, 283–284
  Poiseuille's law, 82, 83, 88, 134
  pressure gradients, 85
Blood pressure, blood forces in, 95
  chemical regulation of, 90
  during cardiac cycle, 269
  history of, 85–86
  hormonal influences, 91–93
  indirect neural control of, 89
  muscle pump and, 94
  principles of, 86–87
Bohr effect, 132, 135. See also *Oxygen disassociation curve*.
Bowditch's law, 19, 22, 78
Boyle's law, 111, 281
Breathing. See *Respiration; Ventilation*.
BTPS, 252, 279, 289

CALCULATION methods. See also
  Conversion factors.
cardiac index, 268–269
cardiac output, 97, 98, 267–268, 280
composition and resolution of forces,
  274–275
expiratory reserve volume, 251
gross cost of exercise, 263
gross efficiency, 264
Hyman index, 269–270
inspiratory capacity, 251
inspiratory reserve volume, 251
kilogram meter (work), 266
kilopond meter (work), 266
maximum breathing capacity, 254
minute volume, 253, 254
  corrected to body surface area, 256
negative energy balance, 265
net cost of work, 194, 263
net efficiency, 264
oxygen debt, 264–265
oxygen pulse, 268
oxygen uptake, closed circuit, 251–252
    nonrecording spirometer, 249–250
    recording spirometer, 247–249
  open circuit, 256–260
oxygen uptake/kilogram body weight,
  265
postural mean blood pressure index,
  269–270
rate of oxygen removal, 253
somatotypology, 270–273
tidal volume, 254
timed capacity, 254–256
  expressed as percentage of vital
    capacity, 255–256
ventilation equivalent for oxygen, 127,
  252–253
vital capacity, 251
work, 261–265 (See also *Bicycle ergometers*.)

Calories, 287
  expenditure of, 196
  values in food, 160
Calorimetry. See also *Metabolism*.
  direct, 161
  indirect, 162–166
    closed circuit, 162–164, 245–247
    open circuit, 164–166, 256–260
  sources of error in, 163, 164, 168
Carbohydrate, as "protein sparer," 172
  distribution in human, 14, 168. See
    also *Metabolism*.
  metabolism of, 168–171
  thermal equivalent of oxygen, 173–174
Carbon dioxide, disassociation curve,
    136–138
  effect on blood pressure, 91
  effect on pulse rate, 91
  effect on ventilation, 112, 113
  removal, 211
  role in blood pH level, 137
  uptake, 129, 135, 136
Cardiac cycle, 99–102
Cardiac evaluation, 269–270
Cardiac muscle. See *Muscle tissue*.
Cardiac output, 130, 206
  control of, 80–84
  dynamics of, 88–89
  factors influencing, 102–103
  formulas for, 79, 97, 98, 268, 280
  heart rate and, 79, 94, 104–107
  measurement of, 97–99, 104–106
    Fick principle in, 97, 267
  stroke volume in, 79, 104–107
Center of gravity, 47, 58–59, 280
Charles' law, 281
Clo unit, 156
Closed circuit. See *Calorimetry, indirect*.
Conduction velocity, 280
Conversion factors, area, 287
  gas volumes to 37°C saturated, 289
  heat, 287
  linear measure, 287
  oxygen, oxidation, 288
  power, 288
  pressure, 288
  reducing volume of moist gas to
    standard conditions, 291
  vapor pressure of water, 290
  velocity, 288
  volume, 288
  weight, 288
  work, 289
Core temperature, 141, 143
Cori cycle, 14, 15, 169. See also *Liver*.
Cramp, heat, 154

DALTON's law, 117–118, 281
Dead space, respiratory, 116–117
Deamination, 171
Density, 280
Dynamogenesis, 60–63

EFFICIENCY, 280
  calculation methods for, 264
Electrocardiographic deflections, 100, 101
Electrogoniometry, 70–73
Electromyography, 67–69
Energy, 281
Energy balance, 172
  negative, 265
Energy cost, gross, 281
  net, 281
Enzyme, 171
Ergogenic aids, nutritional, 215, 221
  oxygen inhalation, 226–228
  pharmaceutical, 221–226
    alkalies, 221–222
    amphetamines, 222–223
    aspartates, 223
    caffeine, 224
    gelatin, 224–225
    hormones, 225–226
    sugar, 226
Esters, 205
Exercise, effects of, on body weight, 192–196
  on capillary bed, 134
  on carbon dioxide disassociation,
    136–138
  on heart volume, 103–107
  on kidney function, 207–208
  on liver function, 205
  on obesity, 188–196
  on oxygen disassociation, 129
  on pulmonary diffusion coefficient,
    120
  on respiratory exchange ratio, 175–176
  on utilization coefficient of oxygen,
    134
Exhaustion, heat, 154

FACILITATION, 43
Fatigue, 25, 228–230
Feedback, 33
Feedback loop, 36
Females, physical activity in, 232–233
Fever. See *Pyrexia*.
Fick principle, 97, 267
Fluid, balance, 203–204
  distribution in body, 202
Foodstuffs, water content of, 204
Force, 64

Gas laws, of Boyle, 111, 281
  of Charles, 281
  combined, of Boyle and Charles, 281.
    See also *STPD.*
  of Dalton and Henry, 282
  of Dalton, 117–118, 281
  of Henry, 282
Gas tension, 126, 132
Glomerular filtration rate, 207

"Health foods," reason for use, 216–218
Heart, anatomy of, 77–78. See also
    Cardiac; Muscle tissue.
  law of Bowditch and, 78
Heat, 287. See also *Pyrexia.*
  balance, 144
  cold and, racial differences, 156
  disorders, 153-154
  gain, 149-156
    endocrine glands and, 149–150
    food and, 150
    metabolism and, 149–150
    shivering and, 150, 154–156
    sun and, 150
  loss, 146–148
    conduction and, 148
    convection and, 147
    evaporation and, 146
    radiation and, 146
Henry's law, 282
Homeostasis, 201
Hooke's law, 282
Hormone, 171. See also *Ergogenic aids.*
Hydrogen ion concentration. See *Acid-base balance; pH*
Hyman index, 269–270
Hyperventilation, 125–126
  effect on blood pH, 125–126

Insulin, 170–171
Intentional response time. See *Reaction time.*

Ketosis, 171
Kidneys, anatomy of, 208
  as fluid reservoirs, 204–207
  control of flow rates in, 207
  discoverers of structure and function
    of, 201–202
  pH regulation, 210–212
  plasma flow, 206–207
  urine production, 207
Kilogram meter, 266–267
Kilopond meter, 266, 282
Kinesthetic sense receptors. See
    Proprioception.

Lactic acid, 14, 15, 82, 168, 183, 184–
    187. See also *Muscle.*
  coefficient of combustion of, 14
Laplace, law of, 282. See also *Blood flow.*
Law of partial pressures. See *Gas laws.*
Lever, 55–58, 282
Lifting, involving memorization and
    association, 33
Lipid. See *Metabolism, fat.*
Liver, anatomy of, 206
  deamination in, 171
  function of, 205–207
Longevity, 236
Lung, capillary bed, 120, 122
  mechanics of breathing and, 110–112
  vascular bed of, 123
  volumes and capacities of, 114–116,
    250–252

Machine, 54
Man, 1–3
  compared to machine, 2
  designed for motion, 54–58
  potential energy value, 1
Mechanical advantage, 282
Metabolic acidosis, 136, 219
  alkalosis, 136
Metabolic activity, classification of,
    176–181
Metabolism, 159
  basal, 159, 167–168
  carbohydrate, 168–171
  fat (lipid), 173
  history of, 159–160
  protein, 171–172
  thermal equivalent of oxygen in,
    173–174
Metric system, 245, 286–287
Moments of force, 57, 72–73
Motion, accelerated, 279
  arthrological considerations in, 54–55
  center of gravity and, 58–59, 280
  Newton's laws and, 58–60
  power source and levers in, 55–58
  resistance to, 60, 65–67
  torque, 57, 72–73
Movement, analysis of, 64–67
  cerebral control of, 44–47
  efficiency of, 62–63
  reflex control of, 31, 49
Muscle, action potential in, 20, 21
  contraction of. See *Muscle contraction.*
  end plate potentials, 19–20
  fiber arrangement, 6, 10
  glycogen in, 168
  pump, 94–96

Muscle, receptors, 32, 33, 36–38
    spindles, 32, 33, 36–38
    stimuli and response, 21–23
    tissue of. See *Muscle tissue.*
    tonicity, 25
    work, 26
Muscle contraction, associated antag-
        onistic, 25
    chemistry of, 11–15, 224
    gradation in, 17, 18, 78
    historical perspective, 11
    innervation ratio, 18
    motor unit, 18
    reciprocal innervation in, 25, 43, 44
    recruitment in, 18, 78
    stimuli and response in, 21–23
    types of, 23–25, 26
Muscle tissue, anatomy of, 5–10
    cardiac, 19, 78–80
    chemical composition of, 11
    fluid storage in, 206
    involuntary, 18–19
    lactic acid in, 14, 15
    properties of, 4
    pyruvic acid in, 15
    red and white types, 16–17
    skeletal, 4–10
    smooth, 18–19
    striated, 4–10
Myotatic reflexes, 40–44

NERVE(s), action potential in, 20, 21
Nervous system, autonomic, 30–31
    somatic, 30–31
Newton's law of motion, 58–60, 283
Nitrogen equilibrium, 172

OBESITY, 189
    calories and, 194–196
    etiology of, 189–191
    physical inactivity and, 192–194
    simple, 189–191
Ohm's law, 283
    applied to elgon, 73
Open circuit. See *Calorimetry, indirect.*
Oxygen, oxidation and, 288
    thermal equivalent of, 173–174
Oxygen debt, 16, 181–184
    alactacid portion of, 184
    lactic acid and, 185–187
    possible errors in calculation of,
        182–183
Oxygen dissociation curve, 129
    Bohr effect and, 129, 132
    effect of exercise on, 129
    Henry's law and, 132
    myoglobin and, 134–135

Oxygen uptake, 130
    maximum, 188
Oxygen utilization coefficient, 133, 283

P WAVE, 100, 101
Partial pressures, law of, 117–118, 281
Pascal's laws, 83, 85, 283–284
Perspiration. See also *Sweat.*
    insensible, 145
    sensible, 145
pH, 136, 204, 209, 226. See also *Acid-
    base balance.*
Physical fitness, 233–237
    folly of single score, 235–236
    vagueness of term, 233–234
Plasma volume, 202
Poiseuille's law, 82, 83, 284
Polarity, 21
Postural hypotensive syndrome, 84
Posture, oxygen cost of, 47
    static and dynamic, 47–49
Power, 284, 288
Power source, 55–58
Pressure, 288
    of water vapor, 290
Pressure gradients, 118, 120
Proprioception, 33, 34, 38–40
Protein ingestion, 172
Pulmonary diffusion coefficient, 119
    effect of exercise on, 120
Pulmonary ventilation. See *Ventilation,
    pulmonary.*
Pyrexia, 141, 151. See also *Heat.*

Q WAVE, 100, 101

R WAVE, 100, 101
Reaction time, complex, 50
    conditioned reflex, 50
    intentional response, 50
    reflex component, 50
    simple, 50
Reflex(es), 40
    statokinetic-tonic, 50–51
    stretch or myotatic, 40–43
Relative humidity, 147, 284
    effect on heart rate, 147
Resistance, 284
Resolution of force of gravity, 285
Respiration, 110. See also *Ventilation,
    pulmonary.*
    Boyle's law and, 111
    break point in, 127
    Dalton's law and, 117
    external phase of, 111, 112
    gas diffusion in, 117–122
    internal phase of, 129–134

Respiration, partial gas pressures in, 118–120, 132
  rapid shallow, 125
  respiratory gases, 130–131
  role of diaphragm in, 112, 127
Respiratory dead space, 116–117
Respiratory exchange ratio, 175–176, 284
Respiratory gymnastics, 126–127
Respiratory quotient, 174–176

S wave, 100, 101
Salt, balance of, 152–153
  supplemental feeding of, 153
Skeleton, function of, 4, 54–55
Slide rule, operation, 243–245
Smoking, 230–232
Somatic nervous system, 30–31
Somatotypology, 270–273
Spatial orientation, 50–51
Sp· cific dynamic action, 167
Specific gravity, 285
  of urine, 146
Steady state, 15–16, 187–188
  apparent, 187
  oxygen debt and, 185
  true, 187
STPD, 285, 290
Stroke, heat, 154
Sweat, 145
  bacterial action on, 146
  chemical composition of, 146
  rates, 150
Sweat glands, apocrine, 146
  eccrine, 146
Symbols for respiratory physiology, 292

T wave, 100, 101
Temperature, 285
  core, 141, 143
  diurnal rhythm in, 142
  effect on heart rate, 147
  effect on work, 143
  shell, 143
Tension, 25. See also *Gas tension.*
Thermodynamics, 166
  law of, 145, 166
Thermogenesis, 166–168
Thermoregulation, neural, 151

Thirst, 153
Tissue respiration, chemical combination, 130
  inadequacy of physical solution in, 130
  oxygen and carbon dioxide transport in, 129–131
Torque, 57, 72–73
Training table, 220

U wave, 100, 101
Urine, 212–213
  composition of, 212
  pH values, 212
    with fluid loss, 149
  specific gravity of, 212
Utilization coefficient of oxygen, 133

Valsalva maneuver, 93
  intrapulmonary pressures in, 97, 112
Vapor pressure of water, 290
Vectors, 64–66
Velocity, 58, 286, 288
Ventilation. See also *Respiration.*
  chemical regulation of, 112–113
  multiple factor theory of Gray, 113–114
  pulmonary, 122–125
    approximate range of values, 124
    oxygen consumption and, 124
    Poiseuille's law and, 125
  role of carbon dioxide in, 112, 113
  role of oxygen in, 113
Vital capacity, measurement of, 251–252
  predicted (formulas), 252
  relationship to fitness, 127–128
Vitamins, 216–218
Volume, 286. See also *Calculation methods.*

Warming-up, 26, 27
Water (fluid) loss, 148–149
Water intake, importance of, to continued performance, 151–152
  in evaporative process, 152
Weight, 288
  control of, 188–196. See also *Exercise; Obesity.*
Work, 60, 261–264, 266–267, 286, 289
  factors influencing, 60–62, 147